Molecular Electronic Devices

Molecular Electronic Devices

FORREST L. CARTER

Naval Research Laboratory
Washington, DC

MARCEL DEKKER, INC.   **New York and Basel**

Library of Congress Cataloging in Publication Data

Main entry under title:

Molecular electronic devices

    Includes index.
    1. Molecular electronics--Congresses. I. Carter,
Forrest L.,
TK7874.M5327 1982   621.381'71   82-18236
ISBN 0-8247-1676-0

MARCEL DEKKER, INC.
270 Madison Avenue, New York, New York 10016

Current printing (last digit):
10 9 8 7 6 5 4 3 2

PRINTED IN THE UNITED STATES OF AMERICA

PREFACE

Simple extrapolation suggests that in approximately two decades electronic switches will be the size of large molecules. It takes little imagination to recognize that the practical realization of this possibility will produce a revolution in the areas of computation, technology, science, medicine, warfare, and lifestyle that will be more significant than any which occurred in the last fifty years. The molecular structure of a 'molecular' sized switch will surely reflect its function, and as such probably will not be based on a silicon technology. If this is the case, the material problems to be solved, both theoretical and experimental, are of such a magnitude that a sizeable effort must be started now in this new direction rather than waiting for the rope to run out in the semiconducting area.

The Workshop on "Molecular" Electronic Devices (WMED) was held at NRL on March 23-24, 1981 under the joint sponsorship of NRL and ONR. Primarily the Workshop was convened to explore the possibilities of developing switches at the molecular level for ultimately controlling and modifying signals. However, other objects of the WMED included: 1) assessing the level of interest in the possibilities of 'molecular' switching; 2) providing a suitable forum for current speculative considerations on the subject (speculative, since no artificial 'molecular' switches have been announced); 3) supporting and emphasizing the growing information concerning molecular biological processes, both of a synthetic and signal controlling nature; 4) alerting a wide variety of scientists of the ever expanding possibilities inherent for 'molecular' switches so that such devices might be worthy of serious consideration. As a historical footnote, this editor's interest in "molecular" switches developed in 1977 when, while participating in NRL's Program on Electroactive Polymers, it became clear that one might communicate electrically with molecules via conducting filaments of polysulfur nitride, $(SN)_x$, and polyacetylene, $(CH)_x$.

1) communication with individual molecules, or rather, moieties, is only one of several problems to be considered with regard to "molecular" electronic devices. Some of the other major problems will involve the fabrication, or possibly, chemical synthesis of device arrays; 2) the minimization and dissipation of heat; 3) the generation of computer "soft" (memory) errors caused by the cosmic rays and the small size of the components, and 4) the development of a new computer architecture which will take advantage of such possibilities as memory redundancy and parallel processing. In fact, only the problem of "soft" errors received more than a passing mention at the Workshop. While it should be noted that these problem areas reside in rather different disciplines they have far ranging effects. Accordingly, Workshop participants were sought among chemists, engineers, molecular biologists, and physicists who would actively participate in both formal presentations and open recorded discussion.

In view of the interdisciplinary nature of this Workshop, it was considered that a glossary of technical terms, processes, and chemical names would be useful to the conferees while at the Workshop. The authors were invited to contribute in advance to the glossary and several did, some authors obviously making an appreciable effort. These include Drs. K.M. Ulmer, T.W. Barrett, D.J. Sandman and A. Aviram. To these were added other terms taken from the manuscripts, then the total was assembled by Dr. H. Wohltjen. Dr. Ulmer's contribution of biotechnical terms was sufficiently complete as to constitute an excellent short course in molecular biology for the Workshop attendees. The glossary included in this volume as an appendix represents a collated and abridged edition of the Workshop version.

Details concerning the Workshop composition will be briefly summarized. Interest in WMED was high as is indicated by the number of selected registrees (~110), of whom 16 were foreign nationals representing 9 different countries. Some of the foreign attendees came specifically for this Workshop. The scientific mix was good (44% chemists, 24% physicists, 25% electrical engineers, and 8% biologists or medical doctors) but, more important perhaps for the excellent interdisciplinary communication achieved, was that about 70% of the attendees individually had strong interdisciplinary backgrounds. The employment mix between industry, academia, and government was also good, corresponding to 30%, 35%, and 35%, respectively.

These Proceedings include the welcoming remarks by Dr. A.I. Schindler, twenty-three planned papers presented by twenty-one authors, a manuscript from Dr. S.L. Matlow submitted on time but not presented, the invited after dinner talk of Dr. A. Berman, and all discussion (edited). Also included are two special commentaries. The invited papers by Drs. Aviram, Guenzer, Ferry, Sandman, and Shipman (Chapter XXIV) were especially valuable in setting the tone of the Workshop.

I am pleased to acknowledge the extended support and encouragement given me by Drs. W. Fox and N.L. Jarvis during the development of the concepts of the chemical computer. Given my meager editorial abilities, I am also happy to praise the cheerful natures and fine secretarial skills of Marilyn Williams and Linda Hollingsworth as well as the proof reading capabilities of Dr. H. Wohltjen. Drs. A. Snow and R. Colton also were generous in their support prior to and during the Workshop. Thanks to the firm leadership of the Session Chairman, the Workshop schedule was maintained while the discussion was stimulating and reasonably complete. The responsible chairmen are: A, David Nelson (ONR); B, K. Wynne (ONR); C, Larry Cooper (ONR); D, Richard F. Greene (NRL); and E, David C. Weber (NRL). Many valuable suggestions were also offered the Organizing Committee, the other members of which are: Larry R. Cooper (ONR); Neldon L. Jarvis (NRL); David Nelson (ONR); Hank Wohltjen (NRL); Kenneth Wynne (ONR). ONR support for the workshop made the preparation of these proceedings possible.

Finally, I note that a survey held at the close of the Workshop was enthusiastic in general and indicated another Workshop in $1\frac{1}{2}$-2 years would be appropriate. Topics suitable for the next Workshop, beyond those noted above as interesting problem areas, include: self-organizing and self-assembling systems as aids to synthetic efforts; surface modification chemistry as a modified inorganic Merrifield technique; and molecular switching species with self-correcting coding capabilities.

Dr. Forrest L. Carter

Figure 1. The WMED participants enjoying the coffee break are Drs. Beverly Giammara (Univ. of Louisville), Tsung-Ein Tsai (Standard Oil, IN), Mark Ratner (Northwestern Univ.), Allen R. Siedle (MMM Central Res. Labs.) and T.W. Barrett (Univ. of Tenn., Memphis).

Figure 2. Dr. Coe Ishimoto (1), of Japan's Sony Corp., talks shop with NRL Chemist, Dr. Oh-Kil Kim.

Figure 3. Dr. Henry Beneking (Germany) checks a map while Drs. Hank Wohltjen (1) and Richard Greene (both of NRL) chat.

Figure 4. Dr. S. Managawa (HISL) contemplates the microprocessor controlled model of a microtubule by S.R. Hameroff and R. Watt (Univ. of Arizona).

CONTENTS

CONTENTS

CONTRIBUTORS

A. AVIRAM IBM Thomas J. Watson Research Center, Yorktown Heights, NY.

T. W. BARRETT* University of Tennessee, Center for the Health Sciences, Memphis, TN.

J. R. BARKER Warwick University, Coventry, United Kingdom.

P. BRANT+ Chemistry Division, Naval Research Laboratory, Washington, DC.

FORREST L. CARTER Naval Research Laboratory, Washington, DC.

DAVID B. COTTS Polymer Science Department, SRI International, Menlo Park, CA.

D. O. COWAN Department of Chemistry, The Johns Hopkins University, Baltimore, MD.

CARL W. DIRK Department of Chemistry and the Materials Research Center, Northwestern University, Evanston, IL.

D. K. FERRY Department of Electrical Engineering, Colorado State University Fort Collins, CO.

B. L. GIAMMARA Department of Anatomy, University of Louisville, School of Medicine, Louisville, KY.

H. L. GRUBIN Scientific Research Associates, Glastonbury, CT.

CHARLES S. GUENZER Naval Research Laboratory, Washington, DC.

R. C. HADDON Bell Laboratories, Murray Hill, NJ.

S. R. HAMEROFF Departments of Anasthesiology and Electrical Engineering, University of Arizona, Tucson, AZ.

J. S. HANKER Dental Research Center, University of North Carolina, Chapel Hill, NC.

DAVID M. HANSON Department of Chemistry, State University of New York, Stony Brook, NY.

A. J. HEEGER† Laboratory for Research on the Structure of Matter, Department of Physics, University of Pennsylvania, Philadelphia, PA.

BARRY HONIG∫ Department of Physiology and Biophysics, University of Illinois, Champaign, IL.

M. ISAACSON School of Applied and Engineering Physics and National Research and Resource Facility for Submicron Structures, Cornell University, Ithaca, NY.

BARBARA J. KINZIG Optical Sciences Division, Naval Research Laboratory, Washington, DC.

RON KOSLOFF Department of Physical Chemistry, Hebrew University, Jerusalem, Israel.

J. W. LYDING Department of Electrical Engineering and Computer Science and the Materials Research Center, Northwestern University, Evanston, IL.

A. G. MACDIARMID Laboratory for Research on the Structure of Matter, Department of Chemistry, University of Pennsylvania, Philadelphia, PA.

---

*CURRENT AFFILIATION Naval Research Laboratory, Washington, DC.

+CURRENT AFFILIATION Chemical Technology Center, Exxon Chemical Co., Baytown, TX.

†CURRENT AFFILIATION Department of Physics, University of California at Santa Barbara, Santa Barbara, CA.

∫CURRENT AFFILIATION Department of Biochemistry, Columbia University, New York, NY.

TOBIN J. MARKS Department of Chemistry and Materials Research Center, North-
    western University, Evanston, IL.
SHELDON L. MATLOW* The Southwall Corporation, Palo Alto, CA.
JAMES H. MCALEAR EMV Associated, Inc., Rockville, MD.
A. MURAY School of Applied and Engineering Physics and National Research
    and Resource Facility for Submicron Structures, Cornell University,
    Ithaca, NY.
T. O. POEHLER Applied Physics Laboratory, Johns Hopkins University, Laurel,
    MD.
MELVIN POMERANTZ IBM Thomas J. Watson Research Center, Yorktown Heights, NY.
R. S. POTEMBER Applied Physics Laboratory, Johns Hopkins University, Laurel
    MD.
M. A. RATNER Department of Chemistry, Northwestern University, Evanston, IL.
DANIEL J. SANDMAN GTE Laboratories, Inc., Walthan, MA.
A. I. SCHINDLER Associate Director of Research, Naval Research Laboratory,
    Washington, DC.
KARL F. SCHOCH,JR.[+] Department of Chemistry and the Materials Research Center,
    Northwestern University, Evanston, IL.
P. E. SEIDEN IBM Thomas J. Watson Research Center, Yorktown Heights, NY.
LESTER L. SHIPMAN[+] Chemistry Division, Argonne National Laboratory,
    Argonne, IL.
F. H. STILLINGER Bell Laboratories, Murray Hill, NJ.
K. M. ULMER Genex Corporation, Rockville, MD.
R. C. WATT Departments of Anesthesiology and Electrical Engineering, Univ-
    ersity of Arizona, Tucson, AZ.
JOHN M. WEHRUNG EMV Associates, Inc., Rockville, MD.
HANK WOHLTJEN Naval Research Laboratory, Washington, DC.

*CURRENT AFFILIATION Conductimer Corporation, Palo Alto, CA.
+CURRENT AFFILIATION Westinghouse Electric Corporation, Research and
    Development Center, Pittsburgh, PA.
+CURRENT AFFILIATION Central Development and Research Department, Experi-
    mental Station, E. I. Dupont de Neimours and Co., Inc., Wilmington, DE.

OPENING REMARKS

WORKSHOP ON 'MOLECULAR' ELECTRONIC DEVICES

A. I. Schindler
Associate Director of Research
Naval Research Laboratory
Washington, DC 20375

Good morning ladies and gentlemen. One of my more enjoyable duties is that of officially welcoming the many scientific and technical groups that meet under the auspices of NRL and ONR. It is a special pleasure to do so today not only because the business of your meeting is very new and exciting, as your abstracts indicate, but because many of you have traveled great distances at a busy time of the year to share with us your excitement and ideas in this new area of endeavor. So I especially welcome our very good friends from the many countries that are represented here today.

I also have noticed your diversity in background as well as in interest; accordingly, I also welcome you as physicists, chemists, biologists, spectroscopists, medical doctors and electrical engineers. But more importantly, I welcome you all here as practioners of the new and exciting field of 'molecular' electronics. The organizing committee and NRL staff will do all in its power to assist you and make this workshop successful.

We are all familiar with the revolution in computer power as exemplified by the hand-held computer. NRL recognizes that this workshop may lead to another revolution of equal if not greater importance. While we are involved in such DOD programs as VLSI, that is the development of high speed, very large-scale integrated circuitry, this workshop may point the way to a quantum jump advancement rather than just incremental improvements.

There are several additional reasons for being excited about this workshop. For example, using the concepts discussed here such as surface chemistry and the self-assembly of molecules, with the concept of molecular sized switches, it may be possible to make detectors for extremely small amounts of specific molecules. Such novel micro-sensors for chemical analysis would be extremely valuable both for military as well as industrial applications.

Artificial Intelligence is another area on which this workshop could have an important impact. A machine which could do useful work with a minimum of human guidance is of extreme use to the Navy for work in the deep sea and other hostile environments. This workshop may ultimately lead to practical memories with a density of 10^{15} bits per cc making possible machines with learning capability. Another use might combine photosensitive surfaces with data recognition processors using molecular switching.

Now it may interest those of you who are interested in communicating with molecules and things very small that NRL has a long history in communication, in a rather big way. One of the first technical groups here was involved in radio communication. Thus, in the communication area we had experimental radar on the Potomac River in 1937 and were the first to bounce a radar signal off the moon. Perhaps you will see while you are at NRL the original Radar dish that was involved in those first moon studies mounted on the roof of the administrative building #43.

Thus, in the past, NRL has thought big about things big and now perhaps it is appropriate to remember Nobel Laureate Richard Feynman's advice, namely that there is "plenty of room at the bottom". That was the approximate title of an article in which Feynman proposed to have small machines making smaller machines making smaller machines, etc.

I note that David Nagel of NRL has initiated a series of talks for a quite different purpose under the title "Think Small", in which "THINK" is given in large letters and "SMALL" in much smaller letters. Accordingly, in this spirit I not only extend our heartiest welcome to you but I invite you to think BIG about Thinking Small.

SECTION ONE
Signal Transmission and Molecular Switching – A

CHAPTER I

THEORETICAL AND EXPERIMENTAL STUDIES OF HEMIQUINONES
AND COMMENTS ON THEIR SUITABILITY FOR MOLECULAR
INFORMATION STORAGE ELEMENTS

A. Aviram and P. E. Seiden
IBM Thomas J. Watson Research Center
Yorktown Heights, NY 10598

M. A. Ratner
Department of Chemistry
Northwestern University
Evanston, IL 60201

INTRODUCTION

The hydrogen bond is nearly unique in its range of energies (approximately 0.1 to 30 kcal/mol), its omnipresence in biological systems, and the variety of species in which it occurs.(1) One fascinating aspect of the hydrogen bond which has received extensive study is the question of protonic motion. In very short hydrogen bonds such as bifluoride (the F-H-F bond distance in KHF_2 is 2.26 Å), the proton moves in a symmetric single well with considerable quartic character.(2) In longer hydrogen bonds, such as that in the formic acid dimer (O-H-O distance of 2.73 Å) the protons move in a symmetric double well; that is, the double well is symmetric if the two formate ($HCOO^-$) species have identical, fixed geometries (rigid potential) or if they are allowed to readjust their geometries completely for the various positions of the two bridging protons (adiabatic potential).(3) The double-well cases allow for localization of the protons on one side or the other of the double well, and thus a double well potential can potentially serve as a memory storage bit. Indeed, in DNA information is stored precisely this way, and motion of the protons can lead to loss of stored genetic information.(4)

THE MODEL

The possibility of utilizing hydrogen bonds for "dynamic molecular information storage" was proposed in a number of publications(5) and from a slightly different point of view more recently.(6) A model system for molecules with symmetric double well potentials is a hemiquinone. As defined previously (5), hemiquinones are valence tautomers that have the unique property of maintaining equal ground state energy in both tautomeric states while flipping the dipole moment due to particle exchange. Fig. 1 illustrates a number of hemiquinones with distinguishable forms indicated by Ia and Ib. Closer examination of the two reveals that Ia and Ib are actually the same molecule.

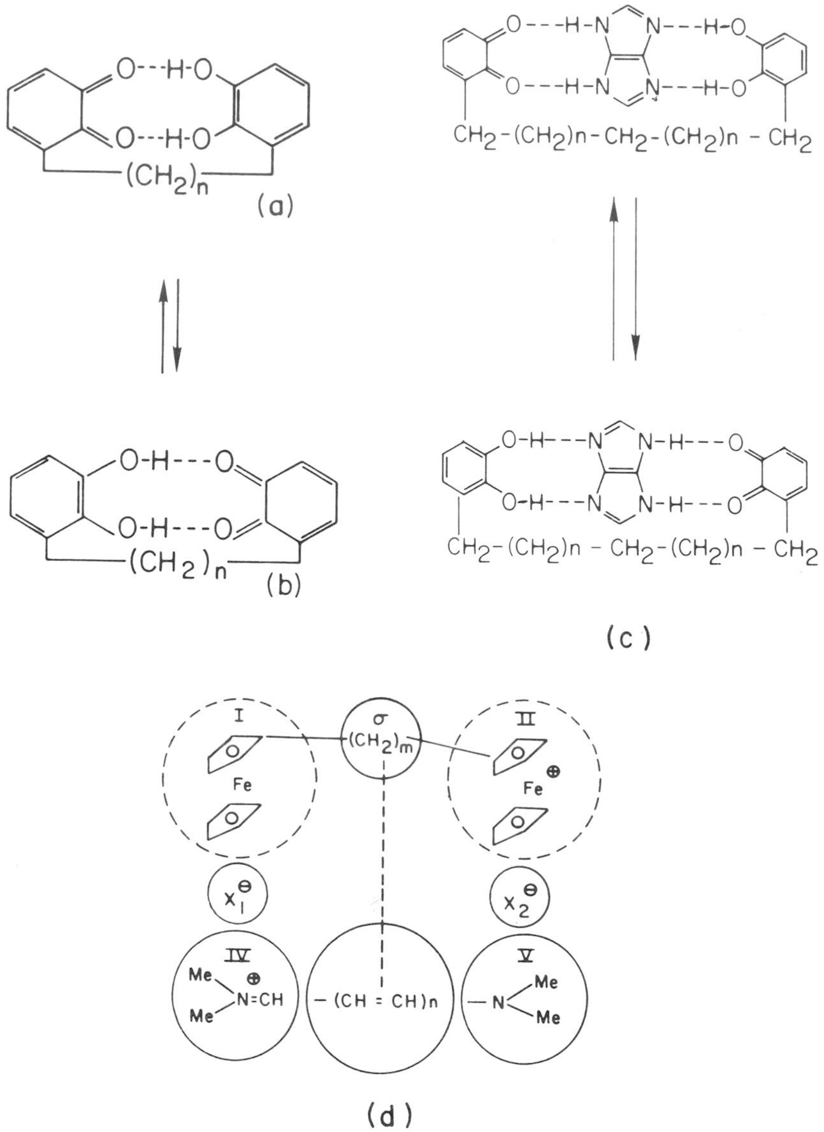

Fig. 1: Examples of three hemiquinones.

One could obtain Ib from Ia by rotation of the carbon frame in space, or
by relocation of two protons simultaneously, with the carbon frame fixed
in space and the electronic wavefunction readjusting adiabatically. Therefore
we describe the two structures Ia and Ib as two valence tautomers(7) (note
that the valences of the redox pair interchange). The hydrogens that are
involved in the valence tautomerism are suspended in a perfectly symmetric
double well potential and are not completely localized in one particular well,
or in one part of the molecule, but migrate left and right, giving rise to an

oscillation of structures Ia and Ib. This resembles the familiar umbrella
inversion oscillation of ammonia(8) or other such systems. This pendulum
alternation of structures I is due both to tunneling penetration of the
hydrogens through the potential barrier of the symmetric double well potential
(9) and to activated passing over the barrier, although the actual motion is a
complex one involving changes in the heavier-atom skeleton as well as proton
transfer. For simplicity we shall use the term "tunneling" to characterize
the proton transfer rate process, both from tunneling and from activation.

The proposed operation of the device is as follows: Information is
coded in a binary form by allowing Ia = "0" and Ib = "1". To do so one should
be able to switch between the two structures at will, to recognize the
structure, and to have a system that, for practical purposes, oscillates very
slowly. In real space and time with an assembly of molecules oriented
parallel to one another and individual molecules that are prevented from
rotating around a perpendicular in-plane axis, the two tautomers become
distinguishable. In electric fields parallel to the long axis of the
molecules the symmetric double well potential is perturbed and becomes
asymmetric. "Downhill" tunneling or trapping of the hydrogens would take
place leading to one particular isomeric structure. "Uphill" tunneling would
be energetically highly unfavorable, therefore for each polarity of applied
electric field only the "reversed" structure would be switched. We note that
the hydrogen motions that lead to interconversion between Ia and Ib also lead
to reorientation of the dipole moment of the molecule by 180°. This in turn
leads to a spike in the current in the external circuit, since the actual
structure resembles a capacitor. Thus, the switching is accomplished by
application of an electric field parallel to the molecular long axis and read
out by the presence or absence of a current in the external circuit.

In a "molecular computer" it is essential that logic operations be
performed on the same dimension and energy scale as that of the storage
elements; therefore we show in Fig. 2 a possible (or) logic circuit based on
hemiquinones. The operation of the circuit is as follows: When a potential
difference is applied across electrodes E_3 and E_4, if a current is read
between E_1 and E_2 it means that one and only one of the two hemiquinones in
the circuit has switched.

Clearly the notions presented above require critical examination and both
solid theoretical and experimental support. Therefore we have undertaken a
rough theoretical study of hemiquinone Ia with the following targets: the
potential surface of hemiquinone Ia; the motion pathway; the exchange frequency
(bit stability); the induced tunneling rate (read/write times); and some
experimental estimation of these parameters. The present preliminary
communication contains some rough estimates of these parameters.

                              THEORETICAL STUDIES

Motion of particles in double well potentials has been treated successfully
in the past by the tunneling approach (4,8,9) and we shall adopt the ideas
that were developed for the treatment of such systems to estimate the expected
frequency of oscillation ν_t of structures such as Ia and Ib. In actually

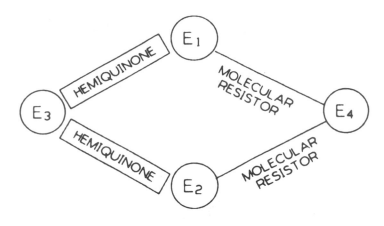

OR CIRCUIT

Fig. 2: A logic circuit of hemiquinones.

calculating a tunneling frequency, attention must be paid to the effective
dimensionality of the problem. We will use the term tunneling generally to
characterize the non-activated motion of the proton between the two minima.
One has to find out whether the motion of the protons is simultaneous or
consecutive. In the case of the simultaneous motion, the tunneling takes
place along one configuration coordinate of the moving hydrogens from their
corresponding oxygens. In this case, our problem would be effectively one-
dimensional. As the particles are displaced, the energy of the system rises
to a maximum, and returns to the original value when the other equilibrium
position is reached. Such a diagram is shown in Fig. 3a. On the other hand
in the case of a consecutive motion, one deals with a two-dimensional motion
along the coordinates of each O-H bond separately. The potential surface of
the system is then three dimensional and the two-dimensional projection is
shown in Fig. 3b. To predict the dominant mechanism is not straightforward.
One has to calculate the tunneling probability in each case separately and
assume that the higher probability motion is the operative one. A more
complicated issue is the separation of the tunneling motion of the protons
from the motions of the other nuclei. A Born-Oppenheimer separation of the
electronic and nuclear motions will be valid in these systems. A further
adiabatic separation of the motion of the nuclei into protonic and other
motions, and defining a potential for motion of the protons decoupled from
the nuclei (1,10), is generally valid only to lowest order.

In the extreme of very strongly coupled motion, we can view the motion
of the protons as polaron-like (11), such that the bond length and angles of
all other nuclei readjust as the protons migrate between the minima. Although
physically it is clear that the protons in fact move and readjust more rapidly
than the heavier nuclei, the effective potential barrier height for tunneling
can nevertheless be that calculated for infinite coupling, since the protonic
jump should occur when the surroundings of the proton in the two wells become
equivalent via thermal fluctuation. (12) The next question involves the actual
shape of the barrier. Numerous ab initio and semiempirical calculations of
similar systems have been performed. (1) Ady and Brickmann (3) investigated
the formic acid dimer, and found a barrier of 59 kcal/mol with a full width
of 0.8 Å for the coupled motion of the two protons. Graegerov (13) determined
experimentally a barrier of 63 kcal/mol for the quinhydrone system. Karlstrom
et al. calculated (14) a smaller barrier (12 kcal/mol) for the malondialdehyde
species, but this work, unlike the formic acid dimer study, did not allow the

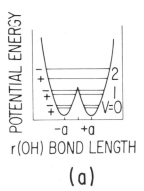

(a)

RELATIVE ENERGIES OF CALCULATED STRUCTURES

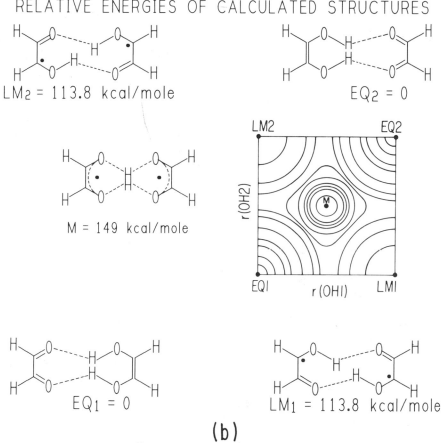

Fig. 3:   Diagrams of "a" the one dimensional double well potential and "b" a
          two dimensional potential surface for hemiquinone I as represented
          by the model molecule that was calculated.

other modes to relax, so this number is not the one relevant to the adiabatic
barrier; in addition, only one proton moves in that system; their calculation
treats the electronic structure properly, via configuration interaction with a
substantial basis. We have carried out calculations on the simple model molecule shown in Fig. 3b. These were ab initio STO-3G and STO 4-31G calculations
using the Gaussian 70 program of Pople and co-workers. The potential is quite
close to adiabatic: all C-O and C-C bond lengths as well as the O-H-O distances
and angles were varied for each position of the proton. This near-adiabatic
barrier height was then found to be 149.7 kcal/mol. This compares with the
value of 145.8 kcal/mol calculated for the same system by Wilcox (15) using
the MINDO 2 semi-empirical method.(16) These barriers are probably in error
due to the small basis sets employed and to the artificiality of the model
species, which is almost certainly unstable. A large error is introduced
by the single-determinant wavefunction, since proper description of the O-H
bond dissociation will require some inclusion of correlation. Nevertheless,
these calculations do indicate that very large barriers to proton motion can
be attained in the limit of infinite coupling. This calculation also indicates
that the minimum-energy path is surprisingly the one on which the two protons
move consecutively rather than simultaneously. Thus the energy for the point
at which one proton is still in its original position but the other has moved
to the saddle point is 113.8 kcal/mol, notably lower than the symmetric barrier
to simultaneous jumping.

PREPARATION AND NMR SPECTRUM OF A MODEL HEMIQUINONE

To investigate the properties of hemiquinones, we have prepared the species
shown in Fig. 4 by the synthetic sequence given in Fig. 5. The NMR obtained
for this flexomer in chloroform solution is given in Fig. 6. If the feature
at 5.57 ppm is taken as due to exchanging protons, an exchange activation
energy of roughly 14.8 kcal/mol can be estimated. An EPR signal is also
observed; this may be due to oxygen reactions with the hemiquinone (17), and
more careful experiments, involving strictly oxygen-free conditions and both
proton and ^{13}C NMR, are in progress.

TUNNELING IN A DOUBLE WELL AND THE EFFECT OF AN ELECTRIC FIELD

The physics of tunneling in double wells is well understood. On the other
hand the electric field induced tunneling merits further consideration. The
influence of the electric field on the hemiquinone on the switching process is
such that the tunneling particles are initially found in the high energy well.
This resembles the case of α particle decay where a particle is caged in a
high energy potential well and tunnels into a lower energy continuum. Thus
the similarity of the two problems justified treating the tunneling due to the
electric field identically to α particle decay.(18)

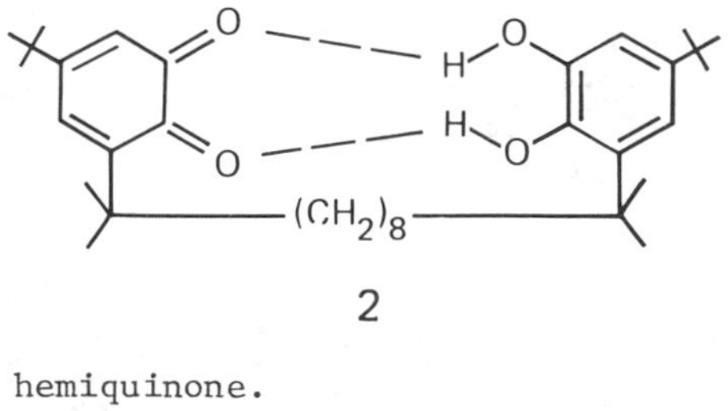

2

Fig. 4: A synthesized hemiquinone.

Suppose we call W_s the tunneling rate in the symmetric barrier and W_a the switching rate in the asymmetric barrier. Then

$$W_s = \frac{\hbar\omega}{2\pi} e^{-\sqrt{2m}} A_s = \hbar/\tau_{st}$$

and following closely calculations for α particle decay, (18)

$$W_a = \frac{\hbar\omega}{2\pi} e^{-\sqrt{2m}} A_a = \hbar/\tau_{sw}$$

Here ω is the proton vibrational frequency, τ_{sw} and τ_{st} are switching and stability times, and A is the WKB integral

$$A = \int_{x'}^{x''} \sqrt{E-V} \; dx/h$$

We want W_s to be small so that the memory element will be stable, but W_a be large to allow fast switching. A field of 10^6 V/cm changes A by <u>roughly</u> 20% for the molecule in Fig. 3. Thus

$$A_a \cong 0.8A_s, \quad \Delta \equiv A_s - A_a \cong 0.2A_s$$

and we have

$$W_a/W_s = e^{-\sqrt{2m}(A_a - A_s)} = e^{-\sqrt{2m}\,\Delta}$$

$$(\omega/2\pi \cong 10^{+15} \; sec^{-1})$$

For the simple molecule in Fig. 3, W_s was calculated to be 10^{-2} sec^{-1} when a barrier of the quartic form was assumed, the STO-3G results for the infinite-coupling limit were used and no thermal effects were included. In performing

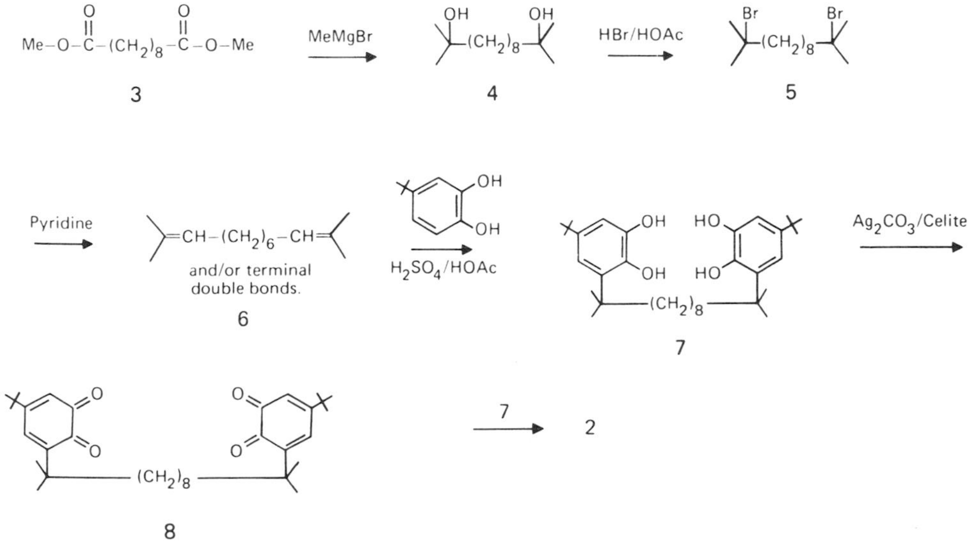

Fig. 5:   The synthetic pathway.

these calculations, we have neglected the zero-point energy. We have also parametrized the effective mass, which will be larger than the bare proton mass, as is usual in polaron transport. (11) It should be noted that both the tunneling frequency and the WKB factor are extremely sensitive to the shape of the barrier and therefore the calculated W_S is merely an estimate of the observable frequency. Using the preliminary NMR results for the hemiquinone of Fig. 4, one obtains a transfer rate of roughly $\omega e^{-E_A/kT} = 10^4$ sec^{-1}.

The argument underlying our use of the infinitely-coupled adiabatic potential for protonic motion in hemiquinone species such as that of Fig. 3 is based on a Franck-Condon like separation of the motion of the tunneling proton from that of the other molecular motions. Then if the protons are to jump they must do so in a geometry such that their energy is the same before and after the jump.(12) This means that the lowest possible barrier would be that found for the proton sitting in its highest-energy position but with all other nuclei adiabatically relaxed. Physically, the Franck-Condon-like picture implies that the relevant proton-transfer rate should be determined by a combination of an activated process (to attain degeneracy of the protonic states localized on the two sides of the double well) and a second process (site-to-site transfer in the activated, symmetric state) which has both tunneling and activated components. This picture may fail due to dynamic coupling of the protonic and oxygen motions (9), but it should constitute a valid first guess.

The reasons for our calculating such unreasonably high barriers in proton motion are not entirely clear, but there appear to be three principal causes, the neglect of activation (cf. above) and the choices of molecule and of method. STO-3G is rather good for near-equilibrium geometries, but the radicaloid nature of the high-energy states in Fig. 3b puts severe demands both on a one-determinant and on a minimum-basis calculation. Also, if the transition states indeed have some radical (or at least strong delocalization) character then they will require for their stabilization (that is, for short switching times) a pi system, such as is found in the hemiquinones of Fig. 1.

It seems that for $\Delta = 0.2A_s$ in the species of Fig. 3 using the calculated infinite-coupling barrier the electric field induced switching is far too slow to be practical, but it should be mentioned that Δ would probably be larger when more polarizable molecules such as those in Figs. 1c and 1d are employed. In addition, the proton coupling to the remainder of the molecule is probably far weaker than we have assumed.

DISCUSSION

Hemiquinones have been shown to be bistable molecules with meaningful interconversion rates. Although our preliminary calculations and spectra do not yield an exact value of the barrier height of these flexomers, the rates clearly can be put in the range 10^{+2}-10^{+12} sec^{-1} by proper molecular design. The calculated result predicting the nonsymmetric transition state is of some interest in itself, and is being pursued in our laboratories.

Both the hemiquinones studied are only initial test study species. A more reasonable candidate as an information storage molecule is represented by the imidazole derivative of Fig. 1c. This collective system of four protons is larger and more polarizable than other similar smaller molecules which have

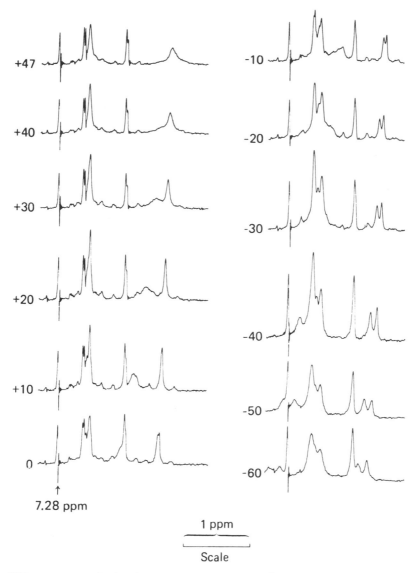

+47

+40

+30

+20

+10

0

7.28 ppm

-10

-20

-30

-40

-50

-60

1 ppm

Scale

Fig. 6: NMR spectra of the hemiquinone of Fig. 4. The number on each spectrum
        is the temperature in degrees Celsius.

been considered here. The collective systems have several advantages over
single protons--they are less susceptible to fluctuation (smaller W_s) should
be more environment-independent and may be easier to prepare. Furthermore,
such collective systems should have higher electrical susceptibility and,
therefore, should switch faster. Also, they are closer to the sorts of
hydrogen-bonded storage devices (ferroelectrics) which have been previously
investigated, but are unsuitable because of hysteresis and the materials
problems associated with macroscopic displacive phase transitions. The
collective effect of true ferroelectric systems ($\sim10^{23}$ protons) will of course

be infinitely stronger than a simple molecular species such as that of Fig. 1, but the essential properties of the ferroelectric, fast τ_{sw} and slow τ_{st}, should be realizable with properly designed molecular species.

Our conclusions thus far support the notion that hemiquinones are suitable candidates for dynamic molecular information storage elements and call for additional studies to further the understanding of these interesting molecules.

ACKNOWLEDGMENT

We thank Drs. T.D. Schultz, C.A. Brown, A.D. MacLean, and M.J. Freiser for helpful discussions. Dr. C. Wilcox of Cornell University carried out the MINDO calculations; we are very grateful to him for these results; we are also indebted to Dr. J.R. Lyerla for the nmr data. M.R. thanks J. Lambert, B. Hoffman, and G.L. Hofacker for helpful comments.

REFERENCES

1. Reviews include G.C. Pimentel and A.L. McClellan, Ann. Revs. Phys. Chem. 22, 347 (1971); G.L. Hofacker, Y. Marechal and M.A. Ratner in P. Schuster et al., eds. The Hydrogen Bond (North Holland, Amsterdam, 1976); M.A. Ratner and J.R. Sabin, in Quantum Mechanics--The First Fifty Years, ed. S.S. Chissick et al. (Butterworth's, London, 1973); P.A. Kollman and L.C. Allen, Chem. Revs. 72, 273 (1972); W.C. Hamilton and J.A. Ibers, Hydrogen Bonding in Solids (Benjamin, New York, 1968); Y. Marechal, in Molecular Interactions; H. Ratajczak and W.J. Orville-Thomas, Eds., (Wiley, New York, 1980).

2. J.A. Ibers, J. Chem. Phys. 41, 25 (1964).

3. E. Clementi et al., J. Chem. Phys. 54, 508 (1971); E. Ady and J. Brickmann Chem. Phys. Lett. 11, 302 (1971); P. Schuster, Int. J. Quantum Chem. 3, 851 (1969). We use the term "adiabatic" simply to denote the potential corresponding to infinitely slow proton motion.

4. P.O. Löwdin has stressed the importance of proton motion in connection with the genetic code, e.g., Adv. Quantum Chem. 2, 216 (1965).

5. A. Aviram, P.E. Seiden, U.S. Patent No. 3,833,894 (1974); A. Aviram, P.E. Seiden, M.A. Ratner, 25th IUPAC Congress, Abstr. page 195 (1975); A. Aviram, P.E. Seiden, M.A. Ratner, IBM Internal Publication RC No. 5919 (1976).

6. F. Carter, NRC Memorandum Report 4335, 35 (1980).

7. R. Gleiter and D. Werthemann, J. Am. Chem. Soc. 94, 651 (1972).

8. D.M. Dennison and G.E. Uhlenbeck, Phys. Rev. 41, 313 (1932).

9. M.D. Harmony, Chem. Soc. Rev. 1, 211 (1972). (Note that eq. 8 of this article contains a misprint).

10. B.I. Stepanov, Zh. Fiz. Khim. 19, 50 (1945); Y. Marechal and A. Witkowkski, J. Chem. Phys., 48, 3697 (1968); N.D. Sokolov and V.A. Savalev, Chem. Phys., 22, 383 (1977); C.A. Coulson and G.N. Robertson, Proc. Roy. Soc.

A342, 289 (1976); S.F. Fischer, G.L. Hofacker, M.A. Ratner, J. Chem.
Phys. 52, 1934 (1970); T.R. Singh and J.L. Wood, J. Chem. Phys. 48, 4567
(1968); S.A. Barton and W.R. Thorson, ibid. 71, 4263 (1979).

11. The small-polaron mobility case is discussed by G.L. Sewell, Phys. Rev.
    129, 597 (1963) and by T. Holstein, Ann. Phys. (NY), 8, 343 (1959).

12. This was first stressed in connection with electron transfer by W. Libby.
    The Franck-Condon barrier is important in most work on proton and on
    electron transfer. Reviews include R.A. Marcus, Ann. Revs. Phys. Chem.,
    15, 155 (1964); W.L. Reynolds and R.W. Lumry, Mechanisms of Electron
    Transfer (Ronald, New York, 1966); J. Ulstrup, Charge Transfer Processes
    in Condensed Media (Springer, New York, 1979).

13. I.P. Gragerov and G.P. Miklukhin, Dokl. Akad. Nauk, S.S.R., 62, 79 (1948);
    Zhur. Fiz. Khim., 24, 582 (1950), A.I. Brodskii and I.P. Gragerov, Dokl.
    Akad, Nauk, S.S.R., 79, 277 (1951). See also A.A. Bothner-By, J. Am.
    Chem. Soc., 73, 4228 (1961).

14. F. Karlstrom et al., J. Am. Chem. Soc., 97, 4186 (1975); 98, 6851 (1978).

15. C. Wilcox, private communication. Wilcox also calculated the potential
    for the molecule in an applied electric field of 10^6 V/cm; the ground
    state energy difference E of 1a is calculated to be 10.08 kcal/mol $\cong$
    3500 cm^{-1}, slightly larger than the classical estimate.

16. M.J.S. Dewar, Science, 187, 1037 (1975) and related papers.

17. G.A. Russell, in E.T. Kaiser and L. Kevan, eds., Radical Ions (Wiley, New
    York, 1968).

18. G. Gamow, Z. Physik, 51, 204 (1928); R.W. Gurney and E.U. Condon, Phys.
    Rev., 33, 127 (1929).

DISCUSSION

Dr. Sandman: GTE - The situation you posed in your model compound
is actually a rather fascinating situation where you are asking different types
of noncovalent interactions to compete. In the hemiquinone calculation where
you are 140 kilocalories above reference, you are roughly one electron volt
above the geometry where you would have a pi complex. Do you feel that
that is a general feature of the type of calculation that you are doing?
Namely, is the pi complex in general going to be a more stable configuration?
The second question refers to your model compound, have you been able to
obtain either an X-ray structure at room temperature or at lower temperatures?

Dr. Aviram: We felt that a charge transfer complex will cause the
barrier to be lowered, and because of the requirement of stability of each bit
that we had in mind, we wanted to avoid this complication, and therefore, we
deliberately designed a molecule, more specifically, the one that we synthesized,
to avoid a charge transfer complex. As to the other question that you asked me--
yes, we started doing an X-ray difraction analysis, and unfortunately as sometimes happens, the scientist passed away and the work was not resumed.

Prof. Marks: NW Univ. - Coming back to the experimental aspects, I
am fascinated by the variable temperature NMR spectra. I don't quite understand

what is going on there. Did you just try a simple dilution experiment to try
to segregate what is intermolecular from what is intramolecular?

Dr. Aviram: We did not do that. At this point, as I mentioned to
you before, the NMR experiments and the EPR experiments are being resumed
at your university. Mark is supervising that.

Prof. Marks: It really is critical to be able to control the
structures of these species, and you could think of so many interesting ways
that those quinones can flex around and dimerize.

Dr. Aviram: Right. Perhaps we should go back and synthesize something that is much more rigid where these degrees of freedom do not exist.

Dr. Honig: Univ. of Ill. - The order of magnitude is somewhat
disconcerting. Is there any precedent for that in the ab initio calculations?
The second question is since the effect of the electric field you calculated
is of the order of, or is almost identical to the experimental barrier, of
what relevance is that calculation to anything? You are working with 13
percent on 140 kilocalories per mole. The total barrier is 14.

Dr. Aviram: Let's take the second one. What we were interested in
was to show that the electric field does have a handle on these molecules and
does lower the barrier. As I told you, these are not the molecules that we
intended for study of switching. We made these molecules for the sole purpose
of studying the motion in a symmetrical double well to confirm that in these
particular double well potentials the particles do migrate from one site to
the other. That was the sole purpose of the synthesis. If we were interested
in doing switching, we would have synthesized something which is much more
polarizable, much larger and on which an electric field has a much greater
effect. As to the first question on the ab initio calculation, factors of
three and four are not something that hasn't been observed before. In our
lab, we have a researcher by the name of Silverman who is constantly doing
molecular calculations, and he told me that he obtains variations of this sort
routinely, so our results are not something peculiar to these calculations.

Dr. Ratner: NW Univ. - I would like to respond a little more to what
you said. Just to complete the response, two things--first, that 14.9 comes
from the interpretation of the NMR that Tobin Marks asked about, and there are
some problems with interpreting that spectrum. As he already indicated, it is
not clear exactly which species you are seeing. There is a process at 14.9, but
it is not clear what the process at 14.9 corresponds to this intramolecular
transfer. The second thing, of course, is the usual sort of hand-waving
argument. These are STO 3G calculations; we know they are wrong, and you must
include correlations, and probably a simple multi-configuration study is
adequate to do that. The third thing is; I think the slide on the NMR may
have been deceptive. The calculations that we were talking about were for
the model molecule without any conjugation. The 14.9 number comes from the
different molecule with aromatic stabilization. There you have a pi on each
side; one would expect the barrier to be considerably lower.

Dr. Shipman: ANL - You have used the temperature dependence of the NMR
lineshape to determine the activation energy for the exchange between two or more
hydrogen bonding environments. The 15 kcal/mole activation energy that you
have measured via NMR lineshape analysis suggests a physical process; in
particular, you could be averaging between two environments, one in which there
are two hydrogen bonds and one in which there are no hydrogen bonds. One
possible way to verify this is to place the molecules in non-hydrogen bonding

solvents; you should find that 5-7 kcal/mole per hydrogen bond are required to break the hydrogen bonds between your molecules. In addition, you should look at the $C=O$ stretching region in the infrared absorption spectrum and see if there is a substantial amount of non-hydrogen bonded $C=O$ in your system. The non-hydrogen bonded $C=O$ stretch will be at a higher frequency than the hydrogen bonded $C=O$ stretch.

Dr. Aviram: You mean couple it with the infrared?

Dr. Shipman: Yes. It will give you some information in addition to that contained in the NMR spectrum.

Dr. Aviram: Thank you very much.

CHAPTER II

MOLECULAR MEMORY AND HYDROGEN BONDING

R.C. Haddon and F.H. Stillinger
Bell Laboratories
Murray Hill, NJ 07974

INTRODUCTION

Characteristic sizes of electronic components in computer hardware have displayed a relentless shrinkage with the passage of time. While 10 cm might be an appropriate length scale to describe vacuum tube equipment available in 1940, 10 μm spacings on semiconductor chips has become routine in 1980. Each passing decade thus has witnessed reduction in linear dimension by a factor of ten. By obvious extrapolation one concludes that 2020 will be "the year of the nanometer," with computing elements reduced to the size of individual molecules.

Does this kind of extrapolation make sense in useful technological terms? Can single molecules actually serve as reliable computing elements? Intriguing support for affirmative answers to these questions emerges from established fact. Certainly molecular biology demonstrates by concrete example that individual molecules (specifically DNA and RNA) can serve as information storage, replication, and transmittal media. But information processing in the regime of molecular biology is notoriously slow, perhaps having had no evolutionary compulsion to be otherwise. Furthermore it is chemically uncertain that the class of compounds produced and selected by terrestrial chemical evolution could ever become substantially more rapid, efficient, or versatile by conservative structural modifications. Fortunately synthetic chemistry offers a much wider set of opportunities, one aspect of which we explore in this paper. Another approach, based on photochemical hole burning, has been previously explored. (1)

If indeed some part of computer technology is headed for the molecular regime it is time to turn creative intellectual effort in chemistry and physics to the question of how best that can be achieved.

TAUTOMERISM AND SWITCHING

The fact that many molecules can switch between alternative tautomeric forms may provide a phenomenological entree into the desired novel technology. In particular many cases are known involving intramolecular hydrogen atom shifts between alternative binding sites (potential minima). An elementary

example is provided by glycine, the simplest amino acid, as it transforms
between undissociated and zwitterionic forms:

$$NH_2-CH_2-COOH \rightleftarrows {}^+NH_3-CH_2-COO^-$$

5-Methylpyrazole also exhibits a tautomeric hydrogen shift in a manner that
obviously couples to the pi electron (double bond) character of the molecular
skeleton:

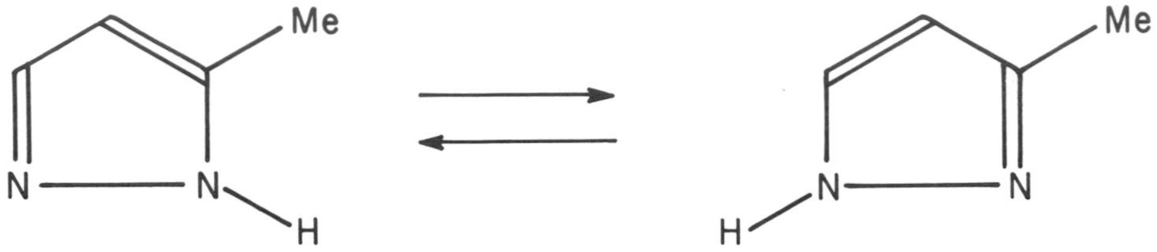

One suspects that switching speeds under appropriate conditions could be
extremely fast for protons, perhaps in the subpicosecond range, owing to the
small mass of that particle. But protons alone are not interesting in this
respect; chemical groups such as methyl or trimethylsilyl could perform with
competitive speeds provided that the distance to be traversed were sufficiently
small. In any event, for information storage applications it is necessary to
have the binding sites inequivalent and separated by a sufficiently high
potential barrier so that neither tunneling nor thermal fluctuations can
inadvertently switch the molecule from one state to the other. Switching
should occur only under external control as by application of a suitable
light pulse.

Figure 1 schematically illustrates an ideal situation for photochemical
switching. It shows three potential energy curves versus a proton positional
coordinate. The lowest curve (a) corresponds to the electronic ground state
and exhibits two inequivalent minima labelled "state 0" and "state 1"; these
are the tautomeric alternatives. The upper two curves (b,c) are a pair of
excited electronic states that afford opportunity for switching. Since the
ground state is asymmetric so too will be these upper states.

It is an established experimental fact that electronic excitation can
drastically alter shapes of potential energy curves. In particular the
relative binding strengths of alternative sites can be reversed, and barriers
reduced or eliminated. For the hypothetical example in Figure 1 we have
permitted the excited states to show such alteration and to tip respectively
right and left.

Optical switching from state 0 to state 1 is initiated by irradiation at
frequency $\nu(0{\rightarrow}1)$. This induces a vertical transition to the lower excited-
state curve, yielding a vibrationally excited molecule in accord with the
Franck-Condon principle. Vibrational relaxation on this upper curve changes
the mean value of the proton's x coordinate to conform to that of state 1,
roughly. Fluorescence decay then returns the system to the ground-state curve
but now with the proton switched. The protonic itinerary is traced out by the
sequence of three solid arrows.

The inverse process whereby state 1 is photochemically switched back to
state 0 requires the higher excited state, but it is otherwise similar. The

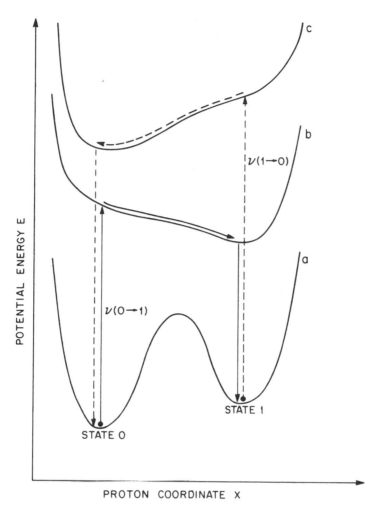

Fig. 1: Idealized photochemical switching scheme for molecules exhibiting inequivalent proton tautomers.

dashed arrows indicate the corresponding process which is initiated by radiation with frequency $\nu(1\rightarrow0)$. Generally $\nu(0\rightarrow1)$ and $\nu(1\rightarrow0)$ would be distinct on account of the basic asymmetry involved, so that the direction of photochemical switching could in principle be controllable. A current photochromic memory system advanced by Heller (2) operates effectively at room temperature by virtue of its holographic basis; the spectral demands in the present context would probably require elimination of absorption band overlap by cooling to very low temperature. (1)

The simple situation just described may in real applications involve considerable complication. It may be necessary to consider only weakly allowed electronic transitions in order to allow enough time to elapse in the upper states for the requisite vibrational relaxation to be effective. This would imply either weak absorptions, or intervention of intersystem crossings to yet other potential curves. However these details do not as a matter of principle eliminate the possibility of photochemical switching.

What we have just described in rudimentary fashion is a passive storage
medium for information encoded in binary form. The difference in spectral
absorbance for the tautomers offers the means to read out a stored message.
The important question of whether one can address single molecules is an
independent issue which we must leave aside for this presentation.

COUPLED SWITCHING

Figure 2 illustrates the fact that two (or more) tautomeric shifts can
occur within the same molecule. Since both labile units (L) interact with
the electronic structure of the entire molecule there inevitably exists a
coupling between them. The excitation frequency required to switch one group
depends on which state the other group is in, and vice versa. Such coupling
provides the opportunity to perform information processing within a single
molecule.

Let x and y represent the coordinates which describe motion of the two
labile units. We are now concerned with energy surfaces in the two-dimensional
x,y space and how they might serve for selective switching. In analogy with
the preceding case of Section. 2 we write the following expressions:

$$E_{aa}(x,y) = E_a^1(x) + E_a^2(y) + F_{aa}(x,y)$$

$$E_{ba}(x,y) = E_b^1(x) + E_a^2(y) + F_{ba}(x,y)$$

$$E_{ab}(x,y) = E_a^1(x) + E_b^2(y) + F_{ab}(x,y)$$

$$E_{ca}(x,y) = E_c^1(x) + E_a^2(y) + F_{ca}(x,y)$$

$$E_{ac}(x,y) = E_a^1(x) + E_c^2(y) + F_{ac}(x,y)$$

The first stands for the electronic ground state and the four that follow are
excited states. The single-variable functions E_a^1, E_b^1, and E_c^1 represent for
the x unit the type of curves illustrated earlier in Figure 1; E_a^2, E_b^2, and
E_c^2 are the corresponding (but not identical!) functions for the y unit. The
F_{ij} give the coupling energies between the units.

The two excitation frequencies $\nu(0{\to}1)$ and $\nu(1{\to}0)$ invoked in the previous
discussion for a single tautomeric unit will now split into four frequencies,
depending on the state of the other unit. The need to eliminate absorption
band overlaps by cooling becomes an even more stringent matter in this case.
We might denote the four resulting frequencies for switching the x unit by

$$\nu(0{\to}1,0), \quad \nu(0{\to}1,1), \quad \nu(1{\to}0,0), \quad \nu(1{\to}0,1)$$

wherein we adhere to the convention that one "variable" denotes the switching
event and the other denotes the state of the unit which remains unchanged.
Similarly there will be four more frequencies

$$\nu(0,0{\to}1), \quad \nu(0,1{\to}0), \quad \nu(1,0{\to}1), \quad \nu(1,1{\to}0)$$

for switching of the y unit. We shall presume that all eight frequencies can
be rendered sufficiently distinct that they can be used in any sequence to
effect the desired switchings.

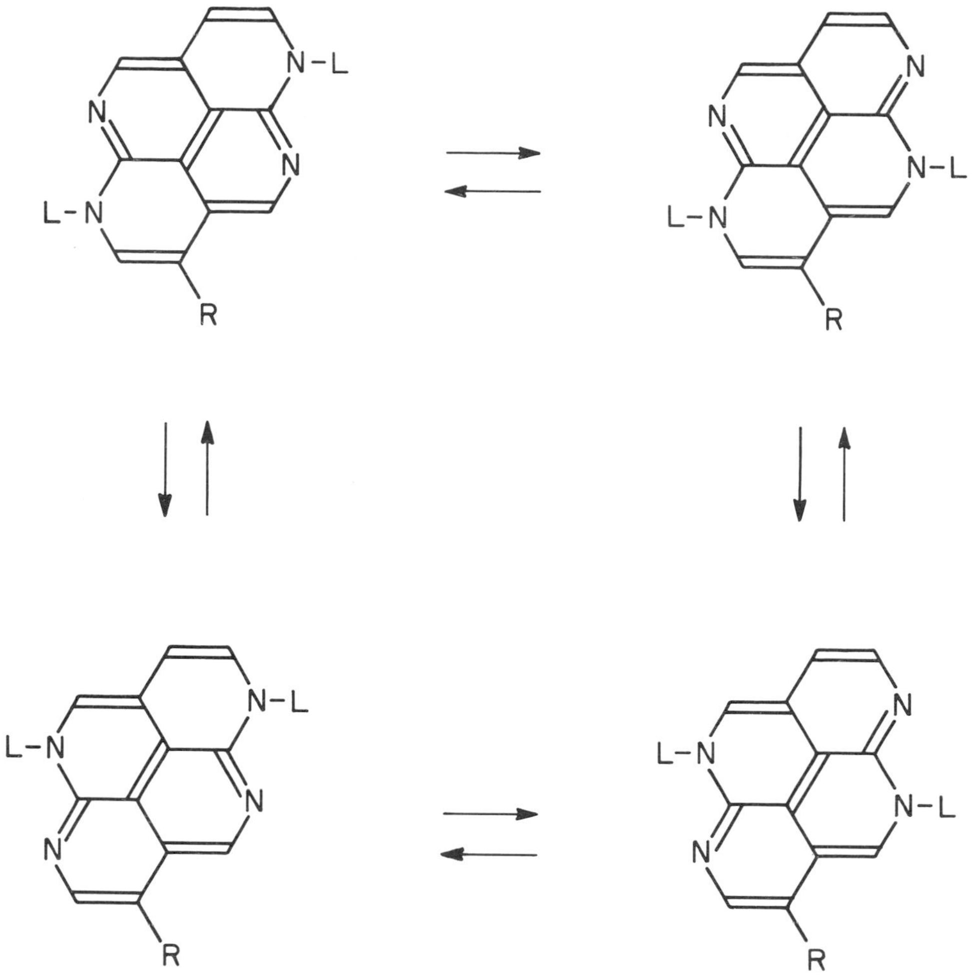

Fig. 2: Coupled shifts of labile groups (L) within a single molecule. The
functional group indicated by R is present to induce asymmetry.

We now observe that adroitly chosen irradiation sequences permit a
rudimentary form of information processing to be carried out intramolecularly.
Starting from any one of the four binary states $(\bar{x}, \bar{y})$ = (0,0), (0,1), (1,0),
or (1,1) it is possible to set $\bar{x}$ and $\bar{y}$ both equal to the maximum of $\bar{x}$ and $\bar{y}$,
or to the minimum of $\bar{x}$ and $\bar{y}$, or one to the maximum and one to the minimum.
The respective irradiation schemes are shown in Figure 3.

Unfortunately, it is not possible to carry out all binary operations with
two-unit molecules. Three interacting units in the same molecule (see Figure
4) are required in order to carry out addition and multiplication functions
for the binary codes carried by two of the three. Figure 5 indicates a five-
pulse sequence that simultaneously yields the binary sum (modulo 2) and the
product (i.e. logical "and") for the numbers initially borne by two units.
Using the foregoing ideas the reader should be able to discover schemes for
generating other binary logical operations such as "or", "nor", and "nand".
It is not our purpose here to belabor the point. It is important to realize
that there can be "smart molecules" capable of carrying out their own information processing in situ. With this concept as a backdrop it becomes crucially
important to mount careful investigations of the potential energy surfaces in
molecules exhibiting tautomerism. Comprehensive and precise understanding of

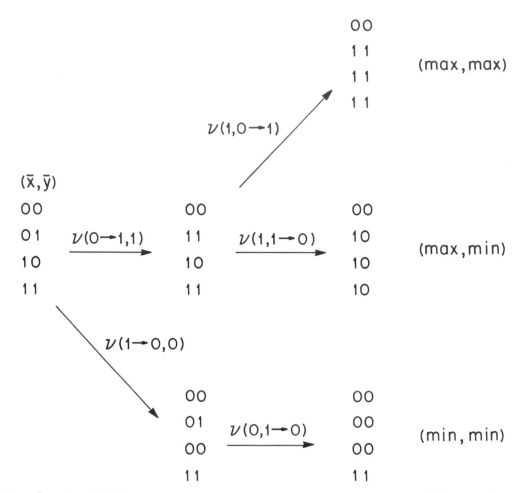

Fig. 3: Irradiation sequences to carry out binary operations within single molecules bearing two labile units.

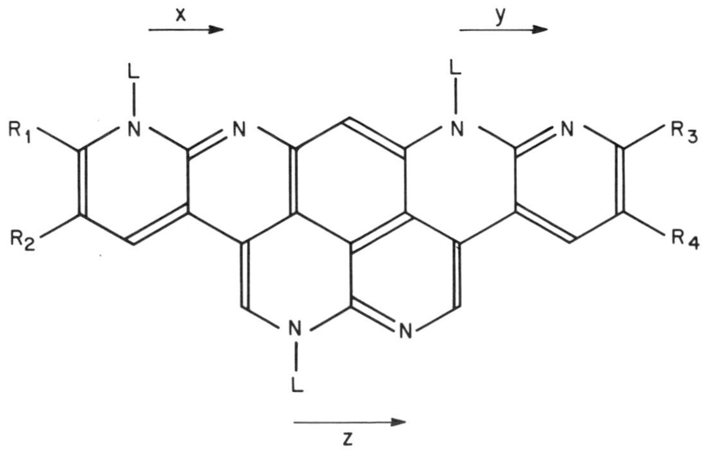

Fig. 4: Molecule possessing three labile units (L), with respective coordinated x, y, and z. The chemical groups R_1....R_4 induce the necessary asymmetry.

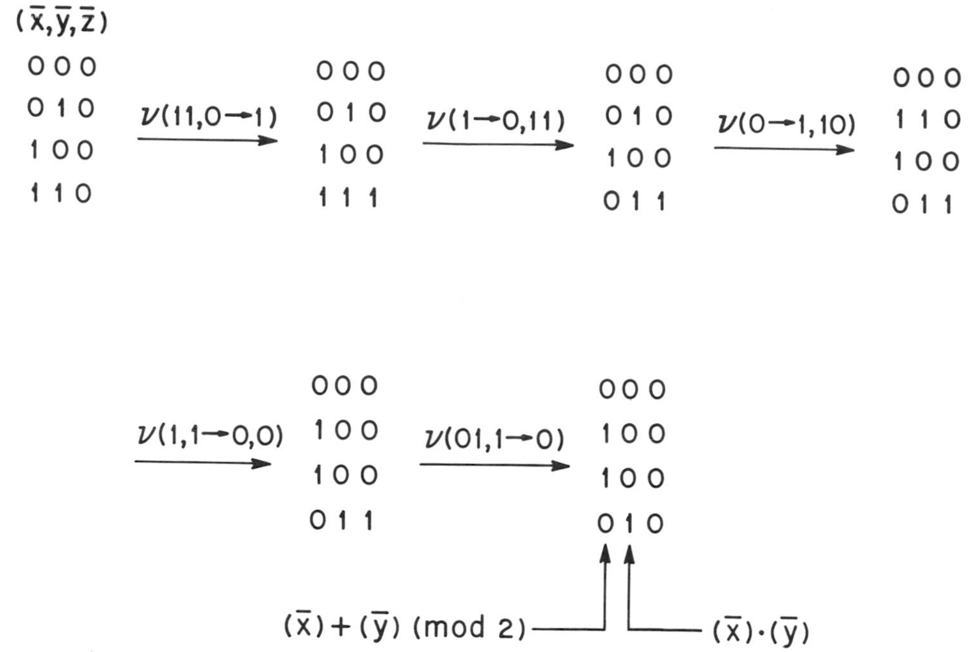

$(\overline{x},\overline{y},\overline{z})$

0 0 0		0 0 0		0 0 0		0 0 0
0 1 0	$\nu(11,0 \to 1)$	0 1 0	$\nu(1 \to 0,11)$	0 1 0	$\nu(0 \to 1,10)$	1 1 0
1 0 0	$\longrightarrow$	1 0 0	$\longrightarrow$	1 0 0	$\longrightarrow$	1 0 0
1 1 0		1 1 1		0 1 1		0 1 1

		0 0 0		0 0 0
$\nu(1,1 \to 0,0)$		1 0 0	$\nu(01,1 \to 0)$	1 0 0
$\longrightarrow$		1 0 0	$\longrightarrow$	1 0 0
		0 1 1		0 1 0

$(\overline{x})+(\overline{y})\;(\mathrm{mod}\;2)\longrightarrow\qquad\qquad(\overline{x})\cdot(\overline{y})$

Fig. 5: Irradiation pulse sequence applicable to a three-unit molecule which
effects sum and product operations.

these surfaces is an obvious prerequisite to the synthesis and use of "smart
molecules".

STUDIES OF HYDROGEN BONDING IN 9-HYDROXYPHENALENONES

As an approach to the preceding ideas we have mounted an in-depth
investigation of a class of compounds based on 9-hydroxyphenalenone (1). The
parent (1) has now been extensively studied and shown to possess a strong
intramolecular hydrogen bond

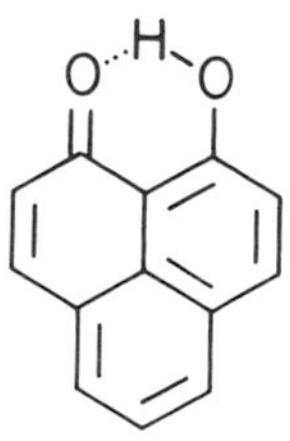

1 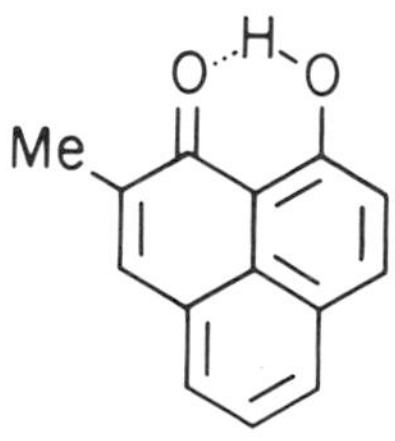   2 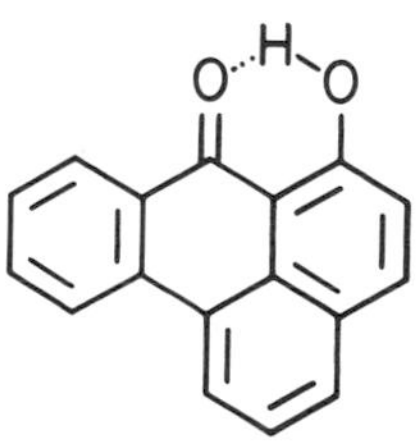   3

The first question we addressed for this molecule concerned the nature
of the ground state potential surface with respect to proton motion between
the two (equivalent) oxygen atoms. In particular, we wished to determine
whether this surface was of the symmetric double (C_s) or single minimum (C_{2v})
type (Figure 6).

ESCA studies by Brown (3) showed that on the relevant time scale (10^{-16}
sec) 1 possessed chemically inequivalent oxygen atoms (Figure 7), thus
demonstrating that 1 is characterized by a double minimum ground state in the

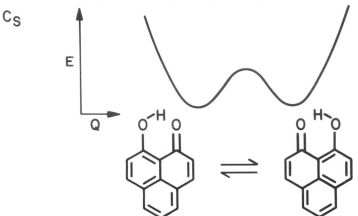

DOUBLE MINIMUM (ASYMMETRICAL HYDROGEN BOND)

C_S

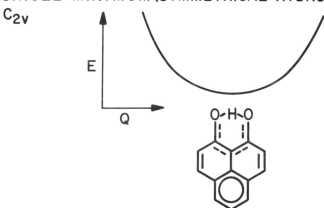

SINGLE MINIMUM (SYMMETRICAL HYDROGEN BOND)

C_2v

Fig. 6: Possible proton transfer potential surfaces for 9-hydroxyphenalenone
         (1).

O_{1s} BINDING
ENERGY (eV)   RELATIVE
                                               AREA

539.23   1.0

536.64   0.99 ± 0.03

Fig. 7: ESCA chemical shifts for 9-hydroxyphenalenone (1) in the gas phase
         (from Ref. 3).

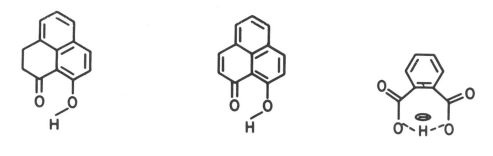

190 ± 7 KHZ   **141 ± 1 KHZ**   **72 ± 2 KHZ**

Fig. 8: DQCCs (kHz) in chloroform solution (from Ref. 4).

gas phase. Deuteron quadrupole coupling constant (DQCC) studies by Jackman (4) gave the same result for the solution state of the molecule. Figure 8 shows the DQCC's of 1 and its dihydroderivative contrasted with the value found for the symmetric hydrogen bond in the phthalate anion. An earlier X-ray crystallographic study by Svensson and Abrahams[5,6] had found a C_{2v} structure for 1 (Figure 9), but this is presumably due to the time scale of the experiment rather than the intrinsic symmetry of the molecule: the O...O separation which was found in this work is characteristic of a strong hydrogen bond in a double minimum potential. Finally, a theory (7) based on the second-order Jahn-Teller (SOJT) effect provided a satisfactory rationalization of the nature of hydrogen bonding in the ground states of 1 and conjugated organic molecules in general, and is consistent with double minimum character.

At this point we turned our attention to the nature of the excited state of 1 and the relationship of the ground and excited state potential surfaces along the proton transfer reaction coordinate.

The results of the fluorescence electronic spectroscopy studies by Brus (8) are embodied in Figure 10. It may be seen that the potential barrier for proton migration in the excited state is less than a third of that in the ground state. The ground state tunneling splittings (Δ) are found to be

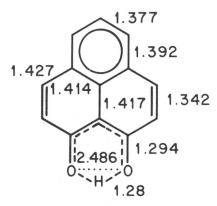

Fig. 9: X-ray crystal structure of 9-hydroxyphenalenone (1) with
         bond lengths (Å) (from Ref.5).

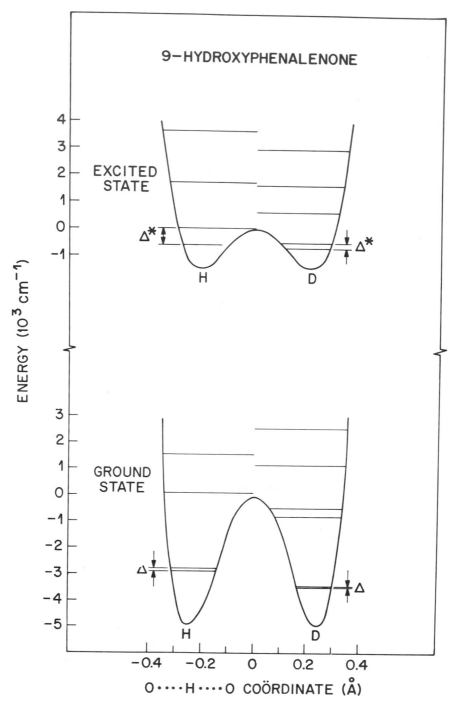

Fig. 10:   Potential energy curves for 9-hydroxyphenalenone (<u>1</u>) derived from
electronic spectroscopic studies (from Ref. 8).

1-h = 130 cm^{-1} and 1-d = 10 cm^{-1}, which lead to tunneling times (τ) of: 1-h = 0.13 psec and 1-d = 1.7 psec (assuming coherent oscillation of the nucleus between potential minima). The excited state tunneling times (τ^*) are found to be: 1-h = 0.02 psec and 1-d = 0.09 psec.

Recent studies (9) of the unsymmetrical 2-methyl-derivative (10) ($\underline{2}$) have shown that the potential minima are split by ~200 cm^{-1} in this compound. This splitting is sufficient to substantially localize the nuclear wave function in the ground state of $\underline{2}$, but not in the excited state. Studies on related molecules where the asymmetry is more pronounced (such as $\underline{3}$ (11)) are currently in progress.

The work to date has allowed a fairly complete characterization of the potential surfaces of $\underline{1}$ and related compounds. Proton transfer via tunneling has been shown to be very fast in these compounds. It seems likely, however, that a more massive group will have to be substituted for the proton if usable memory phenomena are to be observed in these compounds. The trimethylsilyl derivative of $\underline{1}$ (12) has been shown to possess a ground state potential barrier of the same order of magnitude as that found in $\underline{1}$, and may be useful in this connection.

The synthetic effort to produce these molecules, and the experimental studies thus far devoted to their spectroscopic characterization, constitute only the beginning of a long term project. We expect in the near future to expand the set of available tautomeric molecules, to improve the state of knowledge of their ground and excited state potential surfaces, and to examine quantum yields for photochemical switching. Only by concerted effort in all these directions will materials be identified with acceptable performance as molecular memories.

REFERENCES

1. D.M. Burland and D. Haarer, IBM J. Res. Dev. 23, 534 (1979); S. Volker and R.M. Macfarlane, IBM J. Res. Dev. 23, 547 (1979); G. Castro, D. Haarer, R.M. Macfarlane, and H.P. Trommsdorf, US Patent 4,101,976, 1978.

2. H.G. Heller, Chem. Ind. 193 (1978); H.G. Heller, UK Patent 1,464,603, 1977.

3. R.S. Brown, A. Tse, T. Nakashima and R.C. Haddon, J. Am. Chem. Soc. 101, 3157 (1979).

4. L.M. Jackman, J.C. Trewella and R.C. Haddon, J. Am. Chem. Soc. 102, 2519 (1980).

5. C. Svensson, S.C. Abrahams, J.L. Bernstein and R.C. Haddon, J. Am. Chem. Soc. 101, 5759 (1979).

6. S.C. Abrahams, H.E. Bair, R.C. Haddon, F.H. Stillinger and C. Svensson, J. Chem. Phys. 74, 644 (1981).

7. R.C. Haddon, J. Am. Chem. Soc. 102, 1807 (1980).

8. R. Rossetti, R.C. Haddon and L.E. Brus, J. Am. Chem. Soc. 102, 6913 (1980).

9. R. Rossetti, R. Rayford, R.C. Haddon and L.E. Brus, J. Am. Chem. Soc., in press.

10. R.C. Haddon, R. Rayford, and A.M. Hirani, J. Org. Chem., submitted.

11. R.C. Haddon, J. Org. Chem., to be submitted.

12. R.C. Haddon, M.L. Kaplan and A.M. Hirani, unpublished.

DISCUSSION

Dr. Shipman: ANL - If you have tunneling back and forth between two wells in a picosecond or so, how are you going to keep the bit tripped in the state where you want it? Unless you have a computer that can carry out a calculation in much less than a picosecond it is not going to do you much good.

Dr. Haddon: I think ultimately to retain the integrity of the information, one is going to have to go to a more massive mobile group such as trimethylsilyl.

Prof. Ratner: NW Univ. - That structure that you have, involving essentially a 2.5 Å hydrogen bond, is very reminiscent of the old work that Rundle did. In systems where he replaced hydrogen with the deuterium, not only did the hydrogen to oxygen distance change, but the oxygen to oxygen distance also changes in those cases by as much as 0.01 to 0.06 Å. That can result in essentially a completely different spectroscopic characterization. Have you determined the deuteride structure, too, or just the proton structure?

Dr. Haddon: Just the proton structure. Are you suggesting that the structures would be significantly different?

Prof. Ratner: Yes. There are a number of well-documented examples. The standard one is something called chromous acid.

Dr. Haddon: Right. Of course, 9-hydroxyphenalenone is a constrained system.

Prof. Ratner: So are those, or some of them. The chromous acid is not, but I think oxalic acid was the same sort of thing.

Dr. Haddon: We have studied the 9-butoxy. The hydrogen is replaced with a butyl group so that the hydrogen bonding is removed, and we find that the oxygen-oxygen separation opens up from 2.49 to approximately 2.64 Å, so I don't think that there is a great deal of flexibility in this system.

Dr. Siedle: 3M - During the analogue of the system, the phena and hydrogen pentazene system, if the nature of the constituents are high powered, there may be a charge transfer. It would be interesting to speculate. If you start moving those hydrogens that are now bonded to nitrogen instead of oxygen, there might be a significant change in the optimal spectrum.

Dr. Haddon: Yes.

CHAPTER III

INTERGROUP ELECTRON TRANSFER, BACK ELECTRON TRANSFER, BACK TRANSFER
QUENCHING, AND RELAXATION PROCESSES

Ron Kosloff
Department of Physical Chemistry
Hebrew University
Jerusalem, Israel

M. A. Ratner
Department of Chemistry and Materials Research Center
Northwestern University
Evanston, IL 60201

ABSTRACT

For use as switching devices or as photoelectric energy converters, molecular systems must be susceptible to control of the back electron transfer
rates. In natural systems (photosynthetic reaction centers), the back
transfer reaction is at least 10^7 times slower than the downhill electron
transfer process, but the precise roles of the quinones, chlorophylls, iron
atoms, and pheophytins in controlling these relative rates are poorly
understood. We focus on a much more narrowly defined theoretical problem:
how to calculate rates of electron transfer between localization sites in a
generalized molecular crystal model.

The model system which we consider is then one with two electron localization sites linked by a bridge (thus providing both through-bond and through-
space interactions). The localization site is coupled to local vibrons
through both linear (Frohlich-type) and quadratic (frequency-change) terms.
This is a variation of the Holstein molecular crystal model. It is clear that
a fourth timescale (other than those fixed by the vibrational frequency, the
electronic coupling term, and the barrier residence time) must enter into the
problem and that this relates to the relaxation processes which occur on the
localization site. Once the electron has been localized at one site, it will
(within the simple molecular crystal model) continue to undergo multiply
periodic motions. Thus the back transfer rate, within this model, will be
identical to the forward transfer rate. The achievement of switching or of
photoelectric conversion is thus critically dependent upon a relaxation process, which must intervene so as to prevent the back transfer. This relaxation may be provided, for example, by diffusion, by electron energy decay in
bent bands, by rapid intramolecular geometric changes (such as proton
tautomerism) by strain release or by allosteric interactions.

Our calculations are performed using a semigroup approach to reckon the
relaxation effects. This has several advantages over more commonly used

decoupling approximations: it is not dependent upon the assumption of weak
coupling, it can include very high-order relaxation processes, and it is
formally correct even when relaxation effects are stronger than the mixing
terms in the molecular Hamiltonian.

Some of the results of our calculation are not unexpected: when relaxation is ignored, the Robin/Day model valency classifications and the
Goodenough criterion for delocalization are recovered. Simple choices of
relaxation widths reproduce the intervalence transfer line shapes given by
Hush. More generally, however, we predict structure in the intervalence band
and, more strikingly, in the vibrational bands. The dependence of these shapes
on temperature, frequency, and coupling strength is derived straightforwardly.
The Robin/Day classification must be broadened to include relaxation effects,
and we can explain how systems may vary from Robin/Day II (partly delocalized)
to Robin/Day III (fully delocalized) as a function of solvent, surrroundings, or
temperature. Finally, and most suggestively for the purposes of this meeting,
we can derive criteria for when the back-transfer process will become negligible; essentially what is required is relaxation slow enough to permit
some transfer, but fast enough to damp the periodic motions effectively.

I. INTRODUCTION: THE ROLE OF BACK-TRANSFER PROCESSES IN QUENCHING

For use in molecular device applications, we require molecular species
which exhibit either a charge-transfer or an energy-transfer process which can
be controlled selectively. We will be concerned here primarily with electron
transfer and photoexcited electron transfer processes, though similar phenomena and similar theoretical problems are encountered in proton transfer
systems [1-3]. Although their application to switching devices ("rectifiers")
remains uncertain [3,4], ground-state intramolecular electron transfer processes have elicited a great deal of experimental and theoretical study [5-9]
in both biochemical [10] and chemical species, and a good deal is now known
concerning the relevant transfer rates. Even more recently, a significant
literature has been developing on the subject of excited-state electron
transfer phenomena, first because of their role as quenchers of photo-excited
states [11], and later because of their application to photovoltaic and photochemical energy conversion [12-14]. Both the rectification and the photoconversion applications lie clearly within the purview of this conference, and
both can be vitiated if the back transfer event is not either eliminated or
significantly reduced.

As an example, consider [4] the schematic rectifier circuit of reference 4;
if the transfer event through the barrier between the acceptor (A) and donor
(D) ends is fast enough, the molecular orbitals appropriate for discussion of
electron transfer between an external circuit and either D or A ends will be
linear combinations of the A and D local orbitals, and no rectification property will occur.

Similarly, Grätzel and co-workers [12] have investigated the photolysis of
H_2O in a sensitized system containing methylviologen and ruthenium tris
bipyridyl: they point out that "if the chemical potential of A^- and D^+ is to
be used in subsequent fuel-generating processes, it is mandatory to prevent or

retard the energy-wasting back-reaction". We review their chemistry in
equations (1-5):

$$S^{++} + CMV^{++} \xrightarrow{h\nu} S^{+++} + CMV^{+} \qquad (1)$$

$$4S^{+++} + 2H_2O \longrightarrow 4S^{++} + 4H^{+} + O_2 \qquad (2)$$

$$4CMV^{+} + 4H_2O \longrightarrow 4CMV^{++} + 2H_2 + 4OH^{-} \qquad (3)$$

$$4S^{+++} + 4CMV^{+} + 2H_2O \longrightarrow 4S^{++} + 2H_2 + 4CMV^{++} + O_2 \qquad (4a)$$

$$2H_2O \xrightarrow{h\nu} 2H_2 + O_2 \qquad (4b)$$

$$S^{+++} + CMV^{+} \longrightarrow S^{++} + CMV^{++} \text{ spoiler} \qquad (5)$$

The sensitizer S^{++} is $Ru(bpy)_3^{++}$, while CMV is a methylviologen. The photo-
excitation process (1) produces ionic species which (2,3) have proper redox
potentials to oxidize and reduce water; the overall process starting from the
photoexcited state (4a) splits water in going to the ground state, while the
overall cyclic reaction (4b) is simply catalyzed photolysis of water. But if
the backtransfer reaction (5) is not considerably slower than (2,3), the
photolysis quantum yield will be small.

Experimentally, a number of techniques have been suggested to reduce the
interfering back-transfer rates. For ground-state electron transfer systems,
these have stressed the nature of the "tunneling barrier" between D and A,
either in isolated molecules [4-9] or in monolayer assemblies [18]. In photo-
transfer, a number of rather specific schemes have been suggested, mostly
involving phase barriers, and including the use of vesicles [14], micelles
[18], chemical interception [17], monolayer assemblies [19,20], electrode
processes [16], and even rapid reorientation [3]. From a theoretical viewpoint, the first group of schemes (barrier manipulation) can be thought of as
a variation in the off-diagonal (mixing) matrix element between the two
localized orbitals [5-9], while the second group (interception of the
initially-transfered state) corresponds to an irreversible relaxation process
which the transfer state undergoes. Although a great deal of theoretical
effort has been expended in examination of the role of the mixing term [7],
very little has been devoted to the relaxation effect [21]. The present paper
examines how relaxation can affect both the transfer rates themselves and the
experiments which probe them, particularly spectroscopic studies [6]. The
relaxation processes introduce into the problem a fourth timescale beyond the
three which occur in the usual polaron theory of electron transfer and in so
doing they totally change the theoretical decription, just as they totally
change the experimental behavior.

II. THEORETICAL DESCRIPTION OF TRANSFER DYNAMICS: CLASSIFICATION AND MODEL

The rates of intramolecular electron transfer have been addressed largely
in the same language as intermolecular transfer [22], and while this should be

appropriate in the case for which the rates are relatively slow, the more
rapid process involved in average-valency systems requires a more general
discussion including so-called nonadiabatic effects [22,23]. A useful classification was originally put forward by Robin and Day [5,24] in considering
mixed-valency species. They defined class I compounds as those in which the
two types of a given ion have distinct, different valence states, such as the
two Ga species (Ga^{III} in tetrahedral sites, Ga^{I} in dodecahedral coordination)
in GaCl$_2$. Class II behavior is exhibited by species in which the sites are
similar but distinguishable; an example is provided by the two Sb sites in
Cs$_2$SbCl$_6$, and these are properly called mixed-valent. Class III systems do
not have distinguishable valence states; all ions behave identically, and the
correct description is in terms of average valence. A standard example is
provided by Krogmann's salt K$_2$Pt(CN)$_4$Br$_{.3}$·3H$_2$O, although several others of the
charge-transfer reduced-dimensionality conductors are perhaps best thought of
as average-valent [25]. A number of experimental probes have been used to
study the mixed-valency species, and although class I materials are easily
distinguished, the distinction between classes II and III is more difficult,
and has been subject to a great deal of discussion [26]. The mixed-valence
problem is highly appropriate for a discussion of back-transfer and molecular
device applications, since if effective class III behavior obtains, the redox
potential of the molecule will be isotropic and no rectification can be
obtained (analogously, for proton transfer, a class III situation would
correspond to the proton entirely delocalized along the A-H---B bond, as
apparently occurs for most "strong" hydrogen bonds) [27]. For the rectification problem, then, we require a theoretical characterization in terms of
the rate of intramolecular electron transfer [4]. For the excited back-
transfer photoconversion devices, on the other hand, the transfer process is
generally intermolecular, and simple joint diffusion of D$^+$ and A$^-$ can provide
the needed relaxation. (An alternative description of the transfer process
can be given in terms of a pseudo-Jahn-Teller effect, in which localized sites
are mixed by vibronic coupling. This model has been applied both to the
electron transfer [23] and to the proton transfer [28] problems, but the
important effects of relaxation have not been included.)

     Experimentally, these transfer rates can be measured in favorable circum-
stances [29,12], but it would be very useful to have a theoretical construct
which both predicts the transfer rates and relates them to experimental quantities which are easily measured (vibrational spectra, photoemission,
Mossbauer, magnetic resonance) [26]. We would also like to use the theory to
help design the components of a rectifier or photovoltaic/photochemical device
pathway by pinpointing which characteristic parameters determine the transfer
rates. In a typical experiment, for instance, Tom and Taube examine [6] the
infrared behavior of [(NH$_3$)$_5$RuNCCNRu(NH$_3$)$_5$]$^{+5}$. The C≡N stretch, which is seen
at 1960 cm^{-1} in the Ru^{II} species and at 2330 cm^{-1} in Ru^{III}, is measured at
2210 cm^{-1} in the mixed-valent bisruthenium complex, and this was used to argue
[6] that the species is of Robin/Day Class III, since the electron is delocalized on a timescale of $(\Delta\omega)^{-1} \sim 10^{-13}$ sec. This sort of argument is attractive and is often valid, but it can be misleading, since full delocalization
cannot be distinguished from rapid transfer between truly distinct sites
simply by observation of the lineshape, and since relaxation effects can produce an averaged lineshape even in weakly mixed systems. In iron acetates,
for example, recent work by Brown [30] shows that the Mossbauer line narrows
from that corresponding to distinguishable sites to that of average valency as
the temperature is raised. We should like our theory to treat the thermal
effects on the transfer rates as mirrored in the lineshape.

     From the viewpoint of molecular device design then, a theoretical descrip-
tion which includes relaxation, transfer, and vibronic coupling should permit

the prediction of device characteristics (such as I/V characteristic [4] for a
rectifier or the photoconversion quantum yield for a photoconverter) in terms
of simple parameters characterizing the molecular subunits and surroundings.
Although several theoretical discussions are available [7-9], they have not
included relaxation properly, and therefore cannot correctly describe either
lineshapes or the effects of the surroundings (and such important experimental
variations as traps, micelles, or electrodes) on the transfer processes. We
therefore give here a very simple model description for the transfer of an
excitation in a homonuclear mixed-valency-type system (it could, for instance,
describe optical transfer in bisruthenium systems or in oligomer subunits of
one-dimensional conducting polymers or be slightly generalized to include site
inequivalence, forward and backward currents in a rectifier molecule).

Our theoretical discussion of back-transfer rates then must include the
local site energies of the electron or hole, the tunneling interaction between
D and A sites, the vibrational motion of the ligands about a localization
site, the local trapping of the valences by geometry changes in the coordination sites and local selective solvation, the changes in frequency about
local sites caused by variation in effective charge as electrons transfer, and
the relaxation processes which interfere with back-transfer. Adopting a one-
orbital localization site model which is assumed coupled to one local vibration, the molecular hamiltonian to describe transfer may be minimally reduced
to

$$H = H_{el} + H_{vib} + H_{coup} \tag{6}$$

$$H_e = E_a \sigma_a{}^z + E_b \sigma_a{}^z + t(\sigma_a{}^+ \sigma_b{}^- + \sigma_b{}^+ \sigma_a{}^-) \tag{7}$$

$$H_{vib} = (b_a{}^+ b_a + 1/2)\Omega_a + (b_b{}^+ b_b + 1/2)\Omega_b \tag{8}$$

$$H_{coup} = \gamma_a \sigma_a{}^z (b_a{}^+ + b_a) + \mu_a \sigma_a{}^z (b_a{}^+ b_a)$$
$$+ \gamma_b \sigma_b{}^z (b_b{}^+ + b_b) + \mu_b \sigma_b{}^z (b_b{}^+ b_b) \tag{9}$$

Here the electronic states on D,A are limited to two, so that the motion of an
electron can be defined by spin operators. Constant terms have been omitted
from (9), in which $\sigma_a{}^z$ measures the number of excited electrons at site a,
while $\sigma_a{}^z$ promotes an electron from the ground to the excited orbital at site
a. The second term describes the motion of an exciton (or of an electron in
the excited state) between site a and site b. The parameter E_a is the
HOMO-LUMO energy difference (roughly the optical excitation frequency) at site
a, and the parameter t measures the strength of the tunneling interaction
between a and b; if it is much greater than $\gamma_a{}^2/\Omega_a$, one expects the exciton to
be delocalized (in the absence of relaxation) [9,31]. Thus H_{el} models an
excited electron hopping between two localized excitation sites. The vibrational frequency at site a is Ω_a, and the operator $b_a{}^+$ creates one quantum of
vibrational excitation at site a. The coupling term proportion to γ_a is the
Frohlich linear electron-vibron coupling [32] which is responsible for
metallic resistivity; it is proportional to the population of excited
electrons at a given site times the vibrational displacement at that site, and
is responsible for the Stokes spectral shift. Finally, the μ_a term describes
the change in the vibrational energy at site a due to the presence of the
excited electron. For hexammineruthenium, Ω is roughly 440 cm^{-1} and
μ_a roughly 60 cm^{-1}.

(One major failing of the model (6) is that the electron density is never
considered fixed on the tunneling bridge. There is experimental [6] and calcu-
lational [23] data indicating that in several Robin/Day II or III binuclear

metal complexes the electronic orbitals can contain significant contributions
from the bridge. Under these conditions, a more complex four-site or five-
site model is useful [23]).

The hamiltonian (6) is closely related to the usual Holstein-Fröhlich
molecular crystal model for electron transfer [32]. Generally one expects
[9,31] localization for $\gamma^2/\Omega \gg t$, delocalization for $t \gg \gamma^2/\Omega$, and
Robin/Day II behavior for $\Omega t \sim \gamma^2$. But such predictions can be very significantly altered by inclusion of relaxation phenomena.

III. RELAXATION EFFECTS. LINESHAPE FORMULAS.

The theoretical problem involved in the characterization of the relaxation
processes is straightforward: since relaxation processes generally do not
conserve the value of the energy in the hamiltonian subsystem (such as the
two-site model of [6]), their effects must be reckoned differently. Although
there exist a number of ad hoc or weak-coupling-limit procedures for including
the effects of relaxation, the treatments of electron transfer usually neglect
such terms entirely. There exists a rigorously correct method for calculating
relaxation effects, which is based on a semigroup formalism and was first
developed by Sudarshan [33], it is described more completely elsewhere
[21,34]. If the relaxation process couples linearly to a (linear or
nonlinear) hamiltonian variable V of the system, a relaxation time dependence
is introduced, and the equation of motion for the dynamical variables
becomes:[21]

$$\frac{dX}{dt} = i[H,X] + g\{VXV^+ - 1/2[VV^+,X]_+\} \tag{10}$$

where the first term is the ordinary Heisenberg evolution and the second term
is the relaxation contribution; the parameter g is a strength which is non-
negative and can be evaluated in certain limits [21].

Equation (10) gives the dynamical behavior which will characterize
experimental measurements of the system. The vibrational lineshape I and
intramolecular electron transfer rate k are given from linear response theory
by [35]

$$I(\omega) = \mathrm{Re}\int_0^\infty \exp -i\omega t \ \langle \dot{m}(t)\dot{n}(0)\rangle \ dt \tag{11}$$

$$k = \int_0^\infty \langle \dot{\sigma}_a{}^z(t) \ \dot{\sigma}_a{}^x(0)\rangle \ dt \tag{12}$$

where the brackets indicate thermal averages and dots mean time derivatives; m
is the dipole moment operator, which (if we neglect electrical anharmonicity)
is proportional to vibrational displacement. Formally, then, we need merely
solve the equations of motion (10) to find the correlation functions (11,12)
for the model of (6). We take m proportional to $b^+ + b$, so that $I(\omega)$ can be
found from solving for $b(t)$.

The equation of motion for b, however, will involve higher-order operators
on the right side, and the exact dynamics of the system [6,10] then becomes
an infinite set of coupled equations. For simplicity, we assume that the
relaxation process is caused by terms which couple linearly to the vibron

displacement $(b^+ + b)$ and to the excitation operators $\sigma_a^{\pm}, \sigma_b^{\pm}$ (the former might correspond to a solvent quenching, and the latter to a redox process of the type indicated in eqns. (2,30). Under these conditions, the relaxation parts of the equations of motion are

$$\dot{b}_{rel}^{\pm} = -\Gamma_b$$
$$\dot{\sigma}_{rel}^{\pm} = \frac{1}{2}(\alpha \pm \beta)\sigma^{\pm}$$

where the parameters α, β, Γ relate to the strengths of the relaxation processes. To solve for b, then, we perform an approximate decoupling in the vibron manifold:

$$b_i^+ b_j b_k \cong \langle b_i^+ b_j \rangle b_k \qquad (13)$$

This decoupling is consonant with the thermal character of the vibron average. With the decoupling (and, for simplicity, ignoring the linear coupling γ terms of (6)), the equation of motion for b_a becomes closed in a space of six operators: b_a, $b_a \sigma_a^z$, $b_a \sigma_a^+ \sigma_b^-$, $b_a \sigma_a^- \sigma_b^+$, $b_a \sigma_b^z$, $b_a \sigma_a^z \sigma_b^z$. This set of six linear coupled equations of motion can be solved by Fourier inversion and matrix diagonalization techniques, the details are given elsewhere [34].

IV. RELAXATION EFFECTS, LINESHAPES, AND REMARKS

We have solved for the lineshapes $I(\omega)$ using the procedures outlined above, and present some of our computed lineshapes in figure 1. Because of the truncation (13), only six operators enter the equations of motion, and one expects at most six peaks in the vibrational lineshape. The problem is characterized by the parameters Ω, E, t, μ, T, Γ, α, β; we choose α, β via

$$\alpha, \beta = \tau_2(T)^{5/2}(1 \pm \exp -\Omega/T)$$

where the $T^{5/2}$ is a state density factor and τ_2 is a strength caused by relaxation processes of the excited electron. We present here some lineshapes for the model coupled-exciton problem; transfer rates for this system, as well as for the more interesting linearly-coupled electron transfer (rectification) problem will be published elsewhere [34].

The lineshapes show several interesting features. When t is very small, the central line about the frequency Ω splits into doublets at $\Omega \pm \mu/2$, for T $\ll$ E; this is the frequency shift caused by the electron localization, and is analogous to the Ru^{II}/Ru^{III} frequency differences mentioned above. As t increases, these lines collapse into a single line at Ω; this is the behavior which Taube invokes [6] to claim Robin/Day III classification (or at least very fast transfer in a Class II system) for the cyanogen-bridged Ru_2^{5+} species discussed above. But note that a similar lineshape can be produced merely by relaxation effects; raising the temperature or lowering the relaxation time for the vibron can cause lineshapes extremely similar to that of true motional narrowing. Thus although Taube's assignment of average valence to the cyanogen-bridged mixed valence Ru species is probably correct, it is not valid to make such assignments on lineshape alone.

The formal dynamics of the model (6) are not in themselves important. What is important is that the semigroup formalism allows for inclusion of relaxation processes into the calculation of rates of electron transfer processes, as well as the associated spectra. In so doing, it introduces a

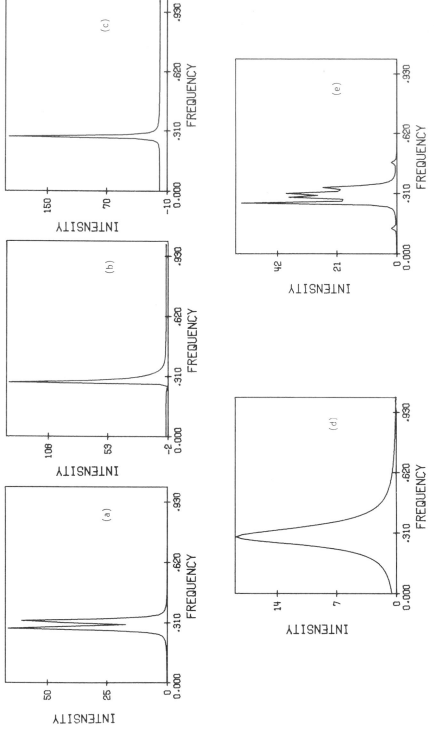

Fig. 1: Computed vibrational lineshapes, from (6,10). The splitting of the vibrational fundamental in (a) is due to the μ coupling of (9). It collapses into a single line in (b) due to rapid exchange (the parameter t has been increased by a factor of 8), but exhibits comparable narrowing in (c) due only to relaxation (α,β were increased by a factor of 100). This can be distinguished from simple vibron lifetime broadening which is shown in (d), where Γ was increased by a factor of 10. In (e), the μ has been increased by a factor of 2 and (α,β) decreased by a factor of 10, compared to (b); it shows the full six-peak feature. Parameters for (a): E = 1, Ω = .3, μ = .04, t = .01, Γ = .005, α = β = .0001, T = .003.

new time scale, the relaxation time, which can in some cases redefine the notion of localized or delocalized behavior. By predicting the transfer rates based on (10), we should be able to understand how the rates depend on tunneling barriers, trapping and quenching, and the other experimental system-surroundings interactions discussed above, and also to see how the experimental lineshapes reflect the true intramolecular dynamics. In this way, the formal transfer theory presented here may help [3] to build a better rectifier, proton storage bit, or photon trap.

ACKNOWLEDGMENT

R.K. is grateful for the grant of a Weizmann Fellowship, and M.R. thanks the Chemistry Division of the National Science Foundation for partial support.

REFERENCES

1. P.-O. Lowdin, Adv. Quantum Chem. 2, 216 (1965); A. Aviram, P. E. Seiden, and M. A. Ratner, this conference, and references therein.

2. C. A. Taylor, M. A. El-Bayoumi, and M. Kasha, Proc. Nat. Acad. Sci. 63 253 (1969); M. Kasha, personal communication.

3. F. L. Carter, N.R.L. Memorandum Report 3960 (1969), 4335 (1980).

4. A. Aviram and M. A. Ratner, Chem. Phys. Lett. 29, 277 (1974)

5. M. B. Robin and P. Day, Adv. Inorg. Radiochem. 10, 247 (1967); N. S. Hush, Prog. Inorg. Chem. 8, 357 (1967).

6. G. M. Tom and H. Taube, J. Am. Chem. Soc. 97, 5130 (1975); H. Krentzein and H. Taube, ibid. 98, 6379 (1976) and many related papers. Also T. J. Meyer, in ref. 8 and references therein.

7. K. Y. Wong, P. N. Schatz, and S. B. Piepho, J. Am. Chem. Soc. 101, 2793 (1979); P. N. Schatz, Prog. Inorg. Chem., in press.

8. D. B. Brown, ed., "Mixed-Valence Compounds", Reidel, Dordrecht, 1980.

9. M. A. Ratner and M. J. Ondrechen, Mol. Phys. 32, 1233 (1976); J. Chem. Phys. 66, 938 (1977); M. A. Ratner, Int. J. Quantum Chem. 14, 675 (1978); M. J. Ondrechen, M. A. Ratner, and J. R. Sabin, J. Chem. Phys. 71, 2244 (1979). The notions were pioneered by J. Halpern and L. E. Orgel, Disc. Far. Soc. 29, 32 (1960).

10. G. R. Moore, R. J. P. Williams, Coord. Chem. Revs. 18, 125 (1976); E. G. Petrov, Int. J. Quantum Chem. 16, 133 (1979).

11. D. Rehm and A. Weller, Israel J. Chem. 8, 259 (1970); M. T. Indella and F. Scandola, J. Am. Chem. Soc. 100, 7733 (1978); J. Erikson and C. S. Foote, J. Phys. Chem. 82, 2659 (1980; N. Agmon and R. D. Levine, Chem. Phys. Lett. 52, 197 (1977).

12. P. A. Brugger, P. P. Infelta, A. M. Braun, and M. Grätzel, J. Am. Chem. Soc. 103, 320 (1981) and references therein.

13. E. Schumacher, Chimia 32, 193 (1978).

14. W. E. Ford, J. W. Otvos, and M. Calvin, Proc. Nat. Acad. Sci. 76, 3590 (1979).

15. C. Creutz and N. Sutin, Proc. Nat. Acad. Sci. 72, 2858 (1975).

16. M. Wrighton, Acc. Chem. Res. 12, 303 (1979).

17. S. J. Milder, R. A. Goldberg, D. S. Kliyer, and H. B. Gray, J. Am. Chem. Soc. 102, 6761 (1980).

18. H. D. Abruna, P. Denisevitch, M. Umana, T. J. Meyer, and R. W. Murray, J. Am. Chem. Soc. 103, 1 (1981).

19. H. Kuhn, J. Photochem. 10, 111 (1979).

20. H. Gerischer and J. J. Katz, Eds., "Light-Induced Charge Separation in Biology and Chemistry," Verlag Chemie, New York, 1979.

21. R. Kosloff and S. A. Rice, J. Chem. Phys. 72, 4591 (1980).

22. W. Reynolds and R. W. Lumry, "Mechanisms of Electron Transfer," Ronald, New York, 1966; R. A. Marcus, Ann. Revs. Phys. Chem. 15, 155 (1966).

23. J. Linderberg and M. A. Ratner, J. Am. Chem. Soc., in press. D. E. Ellis, M. J. Ondrechen and M. A. Ratner, to be published.

24. P. Day, in ref. 8.

25. C. J. Schramm, D. R. Stojakovic, B. M. Hoffman, T. J. Marks, Science 200, 47 (1978); J. Am. Chem. Soc. 99, 280 (1977) and related work.

26. A. Ludi, in ref. 8; N. S. Hush, in ref. 8; N. S. Hush, A. Edgar, and J. K. Beattie, Chem. Phys. Lett. 69, 128 (1980).

27. W. C. Hamilton and J. A. Ibers, "Hydrogen Bonding in Solids," Benjamin, New York, 1968.

28. A. Witkowski, to be published.

29. S. Isied and H. Taube, J. Am. Chem. Soc. 95, 8198 (1973).

30. D. B. Brown, Inorg. Chem., in press.

31. B. Chance et al., eds., "Tunneling in Biological Systems," Academic, New York, 1979; E. K. Kudinov and Y. Firsov, Sov. Phys. Sol. St. 7, 435 (1965); N. R. Kestner, J. Logan, and J. Jortner, J. Phys. Chem. 78, 2168 (1976).

32. T. Holstein, in ref. 31; also Ann. Phys. 8, 325 (1959).

33. V. Gorini, A. Kossakowski, and E. C. G. Sudarshan, J. Math. Phys. 17, 821 (1976); G. Lindblad, Comm. Math. Phys. 48, 119 (1976).

34. R. Kosloff ad M. A. Ratner, to be published.

35. R. Zwanzig, Ann. Revs. Phys. Chem. 16, 67 (1965).

DISCUSSION

Prof. Ferry: Col. St. Univ - In most of the talks this morning people are concerned about the actual switching time for the charge to move from one site to the other. Now that often is not the important time. Switching is something like logic. It is not hard to conceive of making a semiconductor device that is switching on the subpicosecond time scale, but the important aspect is how long it takes to get the charge information out to the outside world, and that can be much longer. The second thing is that in your calculations here, you included the interaction between your molecule and its environment just by a relaxation term. That may not be the most important term to include, especially when you think of including 10^{12} of these molecules in information storage array. In fact, it is well known that probably one of the dominant terms is the self-energy correction that comes in from the interaction, in this case, of the molecule with its environment. That may be the most important thing. It can lead perhaps to other ways than just charge transfer of trying to store information, and I will say a little bit about these tomorrow, but it is important to recognize that that may be the leading term in your treatment that needs to be included.

Prof. Ratner: NW Univ. - There are several dynamic interactions which have not been included, and probably ought to be. The focus really was not so much on information storage as on the non-bidirectional flow processes. As I indicated in the beginning, what I was interested in was a rectification process on the one hand, and a sort of photocatalyzed organic chemistry on the other hand. In both of those I think that difficulty (interactions between species) doesn't arise. You are absolutely right in the case of storage devices where one deals with stability of certain states over long times, self-energies and things like that. Certainly it could be included.

CHAPTER IV

TWO-ELECTRON GATES IN PHOTOSYNTHESIS

Lester L. Shipman
Chemistry Division
Argonne National Laboratory
Argonne, IL 60439

INTRODUCTION

Electron gating by molecules or molecular aggregates will be one of the important aspects in the design of computer components that operate at the molecular level. Fortunately, in the photosynthetic apparatus of green plants and photosynthetic bacteria, Nature has provided a working model for electron gating by molecules (specifically quinones). We can benefit from the study of the photosynthetic electron gates by uncovering the principles underlying the design of the naturally-occurring electron gates. Some of these principles have already been uncovered by the many scientists investigating the structure and function of the photosynthetic apparatus of green plants and photosynthetic bacteria. In the present paper we examine some of these principles and relate them to "molecular" electronics. In a companion paper (1) the primary events of photosynthesis are examined for applications to "molecular" electronics.

PHOTOSYNTHETIC QUINONES

A pair of quinones participates in electron transfer on the reducing side (i.e., the side having electron transfer components reduced by the action of light) of photosystem II of green plants and the photosystem found in purple photosynthetic bacteria (1-29). The quinones are different in the two types of organisms, however. The quinones in PS II are plastoquinones and the quinones in purple photosynthetic bacteria are ubiquinones (see Figure 1). The poly-isoprene side chain in the quinones usually found in these photosystems have n = 9 and n = 10 for green plants and purple photosynthetic bacteria, respectively. The quinones are photochemically reduced by electron transfers from the primary events of photosynthesis (1-29). In each photosystem there are two distinct quinone binding sites; the first quinone to receive the electron after light absorption is denoted Q1. From Q1 the electron hops to the second quinone, denoted Q2. In the green plant photosynthesis literature the symbols most frequently used are Q for Q1 and B (or R) for Q2. We will use the generic symbols Q1 and Q2 and apply them to both green plants and purple photosynthetic bacteria. In both bacteria and green plants, the quinones Q1 and Q2

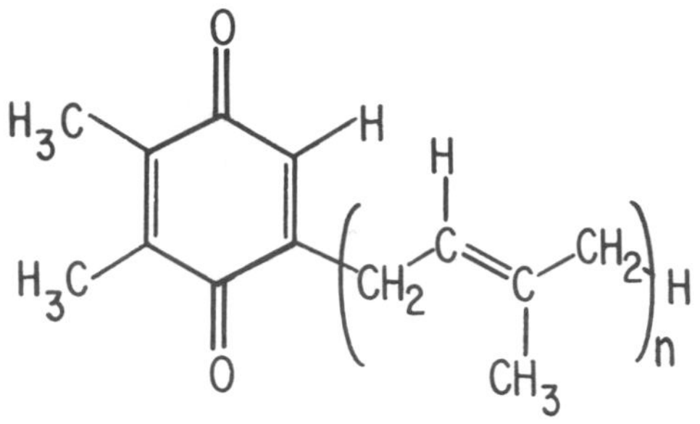

PLASTOQUINONE

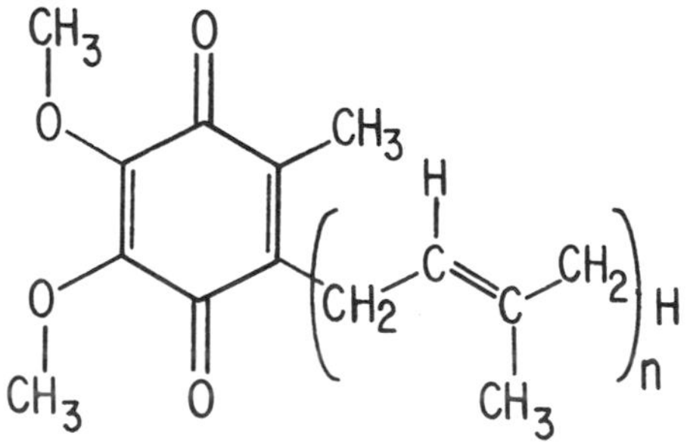

UBIQUINONE

Figure 1. Molecular structures for plastoquinone and ubiquinone.

are noncovalently bound to intrinsic membrane protein. Also in both systems there is a pool of quinones of the same chemical structure which are outside the photosystem, but reside in the same membrane.

TWO-ELECTRON GATING

At rest in the dark, the state normally populated is shown below as S1; both of the quinones are in their fully oxidized state.

$$Q1 \qquad\qquad Q2 \qquad\qquad\qquad\qquad (S1)$$

After absorption of a photon by the photosystem pigments, an electron is transferred from a reduced pheophytin or bacteriopheophytin (22,25,30,31) to the first quinone and state S2 is populated.

$$Q1^- \qquad\qquad Q2 \qquad\qquad\qquad\qquad (S2)$$

In a subsequent electron transfer the electron moves from Q1 to Q2 and the state S3 is populated.

$$Q1 \qquad\qquad Q2^- \qquad\qquad\qquad\qquad (S3)$$

State S3 is lower in free energy than state S2. After absorption of a second photon, an electron is transferred to Q1 and the state S4 is temporarily populated.

$$Q1^- \qquad\qquad Q2^- \qquad\qquad\qquad\qquad\qquad (S4)$$

In a subsequent electron transfer an electron moves from Q1 to Q2 to populate the state S5.

$$Q1 \qquad\qquad Q2^{2-} \qquad\qquad\qquad\qquad\qquad (S5)$$

At this point the pair of electrons on Q2 are released to the electron transfer chain outside the photosystem II complex (green plants) or outside the reaction center (purple photosynthetic bacteria). At this point state S1 is populated again. Thus, quinones Q1 and Q2 function together as a two-electron gate (3,4, 13,14,29) which requires two photons to complete the cycle from S1 to S3 and back again to S1. In terms of stability of the system, the state populated after the first photon is absorbed (S3) is stable for many seconds (4) and the state populated after zero or two photons have been absorbed is stable indefinitely.

THE COMPLEX ROLE OF PROTONS

In the scheme discussed in the preceding section, the quinones Q1 and Q2 are given neutral or negative charges. In the actual photosystem, protons move from aqueous solution outside the photosynthetic membrane onto the quinone-protein complex as electrons are pumped to the quinones. The uptake of protons is coupled to electron transport in complicated ways (20,21,26,29,32). In particular, the rate of proton uptake is almost two-orders of magnitude slower than electron transfer rate to the plastoquinone pool (32). Investigations aimed at uncovering the kinetic and structural aspects of proton uptake as electrons are pumped have been undertaken at several laboratories.

IMPLICATIONS FOR "MOLECULAR" ELECTRONICS

The design and operation of naturally-occurring two-electron gates give insight into some of the design problems associated with such molecular components. In particular, the electron transfer from Q1 to Q2 is temperature dependent and is effectively shut off at the cryogenic temperatures that may be required for the operation of superconducting components. In molecular systems, it is difficult to keep an electron at any particular site for a long period of time because it can tunnel to other components that are either as easy or easier to reduce than the molecule it presently resides upon. As a rule-of-thumb electron transfers between organic pi-systems on different molecules have rates that fall off a decade or so for every 0.2 nm increase in the edge-to-edge gap. Unwanted electron transfers can be prevented by (a) elimination of unwanted electron acceptors easier to reduce than the desired component, and (b) by creating gaps many Angstroms wide between the desired electron acceptors and all other acceptors that are easier to reduce. An additional problem is posed by proton uptake. When organic molecules are reduced by adding an electron, there is often a pK shift such that the reduced form is more basic than the oxidized form. This poses a problem because it can lead to unwanted protonation. Unwanted protonation can be minimized if great care is taken to remove proton donors (e.g., water) from the system or to set up proton barriers (e.g., protein in the case of photosynthetic membranes).

ACKNOWLEDGMENT

My work in photosynthesis has been supported by the Division of Chemical Sciences, Office of Basic Energy Sciences, U.S. Department of Energy, under Contract W-31-109-Eng-38.

REFERENCES

1. L.L. Shipman, "The Primary Events of Photosynthesis", in this volume.

2. J. Amesz, Biochim. Biophys. Acta 301, 35 (1973).

3. B. Bouges-Bouquet, Biochim. Biophys. Acta 314, 250 (1973).

4. B.R. Velthuys and J. Amesz, Biochim. Biophys. Acta 333, 85 (1974).

5. H.J. Van Gorkom, Biochim. Biophys. Acta 347, 439 (1974).

6. W.W. Parson and R.J. Cogdell, Biochim. Biophys. Acta 416, 105 (1975).

7. P.A. Loach, Chemical Properties of the Phototrap in Bacterial Photosynthesis, in "Progress in Bioorganic Chemistry", Vol. 4, E. T. Kaiser, ed., John Wiley & Sons, New York, 1976, pp. 89-192.

8. M.P.J. Pulles, H.J. Van Gorkom, and J.G. Willemsen, Biochim. Biophys. Acta 449, 536 (1976).

9. J. Amesz and L.N.M. Duysens, Primary and Associated Reactions of System II, in "Primary Processes of Photosynthesis," J. Barber, ed., Elsevier, New York, 1977, pp. 149-185.

10. M. Avron, The Electron Transport Chain in Chloroplasts, in "Primary Processes of Photosynthesis", J. Barber, ed., Elsevier, New York, 1977, pp. 373-386.

11. D.B. Knaff, R. Malkin, J.C. Myron, and M. Stoller, Biochim. Biophys. Acta 459, 402 (1977).

12. U. Siggel, R. Khanna, G. Renger, and Govindjee, Biochim. Biophys. Acta 462, 196 (1977).

13. A. Vermeglio, Biochim. Biophys. Acta 459, 516 (1977).

14. C.A. Wraight, Biochim. Biophys. Acta 459, 525 (1977).

15. A.R. Crofts and P.M. Wood, Current Topics in Bioenergetics 7, 175 (1978).

16. P.L. Dutton, R.C. Prince, and D.M. Tiede, Photochem. Photobiol. 28, 939 (1978).

17. P.L. Dutton, J.S. Leigh, Jr., R.C. Prince, and D.M. Tiede, The Photochemical Reaction Center of Photosynthetic Bacteria as a Model for Studying Biological Charge Separation and Electron Transfer, in "Light-Induced Electron Transport in Biology and Chemistry", H. Gerischer and J.J. Katz, eds., Verlag Chemie, New York, 1979, pp. 411-448.

18. G. Feher and M.Y. Okamura, Chemical Composition and Properties of Reaction Centers, in "The Photosynthetic Bacteria", R.K. Clayton and W.R. Sistrom, eds., Plenum Press, New York, 1978, pp. 349-386.

19. W.W. Parson, Quinones as Secondary Electron Acceptors, in "The Photosynthetic Bacteria", R.K. Clayton and W.R. Sistrom, eds., Plenum Press, New York, 1978, pp. 455-469.

20. R.C. Prince and P.L. Dutton, Protonation and Reducing Potential of the Primary Electron Acceptor, in "The Photosynthetic Bacteria", R.K. Clayton and W.R. Sistrom, eds., Plenum Press, New York, 1978, pp. 439-453.

21. A.R. Crofts, The Role of Quinones in Photosynthetic Electron Transport, in "Light-Induced Charge Separation in Biology and Chemistry", H. Gerischer and J.J. Katz, eds., Verlag Chemie, New York, 1979, pp. 389-410.

22. M.Y. Okamura, R.A. Isaacson, and G. Feher, Biochim. Biophys. Acta 546, 394 (1979).

23. K.-I. Takamiya and P.L. Dutton, Biochim Biophys. Acta 546, 1 (1979).

24. R. Tiemann, G. Renger, P. Gräber, and H.T. Witt, Biochim. Biophys. Acta 546, 498 (1979).

25. V.V. Klimov, E. Dolan, E.R. Shaw, and B. Ke, Proc. Natl. Acad. Sci. U.S.A. 77, 7227 (1980).

26. B.R. Velthuys, FEBS Lett. 115, 167 (1980).

27. B.R. Velthuys, Ann. Rev. Plant Physiol. 31, 545 (1980).

28. A. Vermeglio, T. Martinet, and R.K. Clayton, Proc. Natl. Acad. Sci. U.S.A. 77, 1809 (1980).

29. C.A. Wraight and R.R. Stein, FEBS Lett. 113, 73 (1980).

30. D.M. Tiede, R.C. Prince, and P.L. Dutton, Biochim. Biophys. Acta 449, 447 (1976).

31. V.V. Klinov, E. Dolan, and B. Ke, FEBS Lett. 112, 97 (1980).

32. W. Ausländer and W. Junge, Biochim. Biophys. Acta 357, 285 (1974).

DISCUSSION

Prof. Honig: Univ. of Ill. - I am surprised that you require two electrons on the quinone before the protons are taken up externally. I would have thought each proton would move individually. Has anyone thought about that or were there any other mechanisms?

Dr. Shipman: Argonne – Whether zero, one or two protons are taken up on a particular flash depends upon the pH of the external aqueous medium. In a dark adapted system after a single flash a semiquinone anion is seen optically and an ESR signal appears at the same time. The ESR signal is broadened and shifted compared to the ESR signal for a semiquinone anion radical in vitro. A semiquinone anion is formed first and lagging behind by up to two orders of magnitude is proton uptake from the aqueous solution outside the photosynthetic membrane. Proton uptake is detected by observing the changes in the optical spectrum of pH sensitive dyes. The optical signal associated with the semiquinone anion radical does not change when a proton is taken up---implying that the proton goes onto protein (or lipid) rather than the quinone. Under very basic conditions, it should be possible to force the proton uptake to occur on the second flash. Apparently, the protein sheath covering photosystem II functions as a proton buffer that is replenished under conditions such that there is a semiquinone anion nearby. The semiquinone anion cannot be too close to the membrane surface, otherwise the semiquinone anion would readily reduce water soluble electron acceptors such as ferricyanide.

Prof. Honig: Why do you need two electrons before the first proton is taken up internally from the protein? I would have thought that Q^-, Q^{-2} would pick up a proton, and then when the electron was transferred, it would pick up another proton internally?

Dr. Shipman: Q^- is not particularly basic while Q^{-2} is quite basic. If a proton has a choice between going on a semiquinone anion or a lysine side chain, it will go on the lysine. On the other hand quinone double minus will pull a proton off of protonated lysine.

Prof. Marks: NW Univ. - I guess it is probably hard to capsulize photosynthesis in a few minutes. It is fantastic what the photosystem does in terms of irreversible electron transfer. How does it do it? That is the first question.

Dr. Shipman: What part of the photosystem?

Prof. Marks: The inhibition of back electron transfer. Can you give us a capsule summary of how the photosystem does that? Also, are there tricks you can do to it if you really had switched it in one direction, to switch it back? That is, are there external things you can do to the photosystem to deliberately speed up the back electron transfer if you want to. You would be resetting it, if you like.

Dr. Shipman: The way the photosystem achieves a unidirectional electron flow is by having a whole gradation of charge transfer state energies such that the lower energies correspond to a greater separation between cation hole and electron. In other words, as the electron moves out away from the cation hole it hops to molecules that are easier to reduce the farther they are away from the cation hole. It requires thermal excitation to bring the electron back to the hole and recreate the excited singlet state that gave birth to the electron transfer. In addition, the electron transfer rate back to the hole falls off exponentially with the distance between the electron and the hole; the farther the electron is from the hole, the slower the rate for bringing it back. Basically, that is how it works; the electron moves downhill energetically and away from the hole.

Prof. Marks: Is it known if there are any large conformational changes that accompany the various steps to block the back electron transfer?

Dr. Shipman: The first electron transfer step takes a picosecond or less; at such short times the protein can only relax electronically. The next electron transfer step takes a few picoseconds and at these times there could be some relaxation of a protein side chains or a proton transfer. The third electron transfer step takes over a hundred picoseconds and there probably is some conformational adjustment for that step.

Prof. Marks: The second part of the question is: is there any way you can modify the photosystem chemically to permit back electron transfer?

Dr. Shipman: Yes. Under strongly reducing conditions you can reduce both of the quinones and the forward electron transfer is stopped. Alternatively, you can remove both quinones using hexane extraction along with orthophenanthroline; for this case the electron transfers are also stopped. For either of these two cases where the normal forward electron transfers are prevented, the electron eventually returns to recombine with the cation hole.

CHAPTER V

CONFORMATIONAL SWITCHING AT THE MOLECULAR LEVEL

Forrest L. Carter
Naval Research Laboratory
Washington, DC 20375

The dominant trend of modern semiconducting technology is the ever decreasing size of the electronic switches or gates. The extrapolation of this trend strongly suggests that the switching elements will be the size of large molecules in 20 to 30 years (1a) and that the switches will be highly anisotropically structured, unlike isotropic silicon. Possible "molecular" phenomena which might function as switching mechanisms were tabulated in the First Annual Report of the NRL Program on Electroactive Polymers (EAP) (1a). This report also outlined a chemical synthetic scheme for the preparation of a 'molecular' computer. The concepts were extended by a second EAP report (1b) which introduced soliton propagation as a useful device phenomenon and emphasized the importance of self-organization as a synthetic preparation principle. For historical purposes we note that earlier in 1974, Aviram and Ratner (2) had introduced the concept of a "molecular" rectifier but had not discussed linking the particular 'molecular' device directly to external components.

If 'molecular' sized moieties are to function as electronic switches, it is natural for the structural organic or inorganic chemist to assume that different conformational states of the moiety will be in correspondance with the switched states. In order to confirm this assumption and stress the importance of conformational switching, two rather different phenomenon will be explored: the first will emphasize conformational switching in electron tunnel devices; while the second will explore various interesting and new phenomena involving soliton propagation. While signal transport through a tunnel device is apt to be very fast (i.e., the speed of light) we note that signal transport via soliton mode is much slower, i.e., less than the speed of sound. Nevertheless, it will be shown that soliton devices offer the possibility of very high density of switches and memory bits, i.e., as high as 10^{18}/cc. First, however, it is desirable to suggest the enormous versatility of various chemical groups to control periodic tunnel array switches via conformational switching.

Control Group for Tunneling in Short Periodic Structures

Among the most promising of switching mechanisms tabulated earlier (1a) is that of electron tunnelling in short periodic structures. This switching

mechanism is based on the quasi-classical approach of Pschenichnov (3);
elsewhere in this proceedings the mathematics of tunnelling through an
arbitrary set of step function potentials is derived in a standard quantum
mechanical form (4). Molecular analogues of semiconducting NAND and NOR
gates based on electron tunnelling have been illustrated earlier (see Fig. 17
of reference la) with another NOR gate described here (4).

The electron tunnel switch is controlled by the potential characteristics
of its barriers and wells. If for example a potential well depth is
modified by an electric charge rearrangement in a nearby moiety, which we
will call a Control Group (CG), then a switch which is "on" will be rapidly
switched off. For the purposes of this paper, however, we note that any
charge rearrangement will be associated with a conformation change.

In Fig. 1 (top) we schematically indicate the transmission of an
electron through a series of four identical barriers. In the bottom of
Fig. 1 we denote the molecular device as a Body with three Control Groups
(CGi) that regulate the depth of the potential wells and hence the pseudo-
stationary state energies. In this case the Body is a semiconducting molecule with four built-in potential barriers. Attached to the opposite ends of
the Body are the conducting molecular leads of polymeric sulfur nitride, indicated here by $-(SN)_x-$.

What we want to emphasize here is the enormous variability that is permitted by the concept of control groups based on molecular structure. Four
possibilities are indicated in Fig. 2.

In the first, entitled "Charge Flow," the quaternary charged nitrogen
of the control group provides a potential well at the point of attachment to
the Body of the gate. If this + charged nitrogen is neutralized by charge
flow up the $(SN)_x$ chain, then the pseudo-stationary levels at that well would
be dramatically altered and the switch would be turned off, i.e., electron
tunnelling through the Body would be stopped. Note that the conformation of
the quaternary nitrogen is changed upon neutralization.

In the second case the effect is of a smaller magnitude and arises from
the tautomerism associated with an enol-keto system. One method of changing
the dipole direction would be the application of an electric field. If a
tunnel Body contained several such enol-keto control groups, the normal state
of the switch would be "off" in the absence of an electric field. This is
because the rapid equilibration between the two alternatives would quickly
result in a randomization of dipole directions along the Body. In fact,
however, the direction of the dipole can be controlled by using carbon rings
of different sizes. In Fig. 2, part 2, both rings have six carbons. If the
ring furthest from the Body had only five atoms, the enol-keto configuration
to the right would be preferred. Hence, this control group can be readily
made with a built-in bias.

The third example of a control group is intermediate between the charge
flow case and the enol-keto tautomerism of case 2 in terms of the distance the
charge moves. In this case, photo-absorption shifts the plus charge of the
quaternary nitrogen by ten atoms closer to tunnel Body. The control group
indicated here is modeled after the photochromic probe 4-{p-(dipentylamino)-
styryl}-1-methylpyridinum iodide which has been used by Loew, Scully, Simpson,
Waggoner (5) to detect membrane formation. In this work (5) the probe
functions by imbedding its dipentylamino group in the hydrophobic portion
of the membrane, etc.; so situated, its absorption spectra becomes sensitive
to the electric field across the membrane.

ELECTRON   PERIODIC   TUNNELLING

and   CONTROL   GROUPS

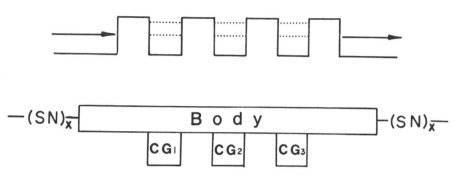

Figure 1. If the energy of the incoming particle matches precisely that of
the pseudostate (dotted lines) then Pschenichnov (3) showed that the transmission coefficient is 1.0. These pseudostate levels, however, can be
changed by the Control Groups (CG) that are attached to the Body of the
molecular device; such a change would turn off the device (i.e. stop electron
tunnelling).

For this case (3) many different zwitterionic or dye molecules could
have been used as examples of photo-activated control groups, however, the
one chosen is useful in that it also clearly indicates bond distances change
significantly during photo-stimulation.

Electron shift between metal atoms is offered as the fourth example of a
control group for a periodic tunnel body. This example is of interest because
it represents a very large class of possible control groups. By the proper
choice of metal atoms and ligands, it is possible to develop either a bimodal
ground state or a ground state and an excited state as indicated in the fourth
example. Further, the separation between cations can be easily adjusted by
the size of the common ligand, here a 5,6 derivative of 2,3-diaminopyrazine.
Such a control group can be photo-activated or possibly driven by an electric
field. The electron transfer rate involved in the relaxation process can be
varied by many orders of magnitude by the proper choice of the common ligand.
These complexes are an area of considerable current interest; for further
details the reader is referred to the work of T. J. Meyer and H. Taube and
their respective co-workers (see references 6 and 7).

By the above four examples, we hope to have illustrated the enormous
variability possible in periodic tunnelling switches. Finally we reemphasize
that although control groups switch the electron tunnelling on or off
primarily by the relocation of charge, there is always associated with that
charge relocation a configurational or conformational change. In switching
phenomena involving solitons, conformational change is of first importance.

Soliton Switching in Conjugated Systems

On a microscopic scale a soliton is a non-linear structural disturbance
that moves in one or two dimensions like a "particle." Associated with this

PERIODIC TUNNELLING
CONTROL GROUPS

1. Charge Flow

2. Electric Field

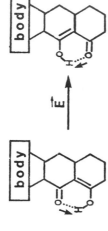

3. Photochromic Groups

4. Electron Shift

Figure 2.   This figure indicates four of the many possible kinds of control moieties for a molecular switch based on periodic tunnelling.

SOLITON TRANSPORT

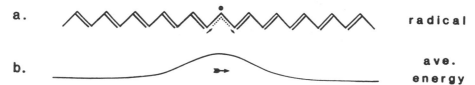

Figure 3.   The motion of a radical soliton in a conjugated system is associated
with the motion of a "phase boundary" or "kink" between ordered
single-double bond domains (adapted from Ref. 1b, Fig. 4)

pseudo-particle is a <u>definite energy</u>, <u>momentum</u> and <u>velocity</u>. Davydov [8]
postulated in 1976 that a soliton traveling thousands of Angstroms down a
α-helix might be the signal transport mechanism associated with bond breaking
in ATP. The bond energy associated with that phenomenon is only four times
thermal background and normally would have been lost in the thermal background before traveling far. Accordingly, soliton transport is associated
with the motion of a disturbance moving without energy loss. In the α-helix
the motion of this 'solitary' wave is necessarily linked to the stretching
of the polypeptide amide bond ($-\overset{\overset{O}{\|}}{C}-\underset{\underset{H}{|}}{N}-$) through its dipole moment.

In conjugated systems the corresponding dipole moment may be absent,
however, single-double bond rearrangement is possible and that presumably
provides the necessary mechanism for soliton propagation. A schematic picture
of a soliton moving from left to right is indicated in Fig. 3. At the soliton
center there exists a moving 'phase' or 'domain' boundary with respect to the
conjugation. It should also be made clear that plus and minus charged
solitons exist as well as radical solitons and that the disturbance at the
soliton center is much larger than suggested in Fig. 3. The passage of a
soliton through a conjugated system generally results in the exchange of
single and double bonds. This effect will play a major role in soliton
switching, as discussed below.

The 'push-pull' disubstituted olefin, 1,1-N,N-dimethyl-2-nitroethenamine
is of special interest because it can be photoactivated to undergo an
electron transfer from the amine nitrogen to the nitro-oxygen (9). At the
same time there is a conformational change involving the olefinic double
bond:

PUSH-PULL OLEFIN

Now imagine that the double bond is part of a larger polyacetylene chain as indicated in Fig. 4. Under polarized photoactivation it should still undergo electron transfer. However if a soliton has been propagated down the polyene chain then that photoactivation process can no longer take place (see Fig. 4). Thus the soliton has <u>switched off</u> the internal charge transfer reaction. (Note also that the absorption spectra of the push-pull olefin can serve as a detector for the passage of the soliton.)

The soliton switching concept can be extended to two chains and two different push-pull structures or extended chromophores. This is indicated in Fig. 5 where the conformation of chain 1 has switched off the nitro-amine chromophore but does not prevent the photoactivation of the sulfur containing chromophore. The passage of a soliton down chain 1 will turn the first chromophore on and the second off; a soliton moving down chain 2 will turn both of them off. In Fig. 6 the concept of soliton gang switching is generalized where A, C, and D, are generalized electron acceptors, conjugated connectors, and electron donors, respectively. Notice that each chromophore, separated from each other by dotted lines, has a different relationship to the conformations of chains 1, 2 and 3. This relationship is summarized in Table 1 where eight different chromophore-chain relationships are indicated as possible. Only the first 4 relationships indicated in Table 1 are illustrated in Fig. 6. For reasons to be offered shortly, the chromophores are identified as channels in Table 1. In Fig. 6 note that the relationship of the leftmost chromophore to each chain is such that the chromophore is subject to photoactivation; in Table 1 this set of relationships is indicated by a vertical row of 1's. However the second chromophore or channel is turned off by the 1st chain, while the third channel is turned off by the 2nd chain. In short the chromophores or channels are so arranged that the passage of a soliton down any of the three chains turns off any soliton that is on and turns on one of the others.

Table 1 then expresses the concept that soliton propagation can be used to perform gang switching where three input states can control 8 different output channels. By separating the chromophores by about 100Å the density of such switches can be estimated to be as high as 10^{18}/cc! It should be remembered however that soliton propagation is less than the speed of sound.

The next generalization as shown in Fig. 7 goes beyond our meager knowledge of soliton propagation. Here we have replaced the electron acceptor and donor groups with molecular 'wires' or filaments of $-(SN)_n-$. Here the question is, "Can the conformation of the chains 1, 2, and 3 control the conduction of electrical charges in the different 8 channels as suggested in Table 1? One question to be asked is, "Does band conduction in $(SN)_x$ convert to soliton propagation across the chains and back again to band conduction?" Note that in such a case, pairs of signals must be sent to restore conformation back to the original state in each channel.

Soliton Valving

Soliton propagation in a conjugated system can lead to a valving behavior as well as to a switching action. This is suggested in Fig. 8 and Table II. Fig. 8 illustrates three conjugated half-chains joining at a single carbon or branch carbon. The passage of a soliton from A to B (or from B to A) moves the double bond at the branch carbon from the A chain to the B chain. In the upper right portion of Fig. 8 we note that a soliton moving from B to C moves the double bond to the C chain. Thus in Fig. 8 we note those soliton propagations that correspond to a clockwise rotation of 120°. In short, those propagations behave like a group operation. The first two entries in the

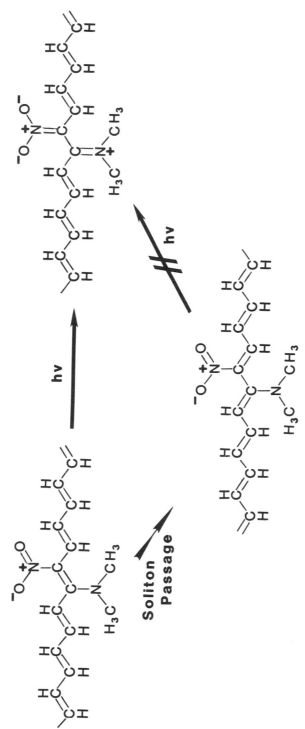

Figure 4. A push-pull disubstituted olefin imbedded in transpolyacetylene can a) be switched off by the propagation of a soliton, or b) be used as a soliton detector.

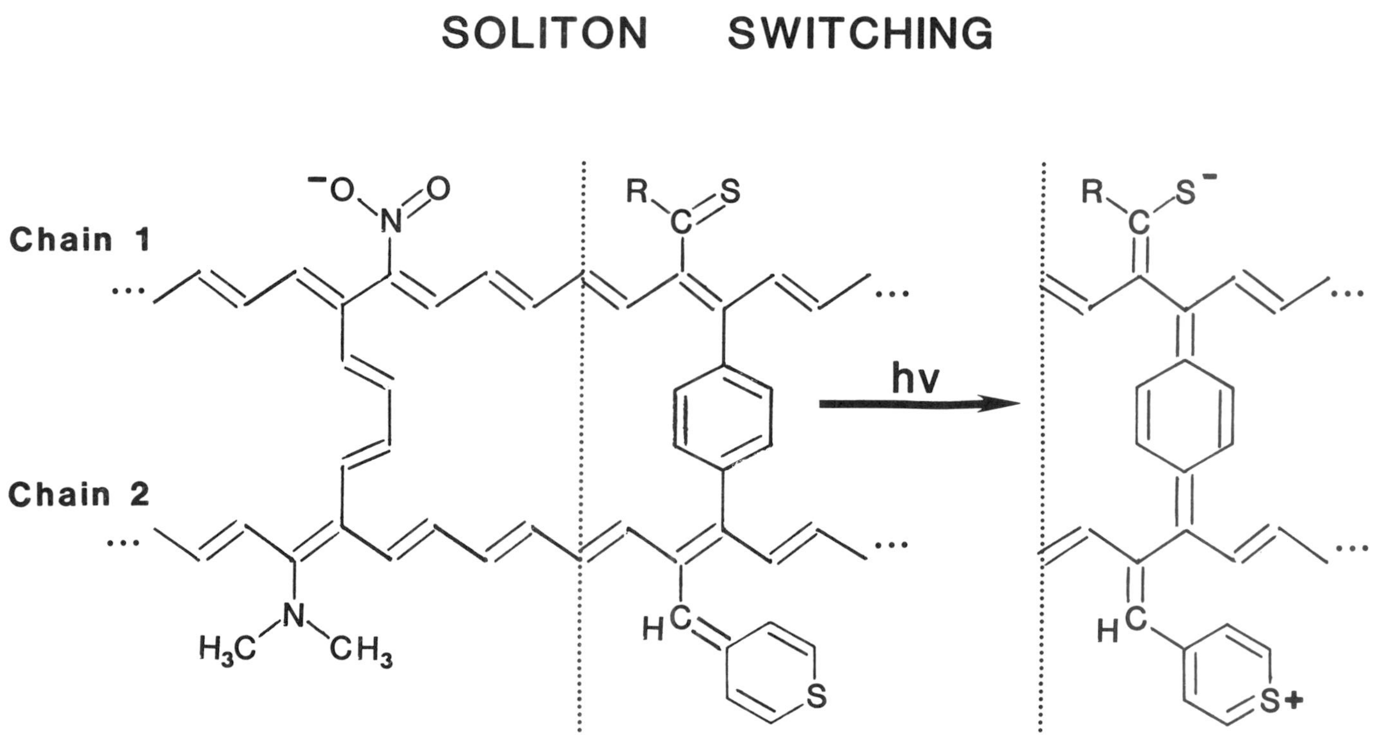

SOLITON SWITCHING

Figure 5. Soliton switching involving two transpolyacetylene chains and two chromophores. The second sulfur chromophore can be photoactivated but not the first.

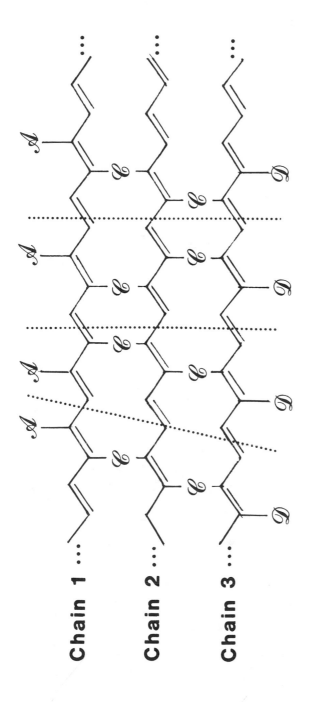

$\mathscr{A}$ electron   acceptor

$\mathscr{C}$ conjugated   connector

$\mathscr{D}$ electron   donor

Figure 6. Soliton gang switch showing four of eight possible different arrangements chromophores can have relative to three conjugated chains.

Table 1.   Three Chain Gang Switching

Channel[a]	1	2	3	4	5	6	7	8
Chain[b] 1.	1	0	1	1	1	0	0	0
Chain 2.	1	1	0	1	0	1	0	0
Chain 3.	1	1	1	0	0	0	1	0

[a]A channel is only open if a vertical column is all ones.

[b]Soliton passage through a chain changes all ones to zeros
and vice versa.

SEND column of Table II in each section correspond to a rotation clockwise,
while the last two of each section correspond to a counter-clockwise
rotation of the bridgehead double bond.

Note that this behavior is not like the operation of a three-way valve
where one branch is cut off from the other two. In this case of soliton
valving, Table II shows that communication is cut off from just one direction,
not two (see NOT SEND column).

It would be surprising to the author if this effect is not used somewhere
in nature in the directed synthesis of natural products.

Proton Tunnelling and Soliton Generation

The asymmetric nature of most hydrogen bonds led to the suggestion of their
possible use as 'molecular' rectifiers (2) and to their tabulation as a possible
switching mechanism in 1979 (1a). In the same EAP report (1a) we included
hydride ion (H^-) as well as proton (H^+) transfer mechanisms in our discussions
but like Aviram and Ratner (2) earlier, omitted suggesting a method for
coupling the tunnelling current to an external current or other phenomenon
(ignoring any displacement current effects). Below we offer a mechanism that
not only relates proton and hydride ion tunnelling to an external current but
also provides a mechanism for the generation of solitons.

In a chemically naive form the proton tunnelling is indicated below as
taking place between a secondary amine and a ketone group in the presence of an
electric field of strength E. The proton donor and acceptor groups are both
adjacent to extended conjugated systems, in this case trans-polyacetylene.

In general the proton transfer gives rise to generation of opposite charges
in the two chains and then the appearance of solitons as below:

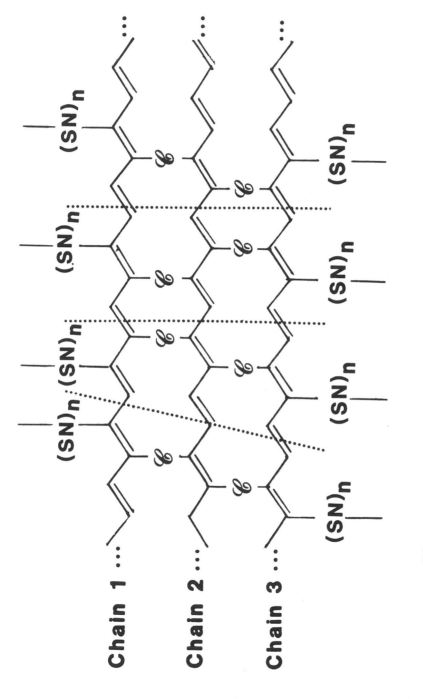

𝒞 conjugated connector

Figure 7. Gang switching is conceptually extended by replacing the electron acceptor and donor of each chromophore or channel with an electron conductor.

SOLITON VALVING

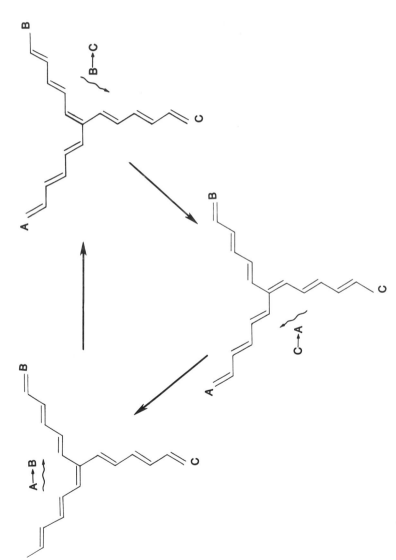

Figure 8.   The propagation of a soliton from A to B corresponds to a clockwise rotation by 120° of the upper left-hand configuration. This valve like action is related to but not isomorphous to a threeway valve.

Table II. Soliton Valving

Double Bond* on Chain	Send	New Double Bond Position	Not Send
A	A → B	B	B → C
	B → A	B	C → B
	A → C	C	
	C → A	C	
B	B → C	C	A → C
	C → B	C	C → A
	A → B	A	
	B → A	A	
C	A → C	A	A → B
	C → A	A	B → A
	B → C	B	
	C → B	B	

*i.e., the double bond on branch carbon.

As the proton, H^+ moves to the left to form a new bond with oxygen, valence electrons (usually π electrons) move to the right as is suggested by the curved arrows. After the conformational changes occur, as indicated in the lower equation, we can imagine a trivalent carbon anion being formed on the right and a carbonium ion being formed on the left. Further motions of these charged states to the right and left respectively are suggested by the curved arrows in the lower equation above. Moreover, since the proton tunnelling is necessarily associated with conformational changes induced by an electric field it seems that the necessary elements for charged soliton formation are present. Accordingly we anticipate that a negative soliton will move to the right while a positive soliton will propagate to the left.

Consider another example:

Several changes are made in the proton tunnelling scheme for soliton generation just above. The electric field direction is reversed and the chemical system is apt to be more stable. In addition, the presence of aromatic terminal groups will mean that the potential at which proton tunnelling is first induced will be higher. That is, a bias can be chemically built in. Furthermore, by the proper choice of terminal groups, the chemist will have considerable control over that bias. In this case, proton tunnelling will occur to the right leaving behind a quinonylidene terminal group.

At this point (lower equation), the system has generated two solitons of opposite charge moving in opposite directions; but then soliton generation stops. If the potential is increased sufficiently, then a hydride ion (H^-) can leave the right hand nitrogen, hopping back to the oxygen and generating two more solitons of the same charges and moving in the same direction as before. Moreover, when the solitons depart and their potential has dropped sufficiently for the hydrogen to see primarily the electric field E, then proton tunnelling will occur again and generate two more solitons. In short we will have an oscillatory generation of solitons.

Soliton Reversal

As a pseudo-particle, a hydrodynamic soliton has a definite energy, shape, and momentum; and like a particle one might consider reflecting it from a suitably stiff surface. At the molecular level the same consideration occurs, but here it is clear that the correct reflector is of molecular origin. Soliton reversal is indicated in two different modes in Fig. 9. The first mode involves two trans-polyacetylene chains connected in a conjugated manner to a tricyclic pentaene. In Fig. 9a we see that the chains are connected in such a way that the number of double bonds in the reversing tricyclic moiety remains constant.

In the single chain soliton reverser of Fig. 9b the reverser moiety is a partially hydrogenated coronene. In this case the soliton advances to the left and proceeds clockwise around the molecule. The valence π electron motion is indicated sequentially by the numbered curved arrows. Note that the electron motion indicated by the tenth arrow can occur only after electron motion indicated by the first arrow is completed. This suggests the theoretical possibility that the soliton never traverses around the hydrocoronene moiety first clockwise and then counterclockwise but is only reflected at the first ring atom while the molecule undergoes a concerted conformation change. In this single chain case, the chain remains in the same conformational state before and after the soliton has been reversed since the soliton passes over the same chain twice.

Soliton Memory Element

In the discussion above we have presented all the components necessary to postulate a Soliton Memory Element. A simple example of such an element is indicated in Fig. 10. In such an element the access time of an information bit (soliton or no soliton) and the number of bits clearly depend on the soliton velocity and the lengths of the conjugated polymer linking the soliton generator and the electron tunnel switch. The velocity of a soliton is energy dependent but only approaches phonon velocity as an upper limit. A soliton is estimated to propagate 100Å in somewhat less than 10^{-10} sec.

In Fig. 10 we show the possibility of storing four bits (in duplicate) at any one time; two on the upper chain and two on the lower chain. The illustration implicitly suggests using the simultaneous arrival of both the positive and negative solitons to trigger the electron tunnel switch. This technique then provides a built-in defense against some soft errors.

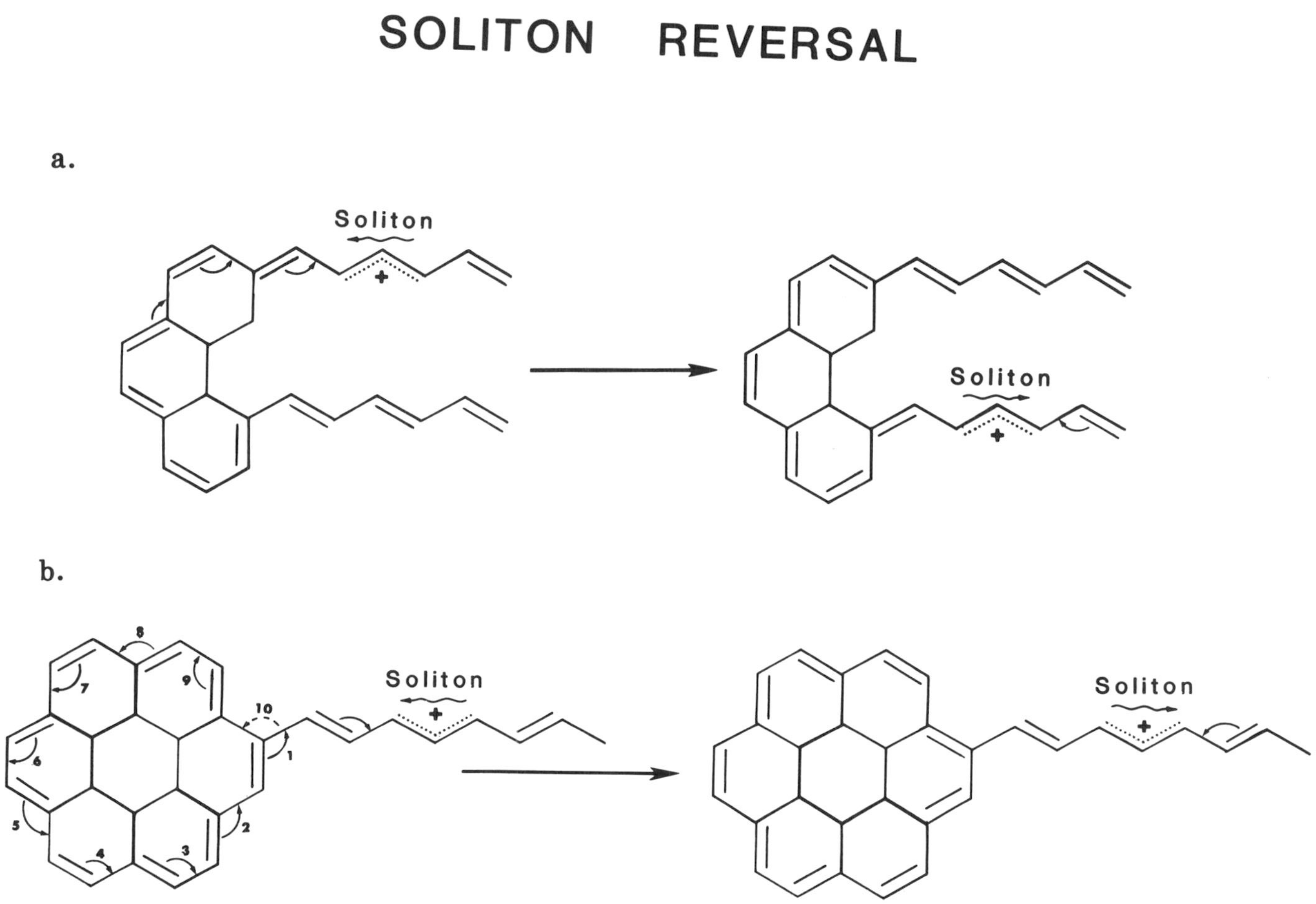

Figure 9. Molecular double chain (a) and single chain (b) soliton reversers are illustrated.

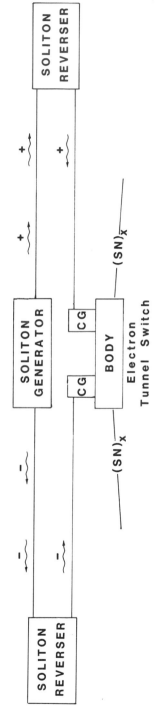

Figure 10. Solitons may be temporarily stored on transpolyacetylene chains connecting the soliton generator first to the soliton reversers and then to the Control Groups (CGs) of the multi-barrier electron tunnel detector (switch).

a. BISTABLE CHEMICAL MEMORY

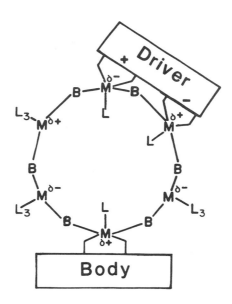

b.

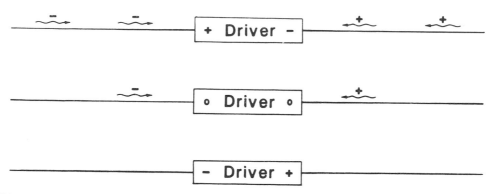

Figure 11. The bistable chemical memory unit of Ref. (1b) is shown in a) while
           b) illustrates the reversal of the Driver charges by two pairs of
           solitons. The read device of the chemical memory is a multibarrier
           tunnel switch whose BODY and one Control Group is shown at the
           bottom of Fig. 11a.

     While soliton devices may not be very fast, one can store information
at great densities. Assume that soliton separations along a trans-polyacetylene

chain are approximately 200Å. If the chains are packed on 50Å centers then the density of soliton information bits can be an astounding 2×10^{18} bits/cc.

Bistable Chemical Memory

The configuration of the soliton generator and the soliton reverser can be used as input to another memory element, namely the bistable chemical memory element, first discussed in Ref. 1b. The element can be independently written and read. It is a static conformational storage device that depends on the existence of two valence states, $M^{0+}_{(low)}$ and $M^{0-}_{(high)}$, of a transition metal. At the bottom of Fig. 11a we see that one metal atom is acting as a Control Group for an electron tunnel switch (the read device) while the Driver controls the valence states in the metal ring by the development of Driver + and - charges. If these Driver charges are reversed to - and + then with the resulting movement of the bridging ligands, B, the valence states of the metal atoms are exchanged, with the ligands B moving toward the new high valence M^{0-} atoms.

While the nature of the Driver moiety has not been specified as yet, it is clear that the Driver charges could be reversed by accepting two pairs of solitons from a soliton generator as suggested in Fig. 11b. Thus the Driver charges can be reversed by three different mechanisms: 1) charge flow under a potential difference; 2) photoactivation (dipole transition); and 3) charged pairs of solitons. Of the three the last would seem to be the most versatile mechanism.

Conclusion

Modern chemistry begins with structural information; from the interatomic distances and angles not only can you predict properties and lifetimes of processes but also synthetic approaches. We have shown that structural or conformational information can provide the key to switching at the molecular level ranging from electron tunnelling and soliton switching to soliton valving, reversal and generation. Since many bulk electrical properties of electroactive polymers are dependent on molecular conformation, these materials may prove to be the key to chemically synthesizing and interconnecting molecular devices. While most of the examples given are drawn from organic chemistry, the bistable chemical memory suggests that inorganic examples will become plentiful; the enormously rich field of transition metal chemistry has hardly been mentioned as an area to be searched for molecular switches.

In short we hope that the universality of conformation changes in molecular electronic switches has been demonstrated above and that the interest of structural chemists in molecular electronic devices has been awakened.

References

1. F. L. Carter in the NRL Program on Electroactive Polymers, a) First Annual Report, Ed. Luther B. Lockhart, Jr., NRL Memorandum Report #3960, p. 121; b) Second Annual Report, Ed. Robert B. Fox, NRL Memorandum Report #4335, p. 35.

2. A. Aviram and M. A. Ratner, Chem. Phys. Letters 29, 277 (1974).

3. E. A. Pschenichnov, Soviet Physics, Solid State 4, 819 (1962).

4. F. L. Carter, "Electron Tunnelling in Short Periodic Arrays," this proceedings.

5. L. M. Loew, S. Scully, L. Simpon, and A. S. Waggoner, Nature 281, 497 (1979).

6. T. J. Meyer, Accounts of Chem. Res. <u>11</u>, 94 (1978); M. J. Powers and T. J.
    Meyer, Inorganic Chem. <u>17</u>, 1785 (1978).

7. A. Von Kameke, G. M. Tom, and H. Taube, Inorganic Chem. <u>17</u>, 1790 (1978).

8. A. S. Davydov and N. I. Kislukha, Phys. Stat. Sol. (b) <u>59</u>, 465 (1973);
    Sov. Phys. JETP <u>44</u>, 571 (1976).

9. A. Hazell and A. Mukhopadhyay, Acta Cryst. B<u>36</u>, 747 (1980).

DISCUSSION

Dr. Nagel: NRL - I would like to ask about the basis for believing
that a conjugated system can support solitons. Solitons require a particular
balance between the dispersive and nonlinear characteristics of a medium. Not
all media will support solitons. What is the basis, either theoretically
or experimentally, for expecting these systems will indeed support solitons?

Dr. Carter: At the moment, the basis is not especially good. The
wave equations themselves, to my knowledge, have only really been solved as time
dependent phenomena by Davydov in the alpha-helix type of situation where the
coupling is via the dipole moment of the polypeptide amide bond. However, Su,
Schrieffer and Heeger have made some Hamiltonian time-independent studies which
certainly indicates the existence of solitons in a conjugated system like polyacetylene. Solitons are an interesting phenomenon and here propose a theoretical
question which is appropriate to ask and to answer in the near future.

Dr. Pomerantz: IBM - Some of the difficulties with building a
large-scale molecular electronic device have been raised, for example, chemical
back reactions and related questions. Another problem not mentioned here yet
is one raised by Bob Keys at our lab, namely, limitation on the packing density
of the electronic devices due to the heat dissipation. Any time a device
changes its state, some energy is dissipated and that thermal energy must be
removed in some fashion or else the device would simply melt. As we go to
molecular densities will that become a limitation on what we are trying to do?
Of course, the thermal problem is one of the background reasons for going to
superconducting technologies where the energy dissipation is extremely low,
and provides one of the motivations for current world-wide computer work.

Dr. Carter: Well, you are absolutely right. There is no question
at all of heat generation being a limiting condition; however, at the molecular level one hopes to avoid resistive elements. All modern circuitry depends strongly on resistive elements in very large numbers. On the other hand,
if you could use the tunnelling phenomena, which are largely non-dissipative,
and soliton propagation, for example, which is largely non-heat generating,
and simultaneously reduce the number of electrons or moving particles that
are involved, then presumably you could minimize some of these heat problems.
The solution is to go to non-dissipative processes as much as possible, and
second, reduce the number of resistive elements of scattering as we usually
know them. Finally of course, one might have to lower the temperature, which
is readily achievable with a very small device. The question is important and
needs much further discussion than what I have given.

Dr. Hagelstein: LLNL - The question concerns having more than one
soliton propagating down the chain, as in the case where one is doing byte
processing. How close in space could you put them on a polyacetylene chain?

Dr. Carter: Two things which I didn't mention--when two solitons
pass one another in the ocean, they do so nondestructively and without

interference. Second, there are three types of solitons--plus, minus, and radical. A plus and minus soliton, if they meet, will not pass but presumably they will annihilate themselves with some considerable energy released. Other combinations could pass unchanged. To answer your question, a soliton probably is maybe 20 Angstroms long in the conjugated system, so you maybe could pack them as close as 100 Angstroms along the chain. I have shown two solitons of the same charge moving one behind the other. That may not be what you want. You may prefer to alternate the charges, in which case perhaps you could get them somewhat closer together.

Prof. Jones: B. Univ. - I need some clarification on the soliton propagation phenomenon. You are envisioning a radical or cation center created at one end of a fully conjugated chain, and propagating along some distance over time. However, according to resonance theory, which is applicable to these systems, the radical center or charge center that is generated does not evolve over time but is in fact part of the delocalized system. As soon as the radical center is created at one end, it is also created at the other end, and what you have is just an ensemble of a resonance structures in which electron density is localized at various sites along the chain. The only way to get around this delocalized feature is to have a gross geometry change that is controllable or predictable. It then isolates one part of the conjugated system, the radical or charge center, from another part of the conjugated system. Could you discuss the distinction between generating a fully delocalized radical center or charge center as opposed to generating valence tautomers and also the time evolution of charge or radicals tautomers?

Dr. Carter: I'm glad you brought the question up because it is a question I should have addressed. One does not know if solitons really exist in polyacetylene, for example. The stationary state type of calculations for solitons are reasonably solid. They usually generate a stationary state midway in the band gap. One does not know whether a charge state traveling down a conjugated system is going to be delocalized or localized, and that may be temperature dependent, but the soliton is necessarily tied to a conformtional distortion in its immediate vicinity, and so that is answering part of your question.

Prof. Jones: One's intuition is that the soliton should not exist unless it is accompanied by some geometry change which hopefully can be controlled. It is true that on creation of a radical center or charge center you do disrupt the type of conjugation that you had in the polymer to begin with. You can effectively isolate one of these intramolecular charge transfer interactions but it is not clear that you would bring to a particular site, the radical or charge character that could be necessary if it were a fully delocalized planar or conjugated system. There would have to be a twist end or some kind of change that would take it out of full resonance.

Dr. Carter: Absolutely, you would take it out of full resonance. There is no doubt about it. It is a problem which perhaps we will attempt to resolve using a finite difference calculation; when we would explore some of your current questions.

Dr. Haddon: Bell - I cannot comment on the dynamics of solitons, but we have done some calculations on conjugated chains (Advances in Chemistry Series 169, 333 (1978)) designed to mimic the situation in polyacetylene when you get a soliton generated, and I don't think as far as organic chemistry is concerned that there is a great deal of mystery about these things. I think many of us are familiar with the sorts of things that happen when you generate a linear conjugated cation, anion, or radical. Solitons are very similar to this sort of species. The results of ab initio calculations on polyenyl cations are in accord with chemical intuition. The bond linkages at the locus of charge density are similar to the bond lengths in aromatic systems such as benzene, but bond alternation becomes pronounced with increasing distance from the locus point. Similarly with the charge densities which are rapidly attenuated with distance from the site of highest charge. Thus these systems show a gradual transition from localized to delocalized bonding. Therefore while the dynamics of solitons may not be fully understood, the organic chemical precedents for the static structures in polyenyl systems are well established.

CHAPTER VI

REVERSIBLE FIELD INDUCED SWITCHING IN COPPER AND SILVER RADICAL-ION SALTS

R. S. Potember and T. O. Poehler
Applied Physics Laboratory
Johns Hopkins University
Laurel, MD 20810

D. O. Cowan
Johns Hopkins University
Baltimore, MD 21218

Forrest L. Carter and P. Brant
Naval Research Laboratory
Washington, DC 20375

SWITCHING AND MEMORY DEVICE: MATERIALS AND FABRICATION

This paper is a report on reproducible current-controlled bistable electrical switching and memory phenomena observed in polycrystalline metal-organic semiconducting films. The effects are observed in films of either copper or silver complexed with the electron acceptors tetracyanoethylene (TNCE), tetracyanonapthoquinodimethane (TNAP), tetracyanoquinodimethane (TCNQ), [1] or other TCNQ derivatives shown below. The character of the switching in going from a high to a low impedance state in these organic charge-transfer complexes is believed to be comparable in many respects to existing inorganic materials.

The basic configuration of the device, shown in Figure 1, consists of a 5-10 μm thick polycrystalline aggregate of a copper or a silver charge-transfer complex sandwiched between two metal electrodes. Electrical connection is made

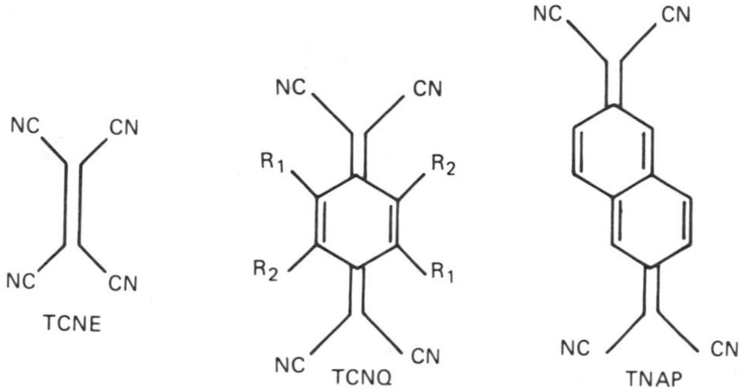

$R_1 = -H, R_2 = -H$
$R_1 = -CH_3, R_2 = -H$
$R_1 = -OCH_3, R_2 = -H$
$R_1 = -F, R_2 = -F$

73

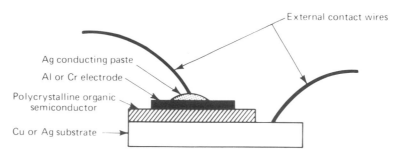

Figure 1. Schematic diagram of an organic switching device.

to the two metal electrodes through silver conducting paste or through liquid
metals of mercury, gallium or gallium-indium eutectic. Fabrication of the
device consists of first mechanically removing any oxide layers and organic
contaminants from either a piece of copper or silver metal foil. The cleaned
metal foil is then placed in a solution of dry and degassed acetonitrile which
has been saturated with a neutral acceptor molecule, for example, TCNQ°. The
neutral acceptors used in all of these experiments are recrystallized twice
from acetonitrile and then sublimed under a high vacuum prior to their use [2].
When the solution saturated with the neutral acceptor is brought in contact
with a metal substrate of either copper or silver, a rapid oxidation-reduction
reaction occurs in which the corresponding metal salt of the ion-radical acceptor molecule is formed. The basic reaction is shown in Equation 1 for copper
and TCNQ°.

$$Cu^{0} + \quad \underset{TCNQ}{\underset{NC}{\overset{NC}{\diagdown}}} \rightleftarrows Cu^{+} \left[\; \right]^{\cdot -} \tag{1}$$

This technique of forming semiconducting films by direct oxidation-
reduction is used to grow highly microcrystalline films directly on the copper
or silver substrate. These films show a metallic sheen and can be grown to a
thickness of 10 μm in a matter of minutes. Once the polycrystalline film has
been grown to the desired thickness, the growth process can be terminated by
simply removing the metal substrate containing the metal organic layer from the
acetonitrile solution; this terminates the redox reaction. The two component
structure is gently washed with additional acetonitrile to remove any excess
neutral acceptor molecules and dried under a vacuum to remove any traces of
solvent. Elemental analysis performed on polycrystalline films of Cu-TCNQ and
Cu-TNAP reveals that the metal/acceptor ratio is 1:1 in both complexes [3].
Finally, the three component structure is complete when a top metal electrode
of either aluminum or chromium is evaporated or sputtered directly on the
metal organic film.

ELECTRICAL BEHAVIOR

Threshold and memory behavior is observed in these materials by examining
current as a function of voltage across the two terminal structure. Figure 2
shows a typical dc current-voltage curve for a 3.75 μm thick Cu/Cu-TNAP/Al
system. The trace in Figure 2, as well as all other I-V measurements presented
in this paper, are made with a 10^{2}-Ω load resistor in series with the device.
Figure 2 shows that there are two stable non-ohmic resistive states in the

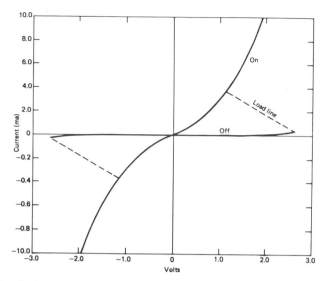

Figure 2. Typical dc current-voltage characteristic showing high- and low-impedance states for a 3.75 μm Cu-TNAP sample.

material. These two states, labeled "OFF" state and "ON" state, are essentially insensitive to moisture, light, and the polarity of the applied voltage. A rapid switching is observed from the "OFF" to the "ON" state along the load line when an applied field across the sample surpasses a threshold value (Vth) of 2.7 V. This corresponds to a field strength of approximately 8.1×10^3 V/cm. At this field strength the initial high impedance of the device, 1.25×10^4 ohms, drops to a low impedance value of 190 ohms. This rise in current to 4 ma and concurrent decrease in the voltage to approximately 1.2 V along the load line is observed in the Cu-TNAP system. It is representative of the switching effects observed in all of the metal charge-transfer salts examined and is characteristic of all two terminal S-shaped or current-controlled negative-resistance switches [4].

In addition, it has been observed in all of the materials investigated that once the film is in the "ON" state it will remain in that state as long as an external field is applied. In every case studied, the film eventually returned to its initial high-impedance state after the applied field was removed. It was also found that the time required to switch back to the initial state appeared to be directly proportional to the film thickness, duration of the applied field, and the amount of power dissipated in the sample while in this state.

Three general trends are noted in the "ON" state character of the copper and silver complexes as related to the different acceptor molecules. The first is that the copper salts consistently exhibited greater stability and reproducibility over the corresponding silver salts of the same acceptor. Second, it is possible to correlate the preferred switching behavior of the different complexes to the reduction potential of the various acceptors. This plot is shown in Figure 3 using copper as a donor in each case. It appears that for devices made from weak electron acceptors, the switching behavior is usually of the threshold type, i.e., when the applied voltage is removed from a device in the "ON" state, the device will immediately return to the "OFF" state. On the other hand, for strong electron acceptors a memory effect is observed. This memory state remains intact from a few minutes up to several days and can often be removed by the application of a short pulse of current in either direction. For intermediate strength acceptors, it is possible to operate the

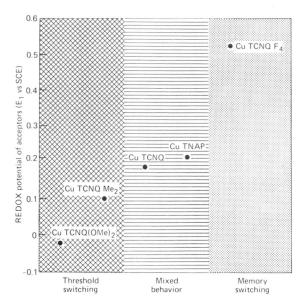

Figure 3. Type of switching behavior plotted versus the reduction potential of the acceptor.

device as either a memory switch or a threshold switch by varying the strength or the duration of the applied field in the low-impedance state. Third, it also recognized that the field strength of the switching threshold tends to parallel the strength of the acceptor. For instance, the copper salt of TCNQ(OMe)$_2$ switches at a field strength of approximately 2×10^3 V/cm, while the copper salt of TCNQF$_4$ is found to switch at a field strength of about 2×10^4 V/cm. It is clear that these three trends are related to the reduction potential of the acceptor calculated from solution redox potentials [5]. However, as these values do not always parallel the values found in the solid phase, a more quantitative description relating to the switching behavior to the acceptor cannot be made unless the various contributions to the binding energy of the different ion-radical salts are considered.

The response to a very short pulse is exemplified in the next figure. Figure 4 is an oscilloscope trace showing both the leading edge of a voltage pulse and current pulse versus time for a Cu-TNAP sample in response to a rectangular voltage pulse with a 4 nsec rise time. This voltage pulse switched the sample from the high- to low-impedance state and contained a 1.0 V overvoltage to eliminate any current oscillations between the "OFF" and "ON" states. Current oscillations arise when the applied voltage is set very close to V_{th}. It is not possible from this experiment to determine values for the conventional delay times and rise times because the combined delay and rise times appear to be less than 4 nsec (the limiting rise time of the pulse generator). This experiment suggests that the mechanism of the switching phenomena is not due to thermal effects [6] which are used to describe switching and memory phenomena in many other systems. From Figure 4, it appears that the delay time is shorter than reported values for inorganic semiconductors under the same experimental conditions. A recent example of delay times in an inorganic amorphous material is given for the composition Te$_{10}$As$_{35}$Ge$_7$Si$_{17}$P$_1$, [7] approximately 1 μm thick, sandwiched between two molybdenum electrodes. A typical delay time reported for this device in response to a single 12 V pulse is about 2 μsec. To reduce the delay time to a value of 10 nsec, a 30 V pulse (18 V overvoltage) was required.

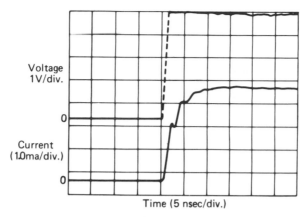

Figure 4. Transient response to a 4 nsec rise time rectangular pulse.

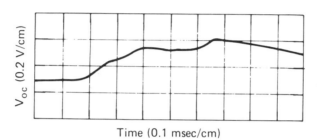

Figure 5. Spontaneous open-circuit potential generated in a Cu/Cu-TNAP/Al sample at room temperature.

An experiment was designed to determine if the device generates an open-circuit voltage or electromotive force (emf) when returning from the low- to high-impedance mode. The appearance of a spontaneous emf [8] would indicate that an electrochemical reaction was responsible for switching phenomena. In this experiment: 1) an applied voltage in excess of the threshold voltage was used to place a Cu-TNAP sample into a low-impedance state where it would remain for a short time after the applied voltage was removed, i.e., memory states; 2) the sample was then externally short-circuited to eliminate any capacitive effects, and finally; 3) a high input impedance storage oscilloscope was used to measure open-circuit discharge voltage when the sample spontaneously returned to its original high-impedance state. The oscilloscope was set to trigger whenever a voltage exceeding a few millivolts appeared across the sample. The results are shown in Figure 5 where the spontaneous open-circuit voltage measured by the oscilloscope is reproduced and is seen to have generated approximately 0.3 volts at discharge.

The open-circuit voltage of 0.3 volts observed in this experiment does show that the mechanism by which the switching occurs is consistent with a field induced solid-state reversible electrochemical reaction associated with the metal charge-transfer salts.

INFRARED REFLECTANCE SPECTRA OF Cu-TCNQ SEMICONDUCTING FILMS

To investigate the formal charge of TCNQ in the semiconducting film of Cu-TCNQ, the infrared reflectance spectra was recorded at room temperature for

crystalline Cu-TCNQ films before and after an external electric field was
applied to the sample. The applied field in this experiment was of a strength
comparable to that in switching device structures, i.e., a field in excess of
10^4 V/cm was used. The results were then compared to the reflection spectra
measured for other crystalline metal-TCNQ radical-anion salts. These salts
are known to exist as either simple or complex salts in the solid-state. The
crystalline materials investigated were lithium-TCNQ, cesium-TCNQ, copper-TCNQ
(prepared by a metathetical reaction) and copper-TCNQ grown on copper substrates in the manner similar to the switching devices. Specifically, the
region of the infrared spectrum measured was between 2000 to 2500 cm^{-1} (0.25
to 0.30 eV). This spectral region corresponds to the ν_2 C≡N stretching mode
in TCNQ. Previous studies have provided evidence to link the frequency assignment of C≡N stretching and C=C stretching modes to the degree of charge transfer in complexes of TCNQ. [9] In these investigations a frequency shift to
lower energy is reported as charge density increases on TCNQ.

The Cu-TCNQ switching material was subjected to electric fields by clamping
a thin highly insulating film of either teflon or polyethylene between the
surface of the Cu-TCNQ film on a copper substrate and an external top metal
electrode. The reflectance spectrum was recorded after removing the field
and separating the Cu-TCNQ (on the copper substrate) from the top electrode
and the insulating plastic film. All of the samples were freshly prepared and
the solid-state diffuse reflectance spectra was recorded on a Perkin-Elmer 621
Grating IR Spectrometer. Wherever possible, elemental analysis was performed
on the samples to verify their composition.

The upper trace in Figure 6 is a reflectance spectrum of a crystalline
film of Cu-TCNQ before the application of an electric field. A moderately

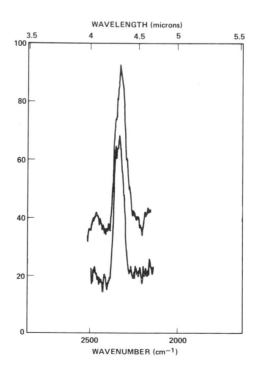

Figure 6. Reflectance spectra of a crystalline film of Cu-TCNQ on copper before (top) and after (bottom) the application of an electric field.

strong infrared active mode for CN is observed to dominate the region characterized by a single line center at approximately 2320 cm^{-1}. The lower
trace (Figure 6) is a reflectance spectrum of the same film of Cu-TCNQ, but
in this spectrum an electric field has been applied to the sample for 72 hours.
In this trace there are two reflectance maxima. One line can be assigned a
value of 2321 cm^{-1} which is nearly identical to the maximum value seen at
2320 cm^{-1} in the original spectrum. However, a second line has appeared as a
shoulder that is shifted to a higher frequency by 21 cm^{-1}. This additional
peak is indicative of a decrease in the electron charge on the CN moiety of
some fraction of the TCNQ molecules [10].

In Table I, the results of this experiment are compared to reflectance
spectra measured for other simple and complex metal-TCNQ salts. We found
that the CN stretching mode in reflectance measurements shifted to higher
frequency by about 100 cm^{-1} from absorption measurements made on the same
material. The peak in the reflectance band at 2320 cm^{-1} for the Cu-TCNQ film
prior to the application of a field is consistent with the values measured for
the simple (1:1) salt of Li$^+$(TCNQ$^{\mp}$) and for Cu-(TCNQ) tabulated in Table I.
On the other hand the spectra of a Cu-TCNQ film after the application of an
applied field closely resembles the spectra of Cs$_2$(TCNQ$^{\mp}$)$_3$ with two CN
stretching modes separated by ~ 20 cm^{-1}. Cs$_2$(TCNQ$^{\mp}$)$_3$ is a complex salt which
contains neutral TCNQ° and radical-anion TCNQ$^{\mp}$ [11].

The diffuse reflectance spectra reported in Table I show that it is
possible to assign a CN stretching frequency to both neutral and radical-
anion TCNQ in crystalline samples of metal-TCNQ complexes because the reflectance peak for neutral TCNQ is shifted ~ 20 cm^{-1} higher in frequency than for
radical-anion TCNQ$^{\mp}$. Specifically, the reflectance data for Cu-TCNQ when compared to other metal-TCNQ salts of known composition strongly suggests that
neutral TCNQ° is not present in the unswitched Cu-TCNQ films. On the other
hand, the additional peak that appears in the spectra of Cu-TCNQ subjected to
an applied field shows a peak superimposable with the peak recorded for neutral
TCNQ° in Cs$_2$(TCNQ$^{\mp}$)$_3$. This evidence suggests that neutral TCNQ° is formed in
a solid-state field induced phase transition when electric fields are applied
to crystalline films of Cu-TCNQ grown on copper substrates.

Table I. Comparison of reflectance maximum for the CN stretching mode in TCNQ
          for various metal-TCNQ salts.

TCNQ Salt	Comments	Reflection Maximum (cm^{-1})
Li TCNQ	Simple 1:1 salt	2320
Cs$_2$ TCNQ$_3$	Complex 2:3 salt	2322 and 2344
Cu-TCNQ	Prepared by metathetical reaction	2323
Cu-TCNQ Switch	Before application of electric field	2320
Cu-TCNQ-Switch	After application of electric field	2321 and 2340

X-ray photoelectron spectroscopy (XPS) has been successfully applied to
the study of oxidation states in mixed valence compounds [12, 13]. Other uses
of XPS include the determination of elemental stoichiometries in unknown materials [14, 15], and the study of concentration gradients in the near surface
region [16]. Consequently, XPS is well suited for characterization of the Cu-
TCNQ switches.

Binding energies provide information regarding charge distribution in
molecules. For insulators or semiconductors B.E. measurement usually requires
the selection of an internal or external B.E. standard or calibration line in
order to eliminate variable charging effects [17]. Without recourse to such
standards B.E.'s are generally unreproducible. However, it has been our experience that under the conditions of our experimental procedure charging
effects have been virtually eliminated for the samples studied in the present
investigation. The B.E. data are summarized in Table II. For comparison, B.E.
data for Cu-TCNQ powder prepared by metathetical reaction, neutral TCNQ°, and
data for Cu metal and the copper oxides, Cu_2O and CuO, are also reported. All
B.E.'s were reproducible to within ± 0.1-0.2eV. Along with the B.E. data we
also include comparisons of the copper Auger parameters [18], which are independent of sample charging, (here defined as B.E. $Cu2p_{3/2}$ - B.E. Cu L_3VV;
AlK_α radiation) for all samples. A representative $Cu2p_{3/2}$ spectrum for a Cu-
TCNQ switch is shown in Figure 7. As a result of comparison of all the B.E.
and Auger parameter data one can conclude that the Cu-TCNQ switch contains
the compound Cu-TCNQ. The reasons for this assignment are as follows. The
presence of Cu(II) in the Cu-TCNQ switch can be ruled out because there are
no high B.E. satellite features in the $Cu2p_{3/2}$ spectra of the switches examined. All copper (II) compounds exhibit this characteristic feature as
found, for example, in the spectrum for CuO [19]. The $Cu2p_{3/2}$, N 1s, and C 1s
B.E.'s of the Cu-TCNQ switch and Cu-TCNQ compound are the same. This result
does not rule out the presence of Cu metal or other Cu(I) compounds in the
switch. However, the Auger parameter for the Cu-TCNQ switch is identical to
that of the genuine Cu-TCNQ compound and the parameter is 2-3 eV different
from those of Cu_2O or Cu metal. Thus, the Auger parameter data rule out the
presence of measurable quantities of Cu metal or Cu(I) compounds other than
Cu-TCNQ on the surface of the switch.
One can independently corroborate these findings by comparison of relative core level intensity data for Cu-TCNQ switches, prepared under a variety
of conditions, with intensity data for the Cu-TCNQ compound. The relative
intensities provide a method of determining sample stoichiometries. The
$Cu2p_{3/2}$/N 1s intensity ratio was determined for Cu-TCNQ switches prepared by
immersing a clean Cu plate in hot or room temperature acetonitrile solutions
of TCNQ for times ranging from 1 to 5 minutes and for the pure Cu^+TCNQ^- compound. The intensity data show that for Cu plate immersion periods of 1 to 5
minutes the $Cu2p_{3/2}$/N 1s ratio for the switch corresponds to that of Cu-TCNQ.

The N 1s spectra of the switches prepared by immersion times of 1-5 minutes were compared with the spectra for the Cu-TCNQ compound and neutral TCNQ°.
The comparisons are shown in Figure 8. Both neutral TCNQ° and the Cu-TCNQ
compound show, in addition to their primary feature centered at 398.7 eV,
characteristic "satellite" features. In the case of TCNQ° the feature is
found at 401.8 eV [20] while for Cu-TCNQ the feature is centered at 400.0 eV.
The N 1s spectrum of the Cu-TCNQ switch is very nearly the same as, although
not identical with, the spectrum recorded for the Cu-TCNQ compound.

Table II. Core Level Binding Energies of Cu-TCNQ Switch and Standard Compounds

	Cu2p3/2	N 1s	ΔB.E. (Cu2p3/2-CuLW)	B.E. C 1s	
Cu-TCNQ	932.1 (1.9)	398.6 (1.5)	361.3	285.0 (2.4)	
Cu-TCNQ Compound	932.0 (2.1)	398.7 (1.7)	361.0	285.1	
Cu	932.3 (1.3)		364.5		
Cu$_2$O	932.3 (1.2)		362.4		
CuO	933.7 (2.0)		364.1		
TCNQ° (sublimed)		399.1 (1.3)		285.5	286.3
Li-TCNQ		397.6 (1.3)		284.3 (2.7)	
Na-TCNQ		397.7 (1.3)		284.4 (2.7)	
K-TCNQ		397.7		284.8 (2.4)	
Cs$_2$-TCNQ$_3$		397.6 (2.7)		284.7 (2.8)	
Ag-TCNQ		398.4 (1.4)		284.6	367.8 (1.4)

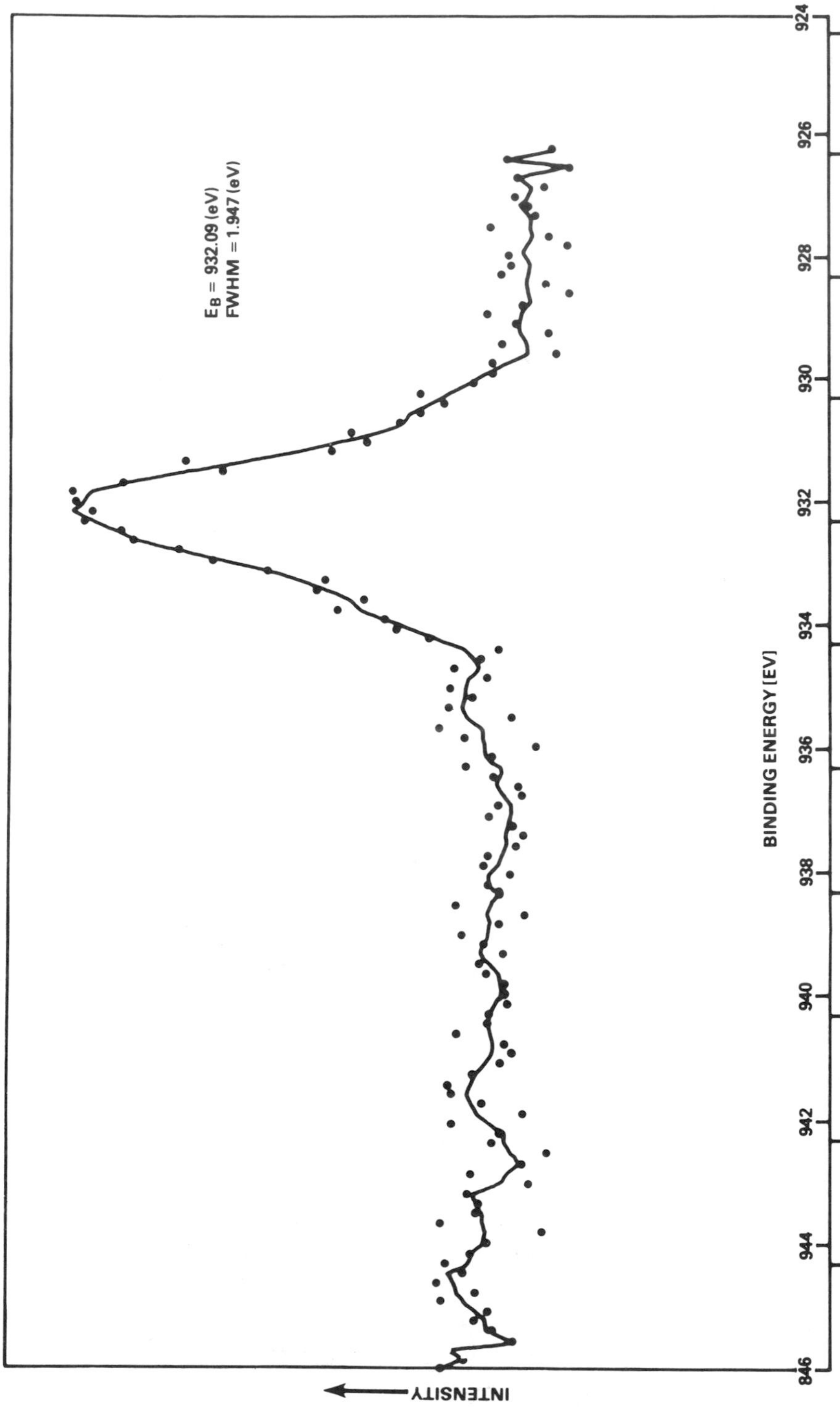

Figure 7. Spectra of Cu(2p$_{3/2}$) region for a 10 μm thick polycrystalline film of Cu-TCNQ (unswitched).

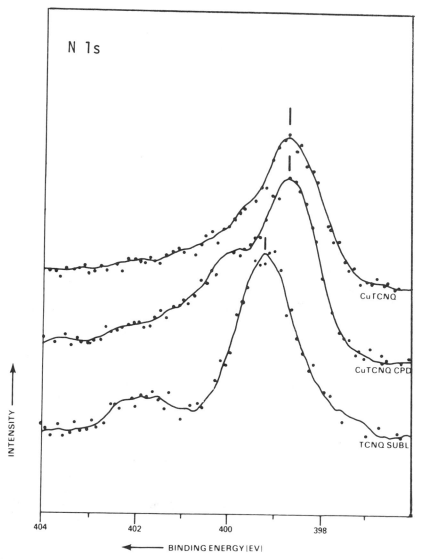

Figure 8. XPS spectrum of nitrogen (1s) for neutral TCNQ° (bottom), Cu-TCNQ powder (center), and a Cu-TCNQ thin film switching device (top).

CONCLUSIONS

It is postulated that mixed-valence species or complex salts [21] formed as a result of this field induced redox reaction control the semiconducting behavior of these films and that these complex salts exist in a solid-state equilibrium with the simple 1:1 salt. Since non-integral oxidation states are common in solids, it is difficult to predict exact stoichiometry in the equilibrium equation, but a likely equation for switching in Cu-TCNQ, for example, may involve

$$[Cu^+(TCNQ^{\bar{}})]_n \; \rightleftarrows \; Cu^o_x + [Cu^+(TCNQ^{\bar{}})]_{n-x} + (TCNQ^o)_x.$$

In addition, an ionic or a molecular displacement associated with this equilibrium would explain the observed memory phenomena and the fact that all the devices show only two stable resistive states.

Since conduction in these narrow band semiconducting salts of TCNQ is believed to be limited by the motion of unpaired electrons along the stacks of TCNQ molecules, this interpretation is in accordance with the electrical behavior reported in these films when fabricated into switching devices [22]. In a simple salt like Cu^+TCNQ^- there is roughly one unpaired electron per molecule which tends to keep electrostatic repulsion in the ground state configuration at a minimum. The low conductivity reported in these simple salts is due in part to an increase in the energy required to overcome the repulsive coulomb forces that result when a conduction electron is removed from one $TCNQ^-$ and placed into a higher energy orbital of another $TCNQ^-$ molecule.

In the case of a mixed-valence salt containing neutral $TCNQ°$ there are more TCNQ molecules than there are unpaired electrons and, therefore, electrostatic repulsion of charge carriers is kept at a minimum by allowing conduction electrons to occupy the empty molecular orbitals of $TCNQ°$. This is a lower energy pathway compared to putting more than one electron on the same TCNQ site and it may explain how mixed-valence semiconducting salts like $Cs_2(TCNQ^-)_3$ and the "switched" form of Cu-TCNQ can exhibit greater conductivity than similar salts with 1:1 stoichiometry.

ACKNOWLEDGMENT

We gratefully acknowledge support by the National Science Foundation (DMR 80-15318) and the Department of the Navy (N00024-81C-5301).

REFERENCES

1. R.S. Potember, T.O. Poehler, and D.O. Cowan, Appl. Phys. Lett. 34 (6), 405 (1979).

2. R.V. Gemmer, D.O. Cowan, T.O. Poehler, A.N. Bloch, R.E. Pyle, and R.H. Banks, J. Org. Chem. 40, 3544 (1975).

3. Elemental analysis was performed by Galbraith Laboratories, Inc., Knoxville, Tennessee 37291.

4. A.E. Owen and J.M. Robertson, IEEE Trans. Electron. Devices 20, 105 (1973).

5. Values for the reduction potential of acceptor were taken from R.C. Wheland and J.L. Gillson, J. Am. Chem. Soc. 98, 3916 (1976).

6. W.D. Buckley and S.H. Holmberg, Solid State Electron. 18, 127 (1975).

7. D.K. Reinhard, App. Phys. Lett. 31, 527 (1977).

8. A spontaneous electrochemical reaction is reported in magnesium-TCNQ salts. See F. Guttmann, A.M. Herman, and A. Rembaum, J. Electrochem. Soc. 114, 323 (1967).

9. S. Matsuzaki, R. Kutwata, and K. Toyoda, Solid State Commun. 33, 403 (1980).

10. M.S. Khatakale and J.P. Devlin, J. Chem. Phys. 70, 1851 (1979).

11.   C.J. Fritchie and P. Arthur, Jr., Acta Cryst. 21, 139 (1966).

12.   P. Brant and Q. Fernando, J. Inorg. Nucl. Chem. 40, 235 (1978).

13.   M. Yamashita, N. Matsumoto, S. Kida, Inorg. Chim. Acta 31, L381 (1978).

14.   P. Brant and R.D. Feltham, J. Electron Spectrosc. and Rel. Phenom.
      16, 379 (1979).

15.   C.D. Wagner, Anal. Chem. 44, 1050 (1972).

16.   D.M. Hercules, Phys. Scripta 16, 275 (1977).

17.   (a) S. Evans, in Handbook of X-Ray and Ultraviolet Photoelectron Spectro-
      scopy, D. Briggs, Ed., Heyden, Philadelphia, 1977, p. 121. (b) J. Finster,
      P. Lorenz, and A. Meisel, Surf. and Interface Analysis 1, 179 (1979).

18.   C.D. Wagner, Faraday Discuss. Chem. Soc. 60, 291 (1975).

19.   D.C. Frost, A. Ishitani, and C.A. McDowell, Mol. Phys. 24, 861 (1972).

20.   (a) C.R. Ginnard, R.S. Swingle, III, and B.M. Monroe, J. Electron. Spectros.
      Relat. Phenom. 6, 77 (1975); (b) A.J: Epstein, N.O. Lipari, P. Nielson,
      and D.J. Sandman, Phys. Rev. Lett. 34, 914 (1975).

21.   For a discussion of complex TCNQ salts see O.H. LeBlanc, Jr., J. Chem.
      Phys. 42, 4307 (1965).

22.   (a) J.B. Torrance, B.A. Scott, and F.B. Kaufman, Solid State Comm. 17,
      1369 (1975); (b) Z.G. Soos, Ann. Rev. Chem. 25, 121 (1974); (c) J.
      Hubbard, Phys. Rev. B17, 494 (1978).

DISCUSSION

Prof. Marks: NW Univ. - Is the crystal structure of copper TCNQ known?

Dr. Potember: No.

Prof. Marks: What is amazing is that you are switching so rapidly with such large electrical changes. Are there major crystal structure changes that have to take place in the polycrystalline film upon switching?

Dr. Potember: In order to see a memory-type switching phenomenon, there must be a change in the crystal structure of the film, i.e., a molecular or ionic displacement. If it was just an oxidation-reduction reaction occurring, the device would switch back to the insulating state as soon as the applied field was removed. We do not, however, believe that a major change in the crystal structure is necessary to invoke the switching phenomena.

Dr. Siedle: 3M - What is the copper to nitrogen ratio in the ESCA analysis?

Dr. Potember: We have not completed that experiment yet, but the copper to nitrogen ratio as determined by CH analysis is approximately one to one with some film thickness dependence being investigated.

SECTION TWO
Signal Transmission and Molecular Switching – B

CHAPTER VII

EFFECTS OF EXTERNAL ELECTRIC FIELDS AND FIELD GRADIENTS

ON THE MOTION OF FRENKEL EXCITONS IN MOLECULAR CRYSTALS

David M. Hanson
Department of Chemistry
State University of New York
Stony Brook, NY 11794

I. INTRODUCTION

The property that generally is used in textbooks on solid state physics to characterize molecular crystals is the weak Van der Waals binding energy between molecules. A classification based on this characteristic is too restrictive because it excludes crystals with hydrogen bond interactions, crystals of electron-donor-acceptor complexes, and crystals with metallic properties. A definition of a molecular crystal must also recognize that a molecule need not be neutral, diamagnetic, and composed of only first row elements. Molecular crystals are best identified by the organization of the unit cell. The unit cells of molecular crystals contain a large number of atoms that are arranged in molecular units. The complexity possible with such a large number of inequivalent atoms is limited by this grouping. Usually to a good approximation, the molecular unit plays the role of an individual atom in phenomena described in solid state physics' texts. It must be kept in mind, however, that the molecule has internal degrees of freedom that often have to be included to account for the properties of these solids.

The energy states of molecular crystals can be classified as phonons, vibrational excitons or vibrons, electronic excitons, charge-transfer excitons, and conduction states. The phonons are intermolecular vibrations, the translational and rotational motion of the molecules considered as rigid bodies on the crystal lattice. The vibrational and electronic excitons are described by the Frenkel model where the excited state is localized on a single molecule in zero order and the intermolecular interaction or coupling is treated as a perturbation. A manifestation of the exciton concept that easily is visualized is the exchange of energy between two coupled pendula. Vibrational excitons stem from the internal vibrational degrees of freedom of the molecules. The use of the vibrational exciton concept requires that the frequency separation of the modes be large compared to the frequency dispersion. The vibrational exciton model is the first order correction to the Einstein model where the dispersion is neglected. This correction often is adequate for the intra-molecular vibrations (vibrons) but not for the intermolecular vibrations

89

(phonons). A full lattice dynamical calculation is necessary to describe the latter and to describe the coupling between the phonons and the vibrons. The electronic Frenkel excitons stem from the excited molecular electronic states. The charge-transfer excitons are excited electronic states in which an electron is transferred from one molecule to its neighbor or neighbors with the electron-hole pair remaining bound. The Wannier model provides a description of some charge-transfer excitons. The conduction states are states in which the electrons and holes are not bound, and charge is transported through the crystal. Proton conduction states also have been observed in some crystals.

Research on the energy states of molecular crystals is concerned with elucidating the energy band structures and associated transport properties and with providing a rationale for them. The transport properties are determined by the same interactions that lead to the band structures plus various scattering or relaxation processes. Important features of the phonon, vibron, and electronic exciton bands have been investigated and are understood for particular cases. Most important, the theoretical and experimental techniques for expanding this knowledge to other systems and for obtaining answers to remaining questions have been developed. On the other hand, not much is known about the band structures associated with charge-transfer excitons and conduc-tion states, and what is known is very likely subject to revision in the light of future experimental results. Similarly little is known about the relaxation or scattering processes that affect any of the transport properties of these crystals.

This paper is concerned with the effects of external electric fields and field gradients on the excitation energy transfer processes associated with the electronic exciton states of molecular crystals. Subsequent sections describe our knowledge of these states and the energy transfer phenomena, predictions of electric field effects and the fundamental information that can be gained from them, observations of electric field effects, applications to systems other than molecular crystals, and the prospects and problems for utilization in technology.

II. EVALUATION OF EXCITATION TRANSFER MATRIX ELEMENTS

The fundamental parameters in Frenkel exciton theory are matrix elements of the form

$$V_{12} \equiv \left(\phi_1^{\,g} \, \phi_2^{\,f} \, | V | \, \phi_1^{\,f} \, \phi_2^{\,g} \right) \tag{1}$$

corresponding to the transfer of excitation energy between molecules 1 and 2, g designates the ground state, f designates an excited state, and V_{12} designates the interaction between the charged particles forming the molecules. These parameters determine the exciton band structure and, in conjunction with various scattering processes and initial conditions, the rates of excitation energy transfer. Frenkel exciton theory has been well reviewed in the literature (1), and the experimental techniques that have been developed for evaluating these excitation transfer matrix elements are summarized in Table I. These techniques also have been reviewed and discussed in two excellent articles (2, 3); consequently, detailed discussion here is not needed.

In systems of aromatic hydrocarbons and their derivatives that have been studied by some or all of these techniques, the excitation transfer interactions have been characterized as being short range with dominating nearest neighbor

Table I. Evaluation of the Excitation Transfer Matrix Elements

Technique	Spectral Observation	Information
Davydov splitting	Multiplet structure in a pure crystal.	Sum of excitation transfer matrix elements.
Quasiresonance shifts	Line shifts in a series of isotopic mixed crystals.	Sum of squares of excitation transfer matrix elements.
Band-to-band transitions vibrational bands phonon bands spin branches	Broad lines.	Density of states.
Rashba effect	Intensity variations in a series of isotopic mixed crystals.	Band structure and location of the band edge.
Alloying	Line shifts and broadening.	Band width in favorable cases, otherwise useful to check consistency of parameters.
Two particle transitions	Broad vibronic lines.	Density of states.
Resonance pairs	Fine structure in isotopic mixed crystals.	Individual excitation transfer matrix elements.

interactions for both the lowest excited singlet and triplet states. Naphthalene appears to be the best characterized system. Other systems on which extensive work has been done are the singlet and triplet states of anthracene and the triplet states of 1,2,4,5-tetrachlorobenzene and 1,4-dibromonaphthalene. Typical values for the matrix elements range from about one wavenumber for triplet states to twenty wavenumbers for singlet states with a small transition dipole moment to a few hundred wavenumbers for states with a large transition dipole moment. Usually only the lowest excited state of a given spin multiplicity is important in energy transfer phenomena because of the rapid intramolecular relaxation from higher excited states.

III. EXCITON MOTION

A. The Limit of Coherence

In the limit of coherent energy transfer, the migration of energy can be described in terms of a wave packet formed by a combination of the exciton eigenfunctions. The wave packet travels through the crystal at its characteristic group velocity which is determined by the exciton band dispersion. For the case of a linear chain of molecules with one molecule per unit cell and only nearest neighbor interactions, the dispersion relation (2), giving the energy E of an exciton state as a function of the wave vector $\underset{\sim}{k}$ is

$$E(\underset{\sim}{k}) = 2 \, V_{11} \, \cos \, (\underset{\sim}{k} \cdot \underset{\sim}{a}) \tag{2}$$

where V_{11} is the excitation transfer matrix element between nearest translationally equivalent molecules separated by the lattice vector $\underset{\sim}{a}$. Using the definition of group velocity

$$\underset{\sim}{V}_g \equiv \underset{\sim}{\nabla}_k \, E(k)/\hbar \tag{3}$$

gives a maximum group velocity for this exciton band of $(2\underset{\sim}{a}V_{11}/\hbar)$ and a minimum velocity of zero.

If the scattering of the exciton by phonons or defects is Markovian and independent of the exciton velocity, then the exciton mean free path d may be given by the thermal average group velocity $\overline{V}_g$ times the mean time between scattering events t_S. In a simple model of scattering, the propagation direction of the exciton after scattering is independent of the direction before (no memory). The exciton then moves in a random walk process with a step size of d, the mean free path. The theory of one dimensional random walks gives the result that after n steps, the root mean square displacement D is $n^{1/2}$ steps. For the case of the exciton, the average number of steps is the lifetime of the excited state t_L divided by the time per step, i.e. the mean scattering time t_S. Consequently we obtain for the mean square displacement,

$$D^2 = d^2 n = d^2 \, t_L/t_S = \overline{V}_g^2 \, t_S t_L \tag{4}$$

While the above picture of exciton motion is extremely simple, it has been applied successfully to real systems (4,5), and more rigorous descriptions of exciton scattering processes are being developed (6).

B. The Regime of Incoherence

In the limit of incoherent energy transfer, the excitation is considered to hop randomly from molecule to molecule (7). This hopping process usually is considered to be Markovian, i.e. there are no memory effects, each hop is independent of what has gone before. Aside from the topology of the lattice, the fundamental physical parameter necessary to describe incoherent energy transfer by using the extensive theoretical development of random walks on lattices is the average number of hops the excitation makes. This number is given by the exciton lifetime t_L, divided by the time between hops t_H.

Memory effects can be incorporated into the hopping model by postulating that the excitation preserves the direction of its motion over a mean free path of d lattice sites, which also can be called the coherence length. At the end of a free path, the exciton is strongly scattered by a lattice defect or phonon and suffers complete loss of directional memory. The correlation time or memory time is the mean time between these scattering events, t_S. The consequences of this modification to the hopping model are described by theories of random walks on lattices with variable step size (8,9). In this excitation transfer process, each Markovian step consists of several non-Markovian hops (10). This idea of quasi-coherence was used above in describing the coherent limit by postulating that between the Markovian steps, the exciton moves with a characteristic group velocity. It is shown later that the nature of the electric field effect on energy transfer for these two ideas of quasi-coherence is qualitatively different, i.e. the nature of the effect depends on whether the excitation hops with memory or moves with a characteristic group velocity between the memory destroying scattering events. The electric field effect therefore probes the degree of localization of the excitation during the energy transfer process.

If an excitation is localized on one molecule of a pair, one has a non-stationary state of the system. The molecules need not be identical and can have excitation energies differing by an amount ΔE. The excitation oscillates from molecule to molecule with the probability of having the second molecule excited being given by

$$Pr(2) = (V_{12}/\Gamma)^2 \sin^2 (\Gamma t/\hbar) \tag{5}$$

where $\Gamma^2 = V_{12}^2 + (\Delta E/2)^2$. This phenomenon is just an example of oscillations in two state systems. The time required to transfer energy from one molecule to the other when $\Delta E = 0$ is just the time required for the $Pr(2)$ to go from 0 to 1. We call this interval the coherent pairwise transfer time, t_{CP}.

$$t_{CP} = h/4V_{12} \tag{6}$$

The use of the coherent pairwise transfer time as the hopping time in random walk models for exciton motion has been quite successful in explaining numerous observations (10-14), and it will be interesting to see if this concept can also account for the influence of an electric field, although it is not rigorously applicable to a many body system (15-17).

In the incoherent limit the time between scattering events is much less than the coherent pairwise transfer time. Consequently, from Eq. 5, we suppose that the probability for energy transfer evolves for a time t until t = t_S, then the scattering occurs, and in a hard scattering model the system starts over at $t = 0$. At this point the probability of energy transfer in an ensemble of pairs is given by

$$\Pr(2 \text{ at } t_S) = (V_{12}/\Gamma)^2 \sin^2(\Gamma t_S /\hbar) \tag{7a}$$

$$\Pr(2 \text{ at } t_S) \approx (V_{12}/\Gamma)^2 (\Gamma t_S /\hbar)^2 = (V_{12} t_S /\hbar)^2 \tag{7b}$$

since $t_S \ll t_{CP}$. For a particular pair in the ensemble, energy transfer will be obtained on the average after a number of attempts equal to the reciprocal of the probability in Eq. 7. The hopping time in this limit then is the time per try t_S times the number of attempts per hop and is given by Eq. 8.

$$t_H = t_S (\hbar/V_{12} t_S)^2 = \hbar^2 /V_{12}^2 \, t_S \tag{8}$$

Table II. Parameters for Exciton Motion

Quantity	Symbol	Value
Excitation transfer matrix element.	V	10 wavenumbers
Exciton lifetime.	t_L	1 msec
Scattering time.	t_S	0.01 psec
Coherent pairwise transfer time (Eq. 6).	t_{CP}	1 psec
Incoherent hopping time (Eq. 8).	t_H	30 psec
Displacement.	D	10^9 lattice constants coherent motion
t_L/t_{CP}		
$(t_L/t_H)^{1/2}$		10^4 lattice constants incoherent motion

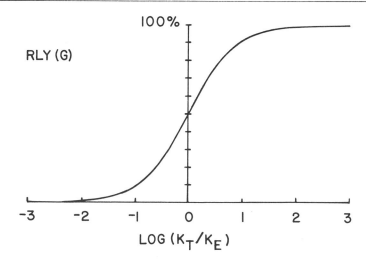

Fig. 1. The relative yield of trap luminescence as a function of the ratio of the energy transfer rate constant to the unimolecular decay rate constant of the host (exciton).

C. The Consequences of Scattering Processes

To appreciate the extent and significance of energy transfer in condensed molecular systems and the drastic consequences of the phonon and defect scattering processes that destroy coherence, consider the distance traveled by the exciton during its lifetime. The relevant parameters and the calculated values for other quantities are given in Table II. For completely coherent motion this distance is simply the average exciton velocity times the exciton lifetime. When kT is large compared to the exciton band width, the thermal average group velocity is about equal to the lattice spacing divided by half the coherent pairwise transfer time. It therefore does not matter much whether one has a highly localized initial state or a more delocalized wave packet except at low temperatures where only certain parts of the exciton band are populated. The effect of scattering in the coherent limit where $t_S \ll t_{CP}$ is to lengthen the pairwise transfer time from t_{CP} to t_H. For the parameters in Table II, the pairwise transfer time increases by a factor of 30 which would result in a factor of 30 decrease in the range of the exciton motion if it were not for the fact that the scattering also changes the motion from being directed to that of a random walk. The number of steps in the random walk is t_L/t_H, and the resulting displacement is the square root of this value, about 6×10^3, a factor of 10^5 less than for coherent motion. Consequently, the important effect of scattering is not to lengthen the time it takes for the exciton to move from one molecule to another but rather to destroy the memory of the motion and turn energy transfer into a random walk. This discussion of scattering only considers scattering processes that destroy coherence. Later the effect of energy exchange between the exciton and phonon systems will be considered along with the use of electric field gradients to return the sense of direction to the exciton.

IV. MACROSCOPIC OBSERVATIONS OF EXCITON MOTION

While energy transfer processes in solids can be monitored in a variety of ways, the sensitized luminescence or energy transfer to guest or defect molecules (x-traps) in the host lattice is considered here. Changes in the rate of energy transfer can be observed by monitoring the relative steady state luminescence yield of the guest and host or by monitoring the time evolution of the guest and host luminescence following pulsed excitation. With the appropriate experimental conditions (5), one can expect these observations to be described by the following kinetic equations.

$$\dot{N}_E(t) = -(K_E + K_T)\, N_E(t) + P(t) \tag{9}$$

$$\dot{N}_G(t) = K_T\, N_E(t) - K_G\, N_G(t) \tag{10}$$

The number of excitons or host molecules in the excited state is N_E, and the number of excited guest molecules is N_G. The pumping rate by the external excitation source is $P(t)$, and the rate constant for unimolecular decay of the host is K_E, of the guest is K_G, and for host to guest energy transfer is K_T. Only the energy transfer rate constant will be considered to depend upon the external electric field. The origin of this dependence is described in the following section.

Under steady state conditions, the ratio of host to guest excitations, from Eq. 10, is K_G/K_T. Since the intensity of luminescence is proportional to the number of excitations, the following expression is obtained for the relative luminescence yield of the guest provided the luminescence quantum yield in the absence of energy transfer is the same for both guest and host. This condition is most likely to be valid for x-traps or isotopic mixed crystals.

$$RLY(G) = I_G/(I_G + I_E) = K_T/(K_T + K_E) \tag{11}$$

One can see from Fig. 1, the graph of Eq. 11, that changes in the guest luminescence yield caused by the electric field will be most dramatic when the energy transfer rate constant is comparable to the host decay rate constant. This constraint poses little difficulty because the energy transfer rate can be varied by varying the guest concentration. Under optimum conditions, the electric field can switch the trap luminescence on and off.

With impulse excitation the effect of P(t) appears as a boundary condition; namely, $N_E(0)$ excitons are formed initially. The subsequent time evolution of the number of excited states and hence the time course of the luminescence is given by

$$N_E(t) = N_E(0) \exp(-K_D t) \tag{12}$$

$$N_G(t) = N_G(0) (\exp(-K_G t) - \exp(-K_D t)) \tag{13}$$

where $K_D = K_T + K_E$ and $N_G(0) = K_T N_E(0)/(K_T + K_H - K_G)$. Measurements of the decay of the exciton luminescence or the corresponding rise of the guest luminescence will reveal changes in the energy transfer rate caused by the external field.

The connection between microscopic models for energy transfer and the measurable energy transfer rate has been made most simply by Wieting, Fayer, and Dlott (18). If C is the fraction of molecules that are traps in a crystal, then the probability that the excitation is not trapped if another new site is sampled during energy transfer is given by (1-C). In time t the number of new sites sampled is given by S(t), the sampling function, so the probability that the excitation has not decayed or been trapped is given by

$$P_E = (1-C)^{S(t)} \exp(-K_E t). \tag{14}$$

Defining K, differentiating Eq. 14 to get the rate of change of the probability, and comparing with Eq. 9, identifies the time derivative of K with the energy transfer rate "constant".

$$K \equiv -S(t) \ln(1-C) \tag{15}$$

$$\dot{P}_E = -(K_K + \dot{K}) P_E \tag{16}$$

$$K_T(t) = \dot{K} = -\ln(1-C) \dot{S}(t) \approx C \dot{S}(t) \tag{17}$$

The leading term of the sampling function has been calculated by Montroll and Weiss (19) for a random walk in one dimension to be

$$S(t) = (8n(t)/\pi)^{1/2} \tag{18}$$

where n(t) is the number of steps made until time t. One therefore sees that the energy transfer rate "constant" is time dependent and is more appropriately called a rate function. This time dependence arises because in the random walk, the excitation revisits the same site; consequently, the rate of sampling new sites and thus the rate of energy transfer to a trap decreases with time.

V. ELECTRIC FIELD EFFECTS ON EXCITON MOTION

External electric fields can influence electronic excitation energy transfer in molecular solids by mixing molecular states, mixing crystal states, changing the crystal structure, changing the axes of spin quantization, and by eliminating or producing resonance conditions for energy transfer. The unimolecular radiative and nonradiative decay rates of host and guest (trap) molecules in solids can be altered by the external field through a mixing of states involving matrix elements of the type $(\Psi_a|\overset{\mu}{\underset{\sim}{}}|\Psi_b)$. $\underset{\sim}{F}$ thus changing the quantum yields of emission as well as fluorescence to phosphorescence ratios. Such mixing is expected to be important for crystals of intermediate size molecules where the states in the above matrix element are near resonance but are not coupled significantly in the absence of the external field. Molecules with inversion symmetry and nearly degenerate g and u states that are mixed by the electric field should be good possibilities for this mechanism.

State mixing effects may also be significant in crystals of large molecules where the states involved belong to different branches of the same exciton band. For example, when the space group of the crystal has a $\underset{i}{C}$ interchange subgroup, the different branches of the exciton band, characterized by g and u symmetry, are coupled by the external field thereby altering the exciton relaxation dynamics. Concomitant energy level shifts may result in exciton level crossing effects. Such mixing can also change the axes of spin quantization or eliminate resonance excitation transfer as further described below.

The electric field can alter significantly molecular orientations and separations, and consequently excitation transfer interactions, in cases where the molecular dipole moment is large and certain phonon frequencies are low. Such coupling between the field and crystal structure also is expected for crystals belonging to the piezoelectric space groups.

The transfer of triplet excitation energy from a host exciton state to a trap depends upon the projection of the spin states of the host onto the spin states of the trap. The electric field can alter these projections by reorienting the molecules or by changing the axes of exciton spin quantization. In molecules the spin quantization is determined by the spin-dipolar interaction and the spin-orbit interaction. In crystals with more than one molecule per unit cell, the excitation transfer interaction between translationally inequivalent molecules V_{12} can change the quantization directions from the molecular frame to the crystal frame (20, 21). If the interaction with the external field $\Delta\underset{\sim}{\mu}\cdot\underset{\sim}{F}$ is large Ω or comparable to V_{12}, then the molecules in the unit cell can be made sufficiently inequivalent by the field to cause the spin quantization to revert to the molecular frame.

In addition to altering the axes of spin quantization, the situation $\Delta\underset{\sim}{\mu}\cdot\underset{\sim}{F}>V_{12}$ destroys resonance and hence inhibits energy transfer. Two or three dimensional energy transfer topology becomes one or two dimensional. In a nonuniform electric field, the exciton may move along the field gradient in a one dimensional topology due to quasiresonance interactions, but perpendicular to the field gradient in a two or three dimensional topology due to the dominance of resonance interactions over quasiresonance interactions. The electric field then controls the nature and the dimensionality of the exciton motion. In this situation, energy exchange between the exciton and phonon systems should be important in compensating for the energy mismatches in order to allow nonresonance transfer to occur. The most spectacular effect should occur if the interaction with the field can scan the energy level spacing past a peak in the phonon density of states or through different phonon modes with significantly different coupling constants.

The most significant effect is expected in systems composed of molecules with large dipole moments. In these cases an electric field or field gradient can be used to make molecules inequivalent and eliminate or reduce the possibility for energy transfer between them by making the energy mismatch comparable to or larger than the excitation transfer interaction and the thermal energy. The energy mismatch, or difference in the excitation energies of the two molecules is given by

$$\Delta E = \Delta \underset{\sim}{\mu}_i \cdot \underset{\sim}{F}_i - \Delta \underset{\sim}{\mu}_j \cdot \underset{\sim}{F}_j \tag{19}$$

where $\underset{\sim}{F}_i$ is the field at molecule i, and $\Delta \underset{\sim}{\mu}_i$ is the vector difference in dipole moments of the ground and excited electronic states. Of course if the dipole moments of the two molecules are parallel and fields are equal, there will be no mismatch.

This picture of an energy mismatch between pairs of molecules is directly relevant to the hopping model for energy transfer where one considers the excitation energy to be localized and hopping from molecule to molecule (7). In recent years research has been directed at describing the case of coherent energy transfer and explicitly incorporating the scattering by lattice defects and phonons that lead to the loss of coherence (4, 6). In what follows we describe the effects of these energy mismatches on both wave packet motion and site to site hopping motion of the exciton. The coherence in this motion is expected to be limited by exciton-phonon and exciton-defect scattering processes. While a linear or one dimensional model is considered in the most detail, the extension to two or three dimensions is not difficult. Furthermore, the description of the motion and the scattering processes is purposely simple in order to bare the essential features of the phenomenon, but similar concepts have been used successfully before (5, 10, 22-24). It is shown that the electric field effect differs for wave packet and hopping motion and is sensitive to whether the coherence is limited by exciton-phonon or exciton-defect scattering (25, 26).

Incorporating the effect of an electric field into more rigorous and mathematically complex descriptions of energy transfer clearly is possible. A complete and rigorous theory of these effects must include the zero field site energies including static disorder, the intersite excitation transfer inter-actions, the exciton-phonon interactions, the site-diagonal electric field shifts, and the possibilities of local and non-local initial conditions for the excitation transfer process. Such a theory has not yet been formulated, but recent progress in treating the dynamical fluctuations (the exciton-phonon interactions) and the static disorder provide a sound basis for the development of such a theory (6, 27-31). Experimental observations of electric field effects on host to guest energy transfer, combined with high resolution spectroscopic techniques, should allow excitation transfer interactions, the

exciton-phonon interactions, the static disorder, and the initial conditions
to be characterized quantitatively.

A. Wave Packet Motion

In the limit of coherent energy transfer, the migration of energy can be
described in terms of a wave packet formed from the exciton eigenfunctions of
a perfect crystal. The group velocity of this wave packet times the mean time
between scattering events gives the exciton mean free path. The effect of an
external electric field on the exciton group velocity and hence on the rate of
energy transfer has been described for a linear antiferroelectric array of
dipolar molecules, shown in Fig. 2, with nearest neighbor interactions (25)
and with next nearest neighbor interactions (26). The external field, applied
in the direction of the dipole moments, causes the electronic excitation energy
of neighboring molecules to differ by $2\Delta\mu F$ which leads to a narrowing of the
exciton band and a decrease in the exciton group velocity.

The exciton dispersion relation for the case of nearest neighbor interactions is given by (4, 32)

$$E(\underset{\sim}{k}) = E_o \pm (4V_{12}^2 \cos(\tfrac{1}{2}ka) + (\Delta\mu F)^2)^{1/2} \tag{20}$$

where E_o is the ideal mixed crystal excitation energy, V_{12} is the excitation
transfer matrix element, a is the lattice constant, and a/2 is the nearest
neighbor spacing, $\Delta\mu$ is the difference in dipole moments of the ground and
excited states, and F is the local electric field. Plots of this dispersion
relation for some values of the field energy $\Delta\mu F$ are given in Fig. 3. At
zero field the dispersion relation is just that for a linear crystal with two
molecules per unit cell separated by half the lattice spacing. Because of
the antiferroelectric arrangement, the external field makes the two molecules
in the unit cell inequivalent, thereby causing the exciton band with two
branches at zero field to split into two inequivalent bands separated by
$2\Delta\mu F$. Since only nearest neighbor interactions are assumed, the dispersion in
these bands comes from the so-called "superexchange" interactions (26, 33, 34).
In the perturbation limit, this interaction scales as $V_{12}^2/2\Delta\mu F$, thus the
interaction decreases, and the bands flatten, the dispersion becomes less, as
the field increases. This flattening has a significant effect on the exciton
group velocity which is determined by the derivative of the dispersion relation.
The thermal average group velocity is calculated as the sum of the group
velocities of all k states of both bands weighted by the appropriate probability

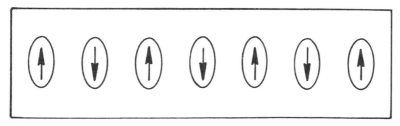

Fig. 2. The antiferroelectric arrangement of polar molecules in a linear
crystal with two molecules per unit cell.

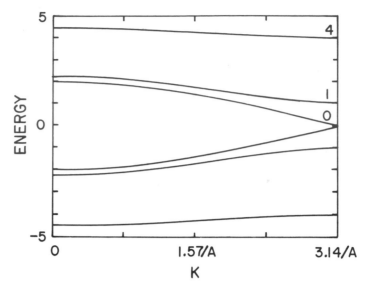

Fig. 3. The exciton energy measured in units of the excitation transfer interaction V_{12} as a function of the wave vector for three values of the field energy: $\Delta\mu F = 0$, V_{12}, and $4V_{12}$.

factor (25). In the high temperature limit, attainable at liquid helium temperatures in some crystals because of the small band width and electric field splitting, the ratio of the average exciton group velocity to the zero field average is given by

$$\frac{\bar{V}_g(F)}{\bar{V}_g(0)} = \left(1 + \left(\frac{\Delta\mu F}{2V_{12}}\right)^2\right)^{1/2} - \frac{\Delta\mu F}{2V_{12}} \cdot \qquad (21)$$

This change in the group velocity is fixed by two measurable parameters: the Davydov splitting and the Stark splitting. Measured in absorption spectra (32), these quantities are simply related to V_{12} and to $\Delta\mu \cdot F$ and uniquely determine the effect of the electric field on the group velocity and on the energy transfer rate.

B. Hopping Motion

The probability for an electronic excitation to "hop" coherently from one molecule to another is given by Eq. 5. In the presence of an electric field ΔE is not zero but equals $2\Delta\mu F$ for the linear antiferroelectric array. As the field increases, Γ thereby increases, and the oscillation frequency for the probability increases, but the probability amplitude decreases. The amplitude factor dominates, and the net result is that it takes longer for energy transfer to occur. A coherent pairwise transfer time can be defined for this situation by multiplying the oscillation period by the number of periods necessary before one can expect to find the second molecule excited. Here one is simply saying that if the Pr(2) goes from 0 to 0.01 during each oscillation period, then on the average in an ensemble, the excitation will be transferred only once in every 100 periods. We therefore have

$$t_{CP} = \tfrac{1}{4}h\Gamma \, V_{12}^{-2}. \tag{22}$$

We call the reciprocal of this time the coherent pairwise transfer rate. This rate is affected by the electric field through the Γ factor.

In the incoherent limit where the scattering time is much shorter than the coherent pairwise transfer time ($t_S \ll t_{CP}$) little if any electric field effect on the transfer rate is expected. If scattering times are so short that the sine function in Eq. 7a can be represented by the first term in the series expansion, the field dependence vanishes entirely as shown by Eq. 7b.

C. Exciton – Phonon Scattering

We suppose that exciton-phonon scattering can be characterized by a mean time between scattering events, t_S, that is independent of the electric field. The coherence length d is then field dependent because of the field dependence of the exciton velocity for either wave packet or site to site hopping motion. As a consequence of the scattering, we imagine the exciton to move through the lattice in a random walk characterized by a mean step size d. Now we use the site sampling function

$$S(t) = d(8n(t)/\pi)^{1/2} \tag{23}$$

where $n(t)$ is the number of steps taken, and the square root gives the number of steps that cover new ground. This quantity is multiplied by d because in the random walk with variable step size, the mean square displacement is $d^2 n(t)$ where d^2 is the mean square step size (8). Since the interval between scattering events determines a step, the number of steps taken in time t is just t/t_S and is independent of the electric field. The energy transfer rate function is then

$$K_T(t) = \tfrac{1}{2}C \, d(8/\pi)^{1/2}(t_S t)^{-1/2}. \tag{24}$$

In the hopping model $d = t_S/t_{CP}$ to give the result

$$K_T(t) = \tfrac{1}{2}C(8/\pi)^{1/2} \, (t_{CP}^2 \, t/t_S)^{-1/2}. \tag{25}$$

In the wave packet model $d = \overline{V}_g \, t_S$ to give the result

$$K_T(t) = \tfrac{1}{2}C(8/\pi)^{1/2} \, \overline{V}_g \, (t/t_S)^{-1/2}. \tag{26}$$

The fractional decrease of these rates as a function of electric field is shown by curves D and E in Fig. 4, respectively.

D. Exciton – Defect Scattering

We suppose that the exciton-defect scattering can be characterized by a mean distance between scattering events, and this coherence length d is independent of the electric field. Now the time between scattering events is field dependent through the field dependence of the exciton velocity which affects the new site sampling function by affecting the number of steps and not the step length: $n = t/t_S$ and $t_S = d/v$.

$$K_T(t) = \tfrac{1}{2}C(8dv/\pi)^{1/2} t^{-1/2}.$$ (27)

In the hopping model $v = 1/t_{CP}$ and

$$K_T(t) = \tfrac{1}{2}C(8d/\pi)^{1/2} (t_{CP}t)^{-1/2}.$$ (28)

In the wave packet group velocity model $v = \overline{V}_g$ and

$$K_T(t) = \tfrac{1}{2}C(8d/\pi)^{1/2} (t/\overline{V}_g)^{-1/2}$$ (29)

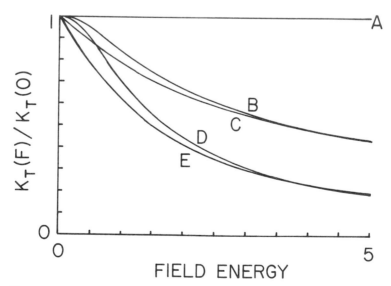

Fig. 4. The energy transfer rate function normalized to the zero field function vs the field energy ($\Delta\mu F$) in units of V_{12} for different models. (A) Random walk model in which coherence is destroyed in a time much less than the coherent pairwise transfer time. (B) Model in which the coherent pairwise transfer time is used and the coherence is limited by exciton-defect scattering. (C) Model in which the average group velocity is used, and the coherence is limited by exciton-defect scattering. (D) Model in which the coherent pairwise transfer time is used, and the coherence is limited by exciton-phonon scattering. (E) Model in which the average group velocity is used, and the coherence is limited by exciton-phonon scattering.

The field dependence of these rates is shown by curves B and C in Fig. 4, respectively.

A summary of the effects of an external field on the various mechanisms of energy transfer is given in Table III. Observations of the field dependence of the transfer rate offers the opportunity to discover whether exciton motion is described by a coherent hopping time or a group velocity and whether the coherence in the motion is limited by exciton-phonon or by exciton-defect scattering. The essential difference in these two scattering processes arises because the field affects the coherence time for the latter and the coherence length for the former. In the random walk, the coherence time determines the number of steps and the coherence length determines the size of the steps.

E.   Energy Exchange between Excitons and Phonons

In the above discussion, scattering by phonons and defects destroyed the coherence in the exciton motion. Account was not taken of the ability of the phonon system to exchange energy with the exciton system in order to compensate energy mismatches. This neglect of inelastic scattering processes may be valid at low temperatures where exciton-phonon interactions produce phase or coherence destroying collisions without energy exchange, and where exciton-defect scattering may dominate.

At higher temperatures phonon assisted energy transfer can take place. In the simplest model one can consider a one phonon process. The rate for one

Table III.   Electric Field Effects on Exciton Motion

Exciton - phonon scattering

    Constant scattering time
    Field dependent scattering length

Hopping model	Eq. 25	Fig. 4 (D)
Group velocity model	26	(E)

Exciton - defect scattering

    Constant scattering length
    Field dependent scattering time

Hopping model	Eq. 28	Fig. 4 (B)
Group velocity model	29	(C)

For coherent energy transfer, the scattering time is a constant and is longer than the exciton lifetime. The electric field effect then follows the form for the case of coherence limited by exciton-phonon scattering.

For a constant step length of one lattice spacing in the hopping model, the electric field effect follows Eq. 28 and curve (B).

For rapid scattering little or no electric field effect is predicted, Fig. 4 (A).

phonon absorption and emission to compensate an energy mismatch of $2\Delta\mu F$ is proportional to the square of the exciton-phonon coupling matrix element, to the density of states, and to the phonon occupation number n, or n+1 for emission (35, 36). Since the energy mismatches can be in the range of 0 to 10 wavenumbers for some molecular crystals, the phonons involved can be the acoustic modes which in the Debye model have a density of states that increases as $(2\Delta\mu F)^{m-1}$ where m is the dimensionality of the crystal. The occupation number varies as

$$n = (\exp{(2\Delta\mu F/k_B T)} - 1)^{-1}. \tag{30}$$

If the effect of exciton-phonon coupling is taken to be proportional to the phonon frequency, then the one phonon assisted rate is expected to be proportional to

$$(2\Delta\mu F)^m (\exp{(2\Delta\mu F/k_B T)} - 1)^{-1}. \tag{31}$$

The phonon assisted rate is small for a small energy mismatch and increases with increasing mismatch in the high temperature limit (36).

The other phonon process that is likely to contribute to the energy transfer rate is the Raman process in which two phonons are involved, and the difference in the phonon energies equals the energy mismatch (27-29). In this case the rate is inversely proportional to the square of the energy mismatch and has a T^7 dependence. The Raman process allows a small energy mismatch to be compensated by much higher frequency phonons. These phonons may couple strongly to the exciton system because of the increased relative motion of neighboring molecules at the higher phonon frequencies. Thus one can see that the effect of the electric field on phonon assisted energy transfer can provide information about the nature of the phonon process involved, the density of phonon states, and the variation in exciton-phonon coupling matrix elements.

F. Relevance to Anderson Localization

The applicability of the concept of Anderson localization to energy transport in isotopically mixed molecular crystals has been a subject of some controversy (37-39). The basic idea is that when the inhomogeneous energy distribution is comparable to the exciton band width then excitations are localized, and energy transfer ceases or is greatly diminished. From Fig. 3, it is clear that the effect of the electric field is to decrease the exciton band width. In systems where the band width can be varied from being greater than the inhomogeneous width to less than the inhomogeneous width, an electric field induced Anderson transition from extended to localized states should be obtained. This transition would be marked by an abrupt decrease in the energy transfer rate.

G. Field Gradient Effects

The model situation that we wish to consider involves a one dimensional array of molecules aligned in a ferroelectric array with their dipole moments parallel. The application of a nonuniform electric field across the crystal shifts the transition energy of each molecule by a different amount and produces the energy level cascade shown in Fig. 5. If the exciton system were

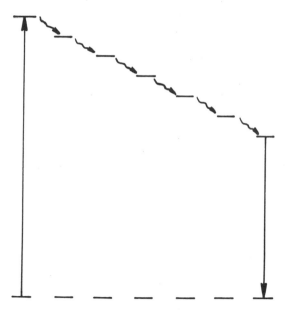

Fig. 5. An energy level cascade obtained by applying an electric field
gradient to a linear array of translationally equivalent dipolar molecules.

in thermal equilibrium across a 1 cm crystal at 1.5°K with the field going from
0 to 100 kV/cm over this 1 cm, the exciton density, and therefore also the
luminescence, at one side of the crystal would be 10,000 times that at the
other side for $\Delta\mu$ = 3D. Such a dramatic redistribution of intensity could
easily be detected. Even larger gradients can be produced at phase boundaries due to the accumulation of space charge. Having a field of 100 kV/cm
develop over a micron distance is not unreasonable. Taking a field to increase
linearly with distance, results in a gradient of 10^9 V/cm^2. Such a gradient
produces an energy mismatch from one lattice site to another of about 0.05
wavenumbers for molecules with dipole moments of 30 D. The theory of
resonance-phonon-assisted energy transfer developed for inhomogeneously
broadened systems can then be applied (27-30). The probability for energy
transfer is modified by a phonon factor which is different for transfer up the
cascade (absorption of energy by the exciton system from the phonon system)
than for transfer down the cascade (absorption of energy by the phonon system
from the exciton system). The difference in these two transfer probabilities,
P_u and P_d, depends upon the temperature, the energy mismatch, and the phonon
process involved. For a one phonon process involving acoustic phonons, the
ratio P_d/P_u is $\exp(\Delta E/kT)$. With the above value for ΔE at 1.5°K, the ratio
of transfer probabilities is 1.05, giving a difference $P_d - P_u$ of 0.024. This
seemingly small difference in transfer probabilities has a drastic effect on
the exciton motion because the distance travelled down the cascade is
determined (8) by multiplying by the number of site to site hops the exciton
makes during its lifetime, about 10^9 from Table II. The electric field
gradient thus has biased the random walk process to increase the displacement
from 10^4 lattice constants to 10^7. Since the probability differences are
multiplied by the large number of hops, even smaller site to site energy
mismatches will have appreciable effects on the energy transfer rate.

H. Topology

Crystals of many polar molecules consist of two sublattices related by an
inversion symmetry operation. A model structure is shown in Fig. 6. The

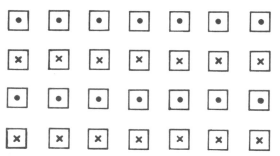

Fig. 6. A model structure of a polar crystal with two sublattices.
Application of an electric field can confine exciton motion to one sublattice
or the other thus transforming a two dimensional energy transfer topology into
one dimension.

application of an electric field parallel to the dipole moments, breaks the
resonance between the two sublattices and turns a two dimensional energy
transfer topology into a one dimensional topology. This transformation has an
effect on the energy transfer rate by changing the new site sampling function.
Eq. 17 relates the energy transfer rate to the sampling function $S(t)$. The
sampling function for a one dimensional random walk is given by Eq. 18. The
sampling function for a two dimensional random walk given by Montroll and
Weiss (19) is

$$S(t) = \pi \, n(t)/\log n(t) \tag{32}$$

If we take $n(t) = t/t_H$, then in a one dimensional topology the energy transfer
rate function decreases with time as $t^{-1/2}$; whereas, in a two dimensional
topology the rate decreases very slowly as $1/\log(t/t_H)$. This change will be
obvious in measurements of the time evolution of the exciton luminescence, and
in a steady state experiment at the optimum trap concentration, the application
of an external field may quench the trap luminescence. This possibility is
enhanced by the effectiveness of reflecting barriers (defects in the lattice)
to limit exciton motion in a one dimensional topology.

VI. EXPERIMENTAL OBSERVATIONS

     For the models of energy transfer considered above, the application of an
external electric field results in a decrease in the extent and rate of the
exciton motion. This decrease should give rise to an increase in exciton
luminescence intensity and lifetime and a decrease in trap luminescence. Such
increases in the exciton intensity have been observed in 4,4'-dichlorobenzo-
phenone. The trap intensities however exhibit a much more complex behavior (40).
The 4,4'-dimethylbenzophenone, the electric field has been observed to lengthen
the exciton lifetime, increase the exciton intensity, and decrease the trap
intensity (41). Examples of these observations are shown in Figs. 7 and 8.
Changes in trap intensities in 1,4-dibromonaphthalene have been attributed
either to an electric field effect on energy transfer or to a field induced
structural modification (42). The relative intensity of phosphorescence from
various x-traps in benzophenone has been observed to depend upon the magnitude
of an external electric field, but this phenomenon has not yet been investigated
in detail (40).

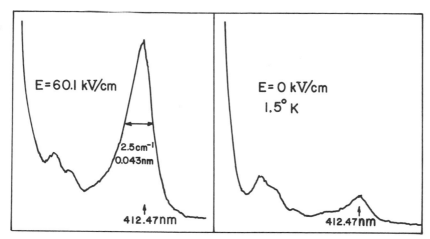

Fig. 7. Phosphorescence spectra showing the enhancement of the exciton origin of 4,4'-dichlorobenzophenone at 412.47 nm presumedly caused by the electric field reducing the rate of energy transfer to traps.

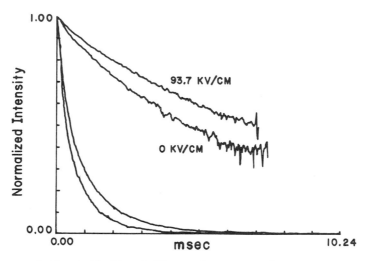

Fig. 8. Decay of the 4,4'-dimethylbenzophenone exciton phosphorescence in the presence and absence of an electric field. The slower decay in the presence of the electric field can be attributed to the decrease in the rate of energy transfer. Both intensity and log intensity are plotted.

VII. OTHER SYSTEMS

Several criteria must be satisfied in selecting systems for the study of electric field effects on energy transfer. We focus here on using the electric field to produce or destroy resonance in the energy transfer process since the properties of systems in relation to the other mechanisms discussed in Sec. V are not easy to assess. The excitation transfer interaction should be smaller than, or at least comparable to, the interaction with the external field. The molecules should luminesce with significant quantum yields and should be polar, or highly polarizable, with a large difference between the ground and excited state dipole moments or polarizabilities. For crystalline systems, the crystal structure should be known along with the magnitudes of the excitation transfer interactions and the resulting band structure. Unfortunately, benzophenone is the only system that meets these criteria. This situation merely demonstrates the vast amount of information that is lacking from our knowledge of molecular solids.

While the crystals of aromatic hydrocarbons and their derivatives are the best characterized in terms of the above desired properties, the application of the concepts discussed in this paper to a wider variety of materials provides the opportunity for the discovery of spectacular effects and new phenomena. Energy transfer donor-acceptor systems doped into plastics, glasses, and thin films allows large electric fields (millions of volts/cm) to be attained. Space charge distributions developed in thin films at interfaces between metals and semiconductors also should provide large electric field gradients. These systems also allow large dye type molecules to be used that are not easily incorporated into crystals, such as ionic dyes, phthalocyanine dyes, and organo-metallic compounds. The electric field should cause large changes in the energy level spacings of such molecules because of the large dipole moments and polarizabilities. Energy transfer chromophores also can be incorporated into polymers or into polymer films. The motion of charge-transfer excitons in crystals of electron-donor-acceptor complexes should be susceptible to electric field effects because there, the motion of the exciton may involve a polarity flipping process (43).

The molecular crystal systems offer the best opportunity, however, to learn about the nature of the exciton motion and the exciton-phonon and exciton-defect scattering processes. These molecules form three different kinds of crystals that should have different properties in these experiments. These crystals can be labeled as antiferroelectric, pyroelectric, and piezoelectric. The antiferroelectric crystals have the polar molecules on sublattices related by an inversion symmetry operation. The mechanisms discussed in Sec. V involving a uniform electric field should be important for these compounds. Examples of such crystals are 4,4'-dichlorobenzophenone, acetophenone, benzaldehyde, 1-indanone, and tetrachlorophthalic anhydride. The last two molecules have rigid structures, and distortions that may contribute to a disordered crystal structure cannot be significant. Such distortions are thought to influence the electric field effects on energy transfer in 4,4'-dichlorobenzophenone (40).

The pyroelectric crystals have the polar molecules arranged so the unit cell has a net dipole moment. Such crystals are of interest because an electric field gradient may cause the excitation energy to be transferred from one end of the crystal to the other. Compounds that have significant luminescence yields and this type of crystal structure are 4,4'-dibromobenzophenone, phthalic anhydride, and several 2,3-substituted-1,4-naphthoquinone derivatives.

The piezoelectric crystals have space groups lacking a center of inversion. Such crystals have the property that a mechanical stress induces a dipole moment in the unit cell, similarly an electric field induces a mechanical strain. All the pyroelectrics are also piezoelectric. Additional examples of molecular crystal piezoelectrics are benzophenone and 4,4'-dimethylbenzophenone.

VIII. PROSPECTS AND PROBLEMS FOR UTILIZATION IN TECHNOLOGY

The concepts discussed in this paper have not yet been applied to characterize systems in the laboratory under well-defined and well-understood conditions. Consequently, a consideration of potential applications to technological problems is extremely speculative. Nevertheless, these ideas may eventually prove significant to technology by allowing photochemical pathways to be controlled or by providing new mechanisms for coupling electronics and light in integrated electro-optic circuits. For example, a five volt potential difference across a thin film optical wave guide can produce an electric field of a million volts per centimeter, and the electric field modulation of the radiative, nonradiative, and energy transfer properties of molecules embedded in the thin film may prove to be a useful capability. If the rate and direction or dimensionality of energy transfer can be controlled by electric fields or electric field gradients, devices based on "excitonics" may prove useful in these integrated circuits. In these devices the electric field could direct or switch sensitized luminescence, photochemistry (useful for information storage), and charge carrier generation at selected interfaces.

The major problem in utilizing these effects in technological devices is finding systems that have the desired properties and work with high efficiency. Following the absorption of light by molecules, energy usually is lost through a number of dissipative processes. This problem can be circumvented by using light of the optimum wavelength and by having the desired process occur on a faster time scale than the dissipative processes.

ACKNOWLEDGMENT

I wish to thank J.S. Patel for his experimental contributions and for his assistance in developing some of these ideas.

Acknowledgment is made to the National Science Foundation and to the donors of the Petroleum Research Fund, administered by the American Chemical Society, for partial support of this research. The award of the 1980-81 Synchrotron Ultraviolet Radiation Facility Fellowship from the Institute of Physical Science and Technology at the University of Maryland and from the National Bureau of Standards is gratefully acknowledged.

REFERENCES

1. Craig, D.P. and Walmsley, S.H., "Excitons in Molecular Crystals", W.A. Benjamin, New York (1968).

2. Robinson, G.W., Ann. Rev. Phys. Chem. 21, 429 (1970).

3. Broude, V.L., and Rashba, E.I., Pure Appl. Chem. 37, 21 (1974).

4. Harris, C.B. and Zwemer, D.A., Ann. Rev. Phys. Chem. 29, 473 (1978).

5. Shelby, R.M., Zewail, A.H., and Harris, C.B., J. Chem. Phys. 64, 3192 (1976).

6. Silbey, R., Ann. Rev. Phys. Chem. 27, 203 (1976).

7. Wolf, H.C., in "Advances in Atomic and Molecular Physics", Vol. 3, D.R. Bates and I. Estermann, eds., Academic Press, New York (1967).

8. Reif, F., "Fundamentals of Statistical and Thermal Physics", McGraw-Hill, New York (1965).

9. Lakatos-Lindenberg, K., and Schuler, K.E., J. Math. Phys. 12, 633 (1971).

10. Kopelman, R., in "Topics in Applied Physics, Vol. 15: Radiationless Processes in Molecules and Condensed Phases", F.K. Fong, ed., Springer-Verlag, Berlin (1976).

11. Argyrakis, P., and Kopelman, R., J. Chem. Phys. 66, 3301 (1977).

12. Argyrakis, P. and Kopelman, R., J. Theor. Biol. 73, 205 (1978).

13. Argyrakis, P. and Kopelman, R., Phys. Rev. B 22, 1830 (1980).

14. Argyrakis, P. and Kopelman, R., Chemical Physics 51, 9 (1980).

15. Kenkre, V.M., and Knox, R.S., Phys. Rev. Letters 33, 803 (1974).

16. Magee, J.L., and Funabashi, K., J. Chem. Phys. 34, 1715 (1961).

17. Stepanov, B.I., and Gribkovskii, V.P., "Theory of Luminescence", Iliffe Books, London (1968) p. 147.

18. Weiting, R.D., Fayer, M.D., and Dlott, D.D., J. Chem. Phys. 69, 1996 (1978).

19. Montroll, E.W. and Weiss, G.H., J. Math. Phys. 6, 167 (1965).

20. Sternlicht, H. and McConnell, H.M., J. Chem. Phys. 35, 1793 (1961).

21. Sheng, S.J., Hanson, D.M., Chem. Phys. Letters 33, 451 (1975).

22. Zwemer, D.A., Harris, C.B., J. Chem. Phys. 68, 2184 (1978).

23. Dlott, D.D., Fayer, M.D., and Wieting, R.D., J. Chem. Phys. 67, 3808 (1977).

24. Dlott, D.D., Fayer, M.D., and Wieting, R.D., J. Chem. Phys. 69, 2752 (1978).

25. Hanson, D.M., Mol. Cryst. Liq. Cryst. 57, 243 (1980).

26. Hanson, D.M., Patel, J.S., Winkler, I.C., and Morrobel-Sosa, A., in "Modern Problems in Solid State Physics: Molecular Spectroscopy", R.M. Hochstrasser and V.M. Agronovich, eds., North Holland, Amsterdam (in press).

27. Holstein, T., Lyo, S.K., and Orbach, R., Phys. Rev. Letters 36, 891 (1976).

28. Holstein, T., Lyo, S.K., and Orbach, R., Phys. Rev. B15, 4693 (1977).

29. Holstein, T., Lyo, S.K. and Orbach, R., Comm. Solid State Phys. 8, 119 (1978).

30. Motegi, N. and Shionoya, S., J. Luminesc. 8, 1 (1973).

31. Klafter, J. and Jortner, J., J. Chem. Phys. 68, 1513 (1978).

32. Hochstrasser, R.M. and Michaluk, J.W., J. Mol. Spectry. 42, 197 (1972).

33. Hong, H.K., and Kopelman, R., Phys. Rev. Letters 25, 1030 (1970).

34. Hong, H.K., and Kopelman, R., J. Chem. Phys. 55, 724 (1971).

35. DiBartolo, B., "Optical Interactions in Solids", John Wiley, New York (1968) pp. 456-458.

36. Orbach, R, in "Optical Properties of Ions in Crystals", H.M. Crosswhite and H.W. Moos, eds. Interscience, New York (1966) pp. 445-455.

37. Klafter, J., and Jortner, J., Chem. Phys. Letters 49, 410 (1977).

38. Monberg, E.M. and Kopelman, R., Chem. Phys. Letters 58, 497 (1978).

39. Klafter, J. and Jortner, J., Chem. Phys. Letters 60, 5 (1978).

40. Hanson, D.M., Kakuta, A., Kato, K., and Sheng, S.J., Proceedings of the Eighth Molecular Crystals Symposium (1977) Santa Barbara, p. 127.

41. Patel, J.S. and Hanson, D.M., to be published.

42. Hochstrasser, R.M., Johnson, L.W., and Klimcak, C.M., J. Chem. Phys. 73, 156 (1980).

43. Haarer, D., Philpott, M.R., and Morawitz, H., J. Chem. Phys. 63, 5238 (1975).

DISCUSSION

Dr. Greene: NRL - A number of people have seen emission in pyroelectrics such as lithium tantalide, but nobody has explained it. That is an area that I think could use some discussion. The other question is if the phonon exciton coupling is strong, then that predicts a Soret effect. If you have a heat flux, that should move the excitons in one direction or the other.

Dr. Hanson: NBS - Yes. For a heat flux, you need a temperature gradient that will affect the exciton motion in the case of strong exciton-phonon coupling. For the pyroelectric luminescence, we see two types of behavior. When the crystal is at one atmosphere ambient pressure, we get very intense flashes which are accompanied by electrical pulses in an external capacitor circuit on the crystal. From work that people have done on triboluminescence, I think that it is due to dielectric breakdown in the ambient atmosphere.

Dr. Greene: It has been seen in very high vacuums.

Dr. Hanson: These are organic crystals that we have looked at. In vacuum conditions, 10^{-2} torr, the luminescence evolves gradually in time and peaks at temperatures which are characteristic of the sample. I think that has to do with charge recombination in the sample, but why it peaks at various specific temperatures is not clear.

CHAPTER VIII

A PROLEGOMENON TO THE STUDY OF SWITCHES FOR CONDUCTIVE POLYMERS

Sheldon L. Matlow
The Southwall Corporation
Palo Alto, CA 94303

INTRODUCTION

In 1925 H. Staudinger was told, '... there can be no such thing as a macromolecule.' (1) In the 1950's several investigators, including the present author, were told in no uncertain terms that the laws of solid state physics forbid the existence of highly conductive polymers. In 1971 Shirakawa and Ikeda succeeded in synthesizing films of poly (acetylene) (2), which on doping has a conductivity as high as $1.2*10**3$/ohm·cm (3). [Note: The required format for this Paper precludes the use of exponents in the body of the text. We have, therefore, elected to use Fortran notation instead. Thus,

$$1.2*10**3 \equiv 1.2 \times 10^3 \quad . \tag{1}]$$

This value is far from the $6.2*10**5$/ohm·cm conductivity of silver, but it is high enough to reinspire the hope that some day the genius of the synthetic organic chemists will provide us with chemically stable, highly conductive polymers. With this hope in mind, it is not premature to explore mechanisms by which this conductivity can be switched on and off. On approaching a frontier of science it is wise to investigate what limitations, if any, are imposed by thermodynamics -- thus, following the dictum, 'If thermodynamics says, "No!", forget it.'

PHILOSOPHICAL AND LINGUISTIC CONSIDERATIONS

From the viewpoint of the philosopher of science the first step which must be taken in creating a new branch of science and its technology is to set up a philosophical model based upon one's epistemology (theory of knowledge). From the philosophical model a mathematical model is developed. In the next stage a physical model is sought which is 'essentially' isomorphic with the mathematical model. Since the mathematics frequently requires the use of numerous approximations to make it tractable, it is unlikely that a completely isomorphic relation can be developed between the mathematical and physical models. If the physical model requires materials with very special properties, it will be necessary that the physical model include a chemical (or molecular) model. Finally, one must develop synthetic procedures for putting the 'raw' materials together in the proper orders to prepare the physical-chemical system.

Space limitations do not permit such a philosophical analysis of molecular electronics here. Instead we shall limit the present discussion to a very small aspect of molecular electronics -- switches for conducting polymers. Even this topic is too extensive, so only an introduction will be presented here. The philosopher's term for 'introduction' is 'prolegomenon' -- from the Greek 'pro' (before) and 'logos' (word). 'Logos', however, can also mean 'law'. Thus, the use of 'prolegomenon' is a play on words. It can mean 'that which comes before the main body of the text', or it can mean 'that which is required before the laws can be developed'.

In this study much of the philosophical considerations are definitional (and, therefore, linguistic) or logical of the type which blurs the distinction between the philosophical and mathematical models to such an extent that the distinction is no longer meaningful. First, let us define some terms. A 'macromolecule' is a molecule consisting of a large number of atoms. A 'polymer' [from the Greek 'poly' (many) and 'meros' (part)] is a macromolecule which can be considered conceptually to be made up of identical or similar small molecules called 'monomers' [from the Greek 'monos' (single) and 'meros' (part)]. If one permits the usage of referring to individual atoms as monomers, then there is no distinction between a <u>macromolecule</u> and a <u>polymer</u>. A single plane in a graphite crystal is a macromolecule, but it is a polymer only if the individual carbon atoms are considered to be monomers.

The monomers of poly (acetylene) are acetylene molecules as the name indicates. The repeating units in poly (acetylene), however, do not have carbon-carbon triple bonds. They are, rather, —CH=CH—. In order to distinguish between the structured units by means of which the polymer is formed and the structural units of the polymer itself, we shall call CH≡CH a <u>monomer</u> of poly (acetylene) and —CH=CH— a <u>mer</u> of poly (acetylene).

A polymer is said to be 'linear' if the atoms of the backbone of the molecule are <u>linearly</u> connected -- a topological relation. Polyenes are, therefore, linear. Polyynes are also linear in the topological sense, but they are also linear in a further sense. The equation for the equilibrium positions of the atoms of the backbone is <u>linear</u>. To distinghish between these two concepts of linearity we shall call the first 'topological linearity' and the second 'metrical linearity'.

[It will be noticed that throughout this paper single quotation marks are used rather than the more typical double quotation marks. This is because we are using the quotation marks in a logically consistent way to distinguish among the different levels of language (4). In this way we ensure that we will avoid the linguistic equivalent of Russell's paradox (5). Thus, red is a color. 'Red' is a word. "Red is a color." is a sentence in language. "'Red' is a word." is a sentence in meta-language. "'"'Red' is a word." is a sentence in meta-language.'" is a sentence in meta-meta-language.]

CONDUCTIVITY CONSIDERATIONS

In this study we shall assume that (1) the polymer is metrically linear, (2) all chains are the same length, and (3) all chains are parallel to the external electric field. The resistance to electron flow can be considered to consist of two terms: the resistance along the polymer chain, R (in) [for

'internal resistance'], and the resistance between polymer chains, R(ex)
[for 'external resistance']. Let ℓ be length and A be cross-sectional
area, then

$$R(total) = R(in) + R(ex)$$

$$= \rho(in) \; \ell(in)/A(in) + \rho(ex) \; \ell(ex)/A(ex)$$

$$= [\rho(in) \; \ell(in) + \rho(ex) \; \ell(ex)]/A , \qquad (2)$$

where we have assumed that

$$A(in) = A(ex) = A . \qquad (3)$$

$\ell(in)$ is the length of the conductive portion of the polymer chain, and $\ell(ex)$
is the distance between the conductive portions of adjacent chains along the
conduction 'line'. (For this purpose the chains are assumed to be end-to-end
and never side-by-side.)

If Ohm's law is obeyed, for a <u>single</u> carrier system,

$$\rho^{-1} = \sigma = n e_o \mu , \qquad (4)$$

where n is the carrier density, μ is the carrier mobility and e-sub-oh is
the charge on an electron, $1.6*10**-19$ Coulombs. The application of (4) to
(2) yields

$$R(total) = [\ell(in)/n(in) \; \mu(in) + \ell(ex)/n(ex) \; \mu(ex)]/e_o A . \qquad (5)$$

In the absence of any knowledge of the structure of the system one would write

$$R(total) = \ell(total)/n(total) \; \mu(total)/e_o A . \qquad (6)$$

It should be noted that

$$\ell(total) = \ell(in) + \ell(ex) . \qquad (7)$$

Thus, we find that

$$[\ell(in) + \ell(ex)]/n(total) \; \mu(total)$$

$$= \ell(in)/n(in) \; \mu(in) + \ell(ex)/n(ex) \; \mu(ex) , \qquad (8)$$

or

$$1/n(total) \; \bar{\mu}(total) = 1/n(in) \; \bar{\mu}(in) + 1/n(ex) \; \bar{\mu}(ex)$$

$$= [n(ex) \; \bar{\mu}(ex) + n(in) \; \bar{\mu}(in)]/$$

$$n(in) \; \bar{\mu}(in) \; n(ex) \; \bar{\mu}(ex) , \qquad (9)$$

or

$$n(total) \; \bar{\mu}(total) = n(in) \; \bar{\mu}(in) \; n(ex) \; \bar{\mu}(ex)/$$

$$[n(ex) \; \bar{\mu}(ex) + n(in) \; \bar{\mu}(in)] , \qquad (10)$$

where

$$\bar{\mu}(j) = \mu(j)/\ell(j) \tag{11}$$

and is a 'mobility per unit length'.

For most conductive polymers

$$n(in)\ \bar{\mu}(in) \gg n(ex)\ \bar{\mu}(ex) . \tag{12}$$

Thus, most bulk resistivity measurements on conductive polymers are, by (10) and (12), measurements of $n(ex)\ \bar{\mu}(ex)$ and tell nothing about $n(in)\ \bar{\mu}(in)$.

A theoretical study which we are conducting (no pun intended), but which is not yet complete, indicates that μ should be proportional to $\ell**2$ provided that all of the atoms in the backbone remain co-planar as ℓ increases. For these cases $\bar{\mu}$ is, therefore, proportional to ℓ. Molecular switches, when turned 'on', convert the individually conductive chains or parts of chains to one large conductive chain. This would cause the polymer to show a dramatic increase in conductivity.

The conductivity is, however, proportional to the product of n and $\bar{\mu}$. We must, therefore also consider the factors which determine n. The valence band of a conductive chain is generally completely filled except for the few holes which result from the thermal excitation of valence band electrons to the conduction band. If there are 'foreign' atoms present in the system, they may produce an occupied band just below the conduction band. The electrons in these levels will be excited thermally into the conduction band provided that a pathway exists between the 'foreign' atom and the conductive chain. Since these 'foreign' atoms donate electrons to the conduction band, they are called 'donors'. ('Foreign' atoms may also produce an unoccupied band just above the valence band. This results in the excitation of holes into the valence band. We shall, however, not consider this case here.) Thus, n will be proportional to the number of donor atoms which have pathways to the conductive chain available to them.

Thus, we find that $\bar{\mu}$(total) will be a function of the number of intramolecular switches which are turned on, which determines the value of $\bar{\mu}(in)$, and the number of inter-molecular switches which are turned on, which determines the value of $\bar{\mu}(ex)$. Furthermore, n(total) will be a function of the number of donor atoms per mer and the number of donor-mer switches which are turned on.

THE MODEL

In setting up our model we have made the following assumptions: (1) The system can be approximated by a one-dimensional conductor model. (2) The dopant is a donor. Thus, the majority carriers are conduction band electrons. (3) The system is sufficiently close to equilibrium to permit the use of the concepts temperature, free energy and Ohm's law. (4) The conduction band electrons are sufficiently independent to permit their being treated as a Boltzmann gas, rather than as a Fermi gas. (5) A domain must be $10**-4$ meters in length to be considered to be a conductor. (6) Switching results from a change in molecular geometry.

In the analysis of the thermodynamics of a switch two factors must be considered, the changes resulting from the change of the geometry of the switch and the changes resulting from carrier delocalization. Thus, four terms must be calculated. $\Delta H(s)$ is the change in enthalpy resulting from the change in the geometry of the switch and is always <u>positive</u>. $\Delta H(c)$ is the change in enthalpy resulting from the delocalization of electrons and is always <u>negative</u>. $\Delta S(s)$ is the change in entropy resulting from the change in the geometry of the switch and is usually <u>negative</u>. $\Delta S(c)$ is the change in entropy resulting from the delocalization of electrons and is always <u>positive</u>.

The Gibbs free energy of switching may be written as

$$G = [\Delta H(s) + \underline{\Delta H(c)}] - T[\underline{\Delta S(s)} + \Delta S(c)] , \qquad (13)$$

where the underlining indicates that the term is negative. At a given temperature switching will occur when

$$[\Delta H(s) + \underline{\Delta H(c)}] = T[\underline{\Delta S(s)} + \Delta S(c)] . \qquad (14)$$

The values of $\Delta H(s)$ and $\Delta S(s)$ cannot be estimated without some knowledge of the before-switching and after-switching geometries of the switches. $\underline{\Delta H(c)}$ and $\Delta S(c)$ can, however, be estimated. Since T in (14) must be positive and have a reasonable value, the values of $\underline{\Delta H(c)}$ and $\Delta S(c)$ will limit the permitted values of $\Delta H(s)$ and $\Delta S(s)$. Thus, restrictions on the permitted geometries of the switches can be established.

Let

m = the number of electrons per mer, taken here as 4,
d = the number of doping atoms per mer, each of which atoms is assumed
    to supply 1 electron,
p = the number of mers per molecule,
q = the number of molecules in the domain,
ℓ(mer) = the length of a single mer, taken here as $2.41*10**-10$ meters, and
ℓ(dop) = the 'length' of a doping atom, taken here as $1*10**-10$ meters.

We assume that the switches themselves are already 'imbedded' in the lengths given. Thus,

$$pq\ell(mer) = 10^{-4} \text{ meters} \qquad (15)$$

or

$$pq = 10^{-4}/2.41 \times 10^{-10}$$

$$= 4.15 \times 10^5 . \qquad (16)$$

We distinguish three different types of switch states:

D, the dopant-mer switches are turned on,
I, the internal (intra-molecular) switches are turned on, and
E, the external (inter-molecular) switches are turned on.

We shall follow the convention here that a tilde over the symbol for a switch type indicates that the switches of that type are in the off state. There are eight possible combination of switch states -- $\tilde{D}\tilde{I}\tilde{E}$, $\tilde{D}\tilde{I}E$, $\tilde{D}I\tilde{E}$, $D\tilde{I}\tilde{E}$, $D\tilde{I}\tilde{E}$, $D\tilde{I}E$, $DI\tilde{E}$ and DIE. We shall consider here only the $\tilde{D}\tilde{I}\tilde{E}$ - DIE transition.

SWITCH THERMODYNAMICS

We shall estimate the entropy of a given state by

$$S = Nk_o \ln L , \qquad (17)$$

where N is the number of electrons, k-sub-oh is Boltzmann's constant ($1.381 * 10^{**}-23$ Joules/deg/electron) and L is the length occupied by the electrons. We shall assume a negligible volume change when switches turn on. We may, therefore, equate the enthalpy with the internal energy. We shall estimate the enthalpy of a state by

$$H = h^2 \sum_{i=1}^{N} n(i)^2 / 8 \, m_o L^2$$

$$= 6.02 \times 10^{-38} \sum_{i=1}^{N} n(i)^2 / L^2 , \qquad (18)$$

where h is Planck's constant ($6.626 * 10^{**}-34$ Joule·sec), m-sub-oh is the rest mass of the electron ($9.110 * 10^{**}-31$ kg) and $n(i)$ is the quantum number of the i-th electron. Since this model does not take account of spin, two electrons can have the same value of $n(i)$. It should be noted that the $n(i)$'s are positive integers and are assigned serially.

For the $\tilde{D}\tilde{I}\tilde{E}$ state the doping electrons are localized on the donor atoms, and the mer electrons are localized on the individual mers. Thus,

$$S(\tilde{D}\tilde{I}\tilde{E}) = dpqk_o \ln \ell(dop) + 4pqk_o \ln \ell(mer)$$

$$= -1.320 \times 10^{-16} d - 5.08 \times 10^{-16} \text{ Joules·deg}^{-1} , \qquad (19)$$

and

$$H(\tilde{D}\tilde{I}\tilde{E}) = 6.02 \times 10^{-38} [dpq/\ell(dop)^2 + 2pq(1^2 + 2^2)/\ell(mer)^2]$$

$$= 2.50 \times 10^{-12} d + 4.30 \times 10^{-12} \text{ Joules} . \qquad (20)$$

The negative sign for the entropy is the result of our having used length rather than multiplicity in (17). The conversion factor cancels out when ΔS is calculated.

For the DIE state both the doping electrons and the mer electrons are delocalized over the entire $1 * 10^{**}-4$ meter length. Since $\ell(dop)$ is small with respect to this length, $\ell(dop)$ is ignored in the following.

$$S(DIE) = dpqk_o \ln(10^{-4}) + 4pqk_o \ln(10^{-4})$$

$$= -5.28 \times 10^{-17} d - 2.11 \times 10^{-16} \text{ Joules·deg}^{-1} , \qquad (21)$$

and

$$\Delta S(\tilde{D}\tilde{I}\tilde{E} \text{ to } DIE) = 7.92 \times 10^{-17} d + 2.97 \times 10^{-16} \text{ Joules·deg}^{-1} . \qquad (22)$$

The evaluation of H(DIE) requires the use of the theorem

$$1^2 + 2^2 + \cdots + a^2 = a(a+1)(2a+1)/6 .$$ (23)

We note, further, that there are $pq(4+d)$ electrons which require $pq(4+d)/2$ energy levels. Thus, for DIE (18) becomes

$$H(DIE) = (6.02 \times 10^{-38}/10^{-8}) \sum_{i=1}^{pq(4+d)/2} n(i)^2$$

$$= 2.51 \times 10^{-31} (pq)^3 (4+d)^3$$

$$= 1.794 \times 10^{-14} (4+d)^3 \text{ Joules },$$ (24)

and

$$\Delta H(\widetilde{DIE} \text{ to DIE}) = 1.794 \times 10^{-14} (4+d)^3 - 2.50 \times 10^{-12}d - 4.30 \times 10^{-12} \text{ Joules}.$$ (25)

A reasonable domain for d is zero to two. Thus,

$$\Delta S(d = 0) = 2.97 \times 10^{-16} \text{ Joules} \cdot \text{deg}^{-1} ,$$ (26)

$$\Delta S(d = 2) = 4.55 \times 10^{-16} \text{ Joules} \cdot \text{deg}^{-1} ,$$ (27)

$$\Delta H(d = 0) = -3.15 \times 10^{-12} \text{ Joules },$$ (28)

and

$$\Delta H(d = 2) = -5.42 \times 10^{-12} \text{ Joules }.$$ (29)

We may now return to equation (14). Let us assume an 'effective' temperature of 400 degrees K, and that $d = 2$, then

$$\Delta H(s) - 5.42 \times 10^{-12} = 400 \underline{\Delta S(s)} + 1.820 \times 10^{-13} ,$$ (30)

or

$$\Delta G(s, 400) = \Delta H(s) - 400 \underline{\Delta S(s)}$$

$$= 5.60 \times 10^{-12} \text{ Joules }.$$ (31)

There are dpq dopant switches, $q(p-1)$ intra-molecular switches and $q-1$ inter-molecular switches for a total of $pq(d+1)-1$ switches. With d equal to two and taking the value of equation (16) we calculate a total of 1.245*10**6 switches. If we assume that all switches have the same Gibbs free energy of transition, the Gibbs free energy change per mole of switches is

$$\Delta G(s, T = 400) = 6.02 \times 10^{23} \times 5.60 \times 10^{-12}/1.245 \times 10^6$$

$$= 2.71 \times 10^6 \text{ Joules.mole}^{-1} .$$ (32)

By comparison, the Gibbs free energy of dissociation of gaseous molecular hydrogen at the same temperature is only 3.96*10**5 Joules/mole. Thus, the

switching Gibbs free energy change is almost seven times as great as the
dissociation Gibbs free energy of hydrogen molecules.

Thus, we conclude that, whatever the chemical composition is for the
switches for conductive polymers, the Gibbs free energy change for the
geometric changes of the switches must be enormous.

REFERENCES

1. R. Olby, 'The Macromolecular Concept and the Origins of Molecular Biology',
    J. Chem. Ed. 47, 171 (1970).

2. H. Shirakawa and S. Ikeda, 'Infrared Spectra of Poly (acetylene)', Polym.
    J. 2, 231 (1971).

3. A.G. MacDiarmid and A.J. Heeger, 'Organic Metals and Semiconductors: The
    Chemistry of Polyacetylene, $(CH)_x$, and Its Derivatives', Synthetic Metals
    1, 101 (1979/80).

4. H. Reichenbach, Elements of Symbolic Logic, The MacMillen Company, New York
    (1947), pp. 9-17.

5. Ibid., pp. 218-226.

CHAPTER IX

ELECTRON TUNNELLING IN SHORT PERIODIC
ARRAYS

Forrest L. Carter
Chemistry Division
Naval Research Laboratory
Washington, DC 20375

INTRODUCTION

Traditionally solutions of the Schrodinger wave equation for square-well and step-function potentials have served primarily heuristic and pedagogical purposes. More recently, however, advances in the use of multibeam evaporators have made possible the growth of layered semiconductors with layers only a few Angstroms thick. In addition we have proposed (1a) that analogues to NAND and NOR switches might be possible at the molecular size level. That proposal relies on the quasi-classical work of Pschenichnov (2) who for a one dimensional system of identical potential barriers anticipated the existence of an electron tunnel effect.

The tunnel effect occurs when the electron's energy, ω, matches that of a pseudo-stationary state, E_n, (i.e. a virtual level) related to an energy level of the well between barriers, when ω is less than the height of the barriers. The work of Pschenichnov (2) suggests that where this condition is met (i.e. $\omega = E_n$) then the transmission coefficient T is equal to 1; in other words, at this energy, the barriers are perfectly transparent. However at a small energy mismatch, transmission falls exponentially with the number of barriers. The extremely rapid decline in electron transmission with the energy mismatch provides the basis for a switching mechanism assuming that one is perturbing one or more of the potential wells or barriers and hence disturbing the energy level of the pseudo-stationary state. We note that both the layered semiconductors and the molecular tunnelling as conceived (1)can be reasonably treated as a one dimensional problem (the approach taken here). In addition, the new results obtained below may be useful for understanding electron transport and scattering along a polymer chain with a non-periodic distribution of substituents or conjugation.

In the first section below an analogue to a NOR gate is suggested which is more properly "molecular" than the one offered previously (1a). Succeeding sections include the development of the continuity equations, the new analytic results obtained for an arbitrary number and arrangement of potential step functions, an algorithm for writing down the exact solution for any number of potential step changes, and finally, the specialized cases of identical potential barriers and wells.

121

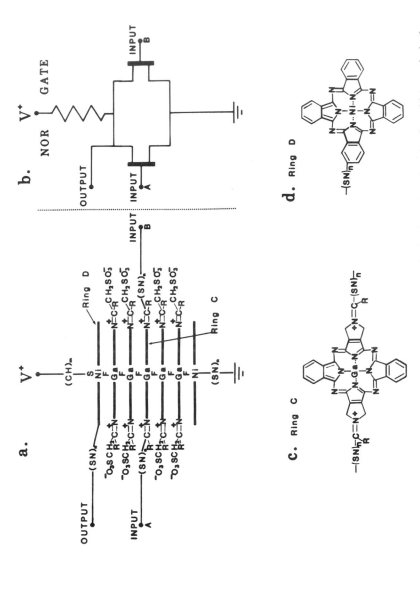

Figure 1. A molecular analogue to a NOR gate based on a stacked fluorine bridged gallium phthalocyanine-type ring. The bridging fluorines result in an insulating barrier between the rings while the terminal sulfurs provide a strong multivalent bond to the $(SN)_n$ and more resistive $(CH)_n$ conductors.

A Molecular Analogue NOR Gate

In the first EAP Review (1a) molecular analogues of semiconducting NAND and NOR gates were offered; however, the NOR gate was based on the special properties of the CuS crystal structure with its alternating insulating and conducting layers. The structure now offered is more properly a 'molecular' analogue.

In Fig. 1a the structure of an analogue to the electronic switch in Fig. 1b is based on a fluorine bridged stack of gallium phthalocyanine rings similar to the compounds recently reported by Kuznesof, Wynne, Nohr, and Kenney (3). The stack is composed primarily of rings of type C (Fig. 1c) where the $-(SN)_x-$ linkage is replaced by the $-CH_2-SO_3$ group. Clearly the rings C are carriers for the Control Group or the Dummy Control Groups having the quaternary imino nitrogen groups $>C=N+$. The two kinds of Control Groups define the periodic potential necessary for tunnelling; Control Groups permit modification of the potential and, hence, the tunnelling to be switched on or off (Ref. 1b).

The D rings (Fig. 1d), nickel phthalocyanine moieties, provide links to both the ground and the negative potential through Ni-S bonds (Fig. 1a); as well as to the $(SN)_n$ - Output lead. These terminating rings also serve to provide a suitable environment for the stacked bridged phthalocyanine rings. Control through the Input $-(SN)_n-$ leads A or B occurs via an electron flow down the $-(SN)_n-$ chain to neutralize the quaternary imino nitrogen. The neutralization of either nitrogen would change the potential of that ring sufficiently to sharply cut off the electron tunnelling through the rings.

Continuity Equations

From the author's (4) earlier result involving a periodic set of an arbitrary number of potential step functions per unit cell it seemed reasonable that an exact expression might be achievable for electron transmission past an arbitrary number of square wells and barriers. That possibility is vindicated in this paper; both the derivation and the generalized analytic expression are given for the transmission coefficient T of an electron past any number of step-function potential changes. The method is classical textbook (see Schiff (5).

Before developing the expression for perfect transmission, it is very useful to understand the relationships for the wave function between the regions of adjacent potentials. The time independent Schrodinger wave equation in atomic units is

$$\frac{d^2\Psi}{dx^2} + 2[E - V(x)]\Psi = 0 \qquad\qquad \text{Eq. 1}$$

where for constant potential V the wave function $\Psi(x)$ can be readily written as

$$\Psi_n(x) = A_n e^{i\beta_n x} + B_n e^{-i\beta_n x} \qquad\qquad \text{Eq. 2}$$

correspondingly to waves of energy $E = \omega$ moving to the right and left with amplitudes A_i and B_n respectively. The exponential multiplier β_n is determined by substituting Ψ_n (Eq. 2) in the differential wave equation (Eq. 1);

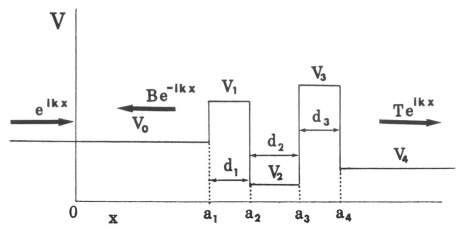

Figure 2. Square well (and barrier) potentials of width d_i and depth (height) V_i in the path of a unit wave approaching from the extreme left.

while the coefficients A_n, B_n, are determined by joining Ψ_n and its first derivative $d\Psi_i/dx$ continuously at each step position a_n of Fig. 2. With $\Psi_n(x)$ corresponding to the wave function with $a_n \leq x \leq a_{n+1}$ the continuity requirements give two equations for each potential step at the positions a_n; thus,

functional continuity and

$$A_{n-1}e^{i\beta_{n-1}a_n} + B_{n-1}e^{-i\beta_{n-1}a_n} = A_n e^{i\beta_n a_n} + B_n e^{-i\beta_n a_n} \qquad \text{Eq. 3}$$

slope continuity

$$\beta_{n-1}A_{n-1}e^{i\beta_{n-1}a_n} - \beta_{n-1}B_{n-1}e^{-i\beta_{n-1}a_n} \qquad \text{Eq. 4}$$

$$= \beta_n A_n e^{i\beta_n a_n} - \beta_n B_n e^{-i\beta_n a_n}$$

Obviously, A_n and B_n can be expressed as a matrix multiplication M_n of the coefficients A_{n-1} and B_{n-1}

$$\begin{pmatrix} A_n \\ B_n \end{pmatrix} = M_n \begin{pmatrix} A_{n-1} \\ B_{n-1} \end{pmatrix} \qquad \text{Eq. 5}$$

This equation can be easily generalized, as was done by Pshenichnov (2) for his quasi-classical approach, to the form:

$$\begin{pmatrix} A_n \\ B_n \end{pmatrix} = M_n \cdot M_{n-1} \cdots M_2 \cdot M_1 \begin{pmatrix} A_o \\ B_o \end{pmatrix} \qquad \text{Eq. 6}$$

where n is the counting index of the potential steps. Clearly since a barrier of finite height requires at least two potential steps, the matrices must be grouped at least by pairs to be compared with Pshenichnov's results.

New Results

The matrices M_n and their successive products, however, are complex (in both senses) and are awkward to write down. It is more convenient to discuss their products like

$$\prod_1^n M_i \quad \text{and} \quad \prod_{k+1}^n M_i$$

in terms of the much simpler analytic expressions $U_{no}^{\pm}$ and $V_{no}^{\pm}$ to be given explicitly below for the first time for various n up to 6.

In these terms $\prod_1^n M_i$ and $\prod_{k+1}^n M_i$ may be related to Eqs. 7 and 8 and Eqs. 9 and 10 respectively. The relationship between the coefficients A_n, B_n, and A_o, B_o in terms of $U_{nk}^{\pm}$ and $V_{ko}^{\pm}$ etc. is indicated by Eqs. 11 and 12.

$$A_n \cdot 2 \cdot e^{i\beta_n a_n} = [U_{no}^+ + iV_{no}^+] A_o e^{i\beta_o a_1} + [U_{no}^- - iV_{no}^-] B_o e^{-i\beta_o a_1} \qquad \text{Eq. 7}$$

$$B_n \cdot 2 \cdot e^{-i\beta_n a_n} = [U_{no}^- + iV_{no}^-] A_o e^{i\beta_o a_1} + [U_{no}^+ - iV_{no}^+] B_o e^{-i\beta_o a_1} \qquad \text{Eq. 8}$$

$$A_n \cdot 2 \cdot e^{i\beta_n a_n} = [U_{nk}^+ + iV_{nk}^+] A_k e^{i\beta_k a_{k+1}} + [U_{nk}^- - iV_{nk}^-] B_k e^{i\beta_k a_{k+1}} \qquad \text{Eq. 9}$$

$$B_n \cdot 2 \cdot e^{-i\beta_n a_n} = [U_{nk}^- + iV_{nk}^-] A_k e^{i\beta_k a_{k+1}} + [U_{nk}^+ - iV_{nk}^+] B_k e^{i\beta_k a_{k+1}} \qquad \text{Eq. 10}$$

The $U_{no}^{\pm}$ and $V_{no}^{\pm}$ are to be given in Table 1 in terms of various β_i, S_i and C_i as defined below where on the left the electron energy ω is greater than the potential V_i, etc:

Low Potential	High Potential
$V_i \leq \omega$	$V_i > \omega$
$\beta_i = \sqrt{\omega - V_i}$	$\beta_i = \sqrt{V_i - \omega}$
$C_i = \cos \beta_i d_i$	$C_i = \cosh \beta_i d_i$
$S_i = \sin \beta_i d_i$	$S_i = \sinh \beta_i d_i$

Although $U_{no}^{\pm}$ and $V_{no}^{\pm}$ functions rapidly become rather complex for increasing n in fact they are rather simple once understood, and they can readily be

GENERATE GENERAL RULE FOR COEFFICIENTS

Substitute for $A_k + B_k$

$$A_n \cdot 2 \cdot e^{i\beta_n a_n}$$

$$= A_o e^{i\beta_o a_1} \left[\frac{e^{i\beta_k(a_{k+1}-a_k)}}{2} (U_{nk}^+ + iV_{nk}^+)(U_{ko}^+ + iV_{ko}^+) + \frac{e^{-i\beta_k(a_{k+1}-a_k)}}{2} (U_{nk}^- - iV_{nk}^-)(U_{ko}^- + iV_{ko}^-) \right]$$

$$+ B_o e^{-i\beta_o a_1} \left[\frac{e^{i\beta_k(a_{k+1}-a_k)}}{2} (U_{nk}^+ + iV_{nk}^+)(U_{ko}^- - iV_{ko}^-) + \frac{e^{-i\beta_k(a_{k+1}-a_k)}}{2} (U_{nk}^- - iV_{nk}^-)(U_{ko}^+ - iV_{ko}^+) \right] \qquad \text{Eq. 11}$$

$$B_n \cdot 2 \cdot e^{-i\beta_n a_n}$$

$$= A_o e^{i\beta_o a_1} \left[\frac{e^{i\beta_k(a_{k+1}-a_k)}}{2} (U_{nk}^- + iV_{nk}^-)(U_{ko}^+ + iV_{ko}^+) + \frac{e^{-i\beta_k(a_{k+1}-a_k)}}{2} (U_{nk}^+ - iV_{nk}^+)(U_{ko}^- + iV_{ko}^-) \right]$$

$$+ B_o e^{-i\beta_o a_1} \left[\frac{e^{i\beta_k(a_{k+1}-a_k)}}{2} (U_{nk}^- + iV_{nk}^-)(U_{ko}^- - iV_{ko}^-) + \frac{e^{-i\beta_k(a_{k+1}-a_k)}}{2} (U_{nk}^+ - iV_{nk}^+)(U_{ko}^+ - iV_{ko}^+) \right] \qquad \text{Eq. 12}$$

TABLE I OF COEFFICIENTS $U_{no}^{\pm}$ AND $V_{no}^{\pm}$

$n = 1$

$$U_{10}^{\pm} = (1 \pm \frac{\beta_o}{\beta_1})$$

$$V_{10}^{+} = V_{10}^{-} = 0$$

$n = 2$

$$U_{20}^{\pm} = (1 \pm \frac{\beta_o}{\beta_2}) C_1$$

$$V_{20}^{\pm} = (\frac{\beta_o}{\beta_1} \pm \frac{\beta_1}{\beta_2}) S_1$$

$n = 3$

$$U_{30}^{\pm} = (1 \pm \frac{\beta_o}{\beta_3}) C_1 C_2 - (\frac{\beta_1}{\beta_2} \pm \frac{\beta_o}{\beta_1}\frac{\beta_2}{\beta_3}) S_1 S_2$$

$$V_{30}^{+} = (\frac{\beta_o}{\beta_2} \pm \frac{\beta_2}{\beta_3}) C_1 S_2 + (\frac{\beta_o}{\beta_1} \pm \frac{\beta_1}{\beta_3}) S_1 C_2$$

$n = 4$

$$U_{40}^{\pm} = (1 \pm \frac{\beta_o}{\beta_4}) C_1 C_2 C_3 - (\frac{\beta_2}{\beta_3} \pm \frac{\beta_o}{\beta_2}\frac{\beta_3}{\beta_4}) C_1 S_2 S_3 - (\frac{\beta_1}{\beta_2} \pm \frac{\beta_o}{\beta_1}\frac{\beta_2}{\beta_4}) S_1 S_2 C_3$$

$$V_{40}^{\pm} = (\frac{\beta_o}{\beta_3} \pm \frac{\beta_3}{\beta_4}) C_1 C_2 S_3 + (\frac{\beta_o}{\beta_2} \pm \frac{\beta_2}{\beta_4}) C_1 S_2 C_3 + (\frac{\beta_o}{\beta_1} \pm \frac{\beta_1}{\beta_4}) S_1 C_2 C_3 - (\frac{\beta_o}{\beta_1} \pm \frac{\beta_1\beta_3}{\beta_2\beta_4}) S_1 S_2 S_3$$

$n = 5$

$$U_{50}^{\pm} = (1 \pm \frac{\beta_o}{\beta_5}) C_1 C_2 C_3 C_4 - (\frac{\beta_3}{\beta_4} \pm \frac{\beta_o}{\beta_3}\frac{\beta_4}{\beta_5}) C_1 C_2 S_3 S_4 - (\frac{\beta_1}{\beta_4} \pm \frac{\beta_o}{\beta_1}\frac{\beta_4}{\beta_5}) S_1 C_2 C_3 S_4$$

$$- (\frac{\beta_1}{\beta_2} \pm \frac{\beta_o}{\beta_1}\frac{\beta_2}{\beta_5}) S_1 S_2 C_3 C_4 - (\frac{\beta_2}{\beta_3} \pm \frac{\beta_o\beta_3}{\beta_2\beta_5}) C_1 S_2 S_3 C_4 + (\frac{\beta_o\beta_2\beta_4}{\beta_1\beta_3\beta_5} \pm \frac{\beta_1\beta_3}{\beta_2\beta_5}) S_1 S_2 S_3 S_4$$

$$V_{50}^{\pm} = (\frac{\beta_o}{\beta_4} \pm \frac{\beta_4}{\beta_5}) C_1 C_2 C_3 S_4 + (\frac{\beta_o}{\beta_3} \pm \frac{\beta_3}{\beta_5}) C_1 C_2 S_3 C_4 + (\frac{\beta_o}{\beta_2} \pm \frac{\beta_2}{\beta_5}) C_1 S_2 C_3 C_4 + (\frac{\beta_o}{\beta_1} \pm \frac{\beta_1}{\beta_5}) S_1 C_2 C_3 C_4$$

$$- (\frac{\beta_o\beta_3}{\beta_1\beta_4} \pm \frac{\beta_1\beta_4}{\beta_3\beta_5}) S_1 C_2 S_3 S_4 - (\frac{\beta_o\beta_2}{\beta_1\beta_3} \pm \frac{\beta_1\beta_3}{\beta_2\beta_5}) S_1 S_2 S_3 C_4 - (\frac{\beta_o\beta_2}{\beta_1\beta_4} \pm \frac{\beta_2\beta_4}{\beta_3\beta_5}) C_1 S_2 S_3 S_4$$

TABLE I OF COEFFICIENTS $U_{no}^{\pm}$ AND $V_{no}^{\pm}$ (CONT'D)

n = 6

$$U_{60}^{\pm} = (1 \pm \frac{\beta_0}{\beta_6})C_1C_2C_3C_4C_5 - (\frac{\beta_4}{\beta_5} \pm \frac{\beta_0\beta_5}{\beta_4\beta_6})C_1C_2C_3S_4S_5 - (\frac{\beta_3}{\beta_5} \pm \frac{\beta_0\beta_5}{\beta_3\beta_6})C_1C_2S_3C_4S_5 - (\frac{\beta_2}{\beta_5} \pm \frac{\beta_0\beta_5}{\beta_2\beta_6})C_1S_2C_3C_4S_5$$

$$- (\frac{\beta_1}{\beta_5} \pm \frac{\beta_0\beta_5}{\beta_1\beta_6})S_1C_2C_3C_4S_5 - (\frac{\beta_3}{\beta_4} \pm \frac{\beta_0\beta_4}{\beta_3\beta_6})C_1C_2S_3S_4C_5 - (\frac{\beta_2}{\beta_4} \pm \frac{\beta_0\beta_4}{\beta_2\beta_6})C_1S_2C_3S_4C_5 - (\frac{\beta_1}{\beta_4} \pm \frac{\beta_0\beta_4}{\beta_1\beta_6})S_1C_2C_3S_4C_5$$

$$- (\frac{\beta_2}{\beta_3} \pm \frac{\beta_0\beta_3}{\beta_2\beta_6})C_1S_2S_3C_4C_5 - (\frac{\beta_1}{\beta_3} \pm \frac{\beta_0\beta_3}{\beta_1\beta_6})S_1C_2S_3C_4C_5 - (\frac{\beta_1}{\beta_2} \pm \frac{\beta_0\beta_2}{\beta_1\beta_6})S_1S_2C_3C_4C_5$$

$$+ (\frac{\beta_1\beta_4}{\beta_3\beta_5} \pm \frac{\beta_0\beta_3\beta_5}{\beta_1\beta_4\beta_6})S_1C_2S_3S_4S_5 + (\frac{\beta_1\beta_4}{\beta_2\beta_5} \pm \frac{\beta_0\beta_2\beta_5}{\beta_1\beta_4\beta_6})S_1S_2C_3S_4S_5 + (\frac{\beta_2\beta_4}{\beta_3\beta_5} \pm \frac{\beta_0\beta_3\beta_5}{\beta_2\beta_4\beta_6})C_1S_2S_3S_4S_5$$

$$+ (\frac{\beta_1\beta_3}{\beta_2\beta_4} \pm \frac{\beta_0\beta_2\beta_4}{\beta_1\beta_3\beta_6})S_1S_2S_3S_4C_5$$

$$V_{60}^{\pm} = (\frac{\beta_0}{\beta_5} \pm \frac{\beta_5}{\beta_6})C_1C_2C_3C_4S_5 + (\frac{\beta_0}{\beta_4} \pm \frac{\beta_4}{\beta_6})C_1C_2C_3S_4C_5 + (\frac{\beta_0}{\beta_3} \pm \frac{\beta_3}{\beta_6})C_1C_2S_3C_4C_5 + (\frac{\beta_0}{\beta_2} \pm \frac{\beta_2}{\beta_6})C_1S_2C_3C_4C_5$$

$$+ (\frac{\beta_0}{\beta_1} \pm \frac{\beta_1}{\beta_6})S_1C_2C_3C_4C_5 - (\frac{\beta_0\beta_4}{\beta_3\beta_5} \pm \frac{\beta_3\beta_5}{\beta_4\beta_6})C_1C_2S_3S_4S_5 - (\frac{\beta_0\beta_4}{\beta_2\beta_5} \pm \frac{\beta_2\beta_5}{\beta_4\beta_6})C_1S_2C_3S_4S_5 - (\frac{\beta_0\beta_4}{\beta_1\beta_5} \pm \frac{\beta_1\beta_5}{\beta_4\beta_6})S_1C_2C_3S_4S_5$$

$$- (\frac{\beta_0\beta_3}{\beta_2\beta_5} \pm \frac{\beta_2\beta_5}{\beta_3\beta_6})C_1S_2S_3C_4S_5 - (\frac{\beta_0\beta_3}{\beta_1\beta_5} \pm \frac{\beta_1\beta_5}{\beta_3\beta_6})S_1C_2S_3C_4S_5 - (\frac{\beta_0\beta_2}{\beta_1\beta_5} \pm \frac{\beta_1\beta_5}{\beta_2\beta_6})S_1S_2C_3C_4S_5$$

$$+ (\frac{\beta_0\beta_2\beta_4}{\beta_1\beta_3\beta_5} \pm \frac{\beta_1\beta_3\beta_5}{\beta_2\beta_4\beta_6})S_1S_2S_3S_4S_5$$

generalized. The verbal algorithm for doing so will be indicated after the formula for the transmission coefficient T is developed.

In terms of Fig. 2 and the coefficient pairs A_o, B_o and A_n, B_n the calculation for T is readily described. Approaching the first potential step at A_1 from infinity is the unit wave $e^{i\beta x}$, thus $A_o = 1$. Reflected from that first potential step is the wave with unknown amplitude $B = B_o$. The coefficient of the wave that gets through to the region V_4, $x > a4$ is the desired transmission amplitude T. Note that there is no wave coming from the right in this region; hence $A_n = T$ and $B_n = 0$. From Eqs. 7 and 8 and the coefficients just specified one can then readily obtain Eq. 13

$$T = A_n = A_o \frac{e^{i(\beta_o a_1 - \beta_n a_n)}}{2} \left[\frac{(U_{no}^+)^2 + (V_{no}^+)^2 - (U_{no}^-)^2 - (V_{no}^-)^2}{U_{no}^+ - i V_{no}^+} \right] \qquad \text{Eq. 13}$$

then with $A_o = 1$ we have for the transmission coefficient

$$|T|^2 = \frac{\left[(U_{no}^+)^2 + (V_{no}^+)^2 - (U_{no}^-)^2 - (V_{no}^-)^2 \right]^2}{4[(U_{no}^+)^2 + (V_{no}^+)^2]} \qquad \text{Eq. 14}$$

Equation 14 informs us that the transmission is maximized when U_{no}^+ and V_{no}^+ approach zero while the numerator remains finite. Table 2 indicates the behavior of the numerator for the first few values of n, the number of step potential changes. Generally it is not a fast varying function.

TABLE II

TRANSMISSION COEFFICIENT NUMERATOR

$$N_{no} = (U_{no}^+)^2 + (V_{no}^+)^2 - (U_{no}^-)^2 - (V_{no}^-)^2$$

$$N_{10} = 4 \frac{\beta_0}{\beta_1}$$

$$N_{20} = 4 \frac{\beta_0}{\beta_2} (C_1^2 + S_1^2)$$

$$N_{30} = 4 \frac{\beta_0}{\beta_3} \left[C_1^2 C_2^2 + C_1^2 S_2^2 + S_2^2 C_1^2 + S_1^2 S_2^2 \right]$$

$$N_{40} = 4 \frac{\beta_0}{\beta_3} \left[C_1^2 C_2^2 C_3^2 + C_1^2 C_2^2 S_3^2 + C_1^2 S_2^2 C_3^2 + S_1^2 C_2^2 C_3^2 + \right.$$
$$\left. C_1^2 S_2^2 S_3^2 + S_1^2 C_2^2 S_3^2 + S_1^2 S_2^2 C_3^2 + S_1^2 S_2^2 S_3^2 \right]$$

The relationship of the function U_{no}^+ (obtained here) to the solution of the wave equation for a periodic set of square well potentials is rather interesting. This is readily illustrated for the Konig-Penny square well model (4) when expressed in the notation above. Given that k is the wave vector and c is the unit cell edge we have (4):

$$\cos kc = C_1 C_2 - \frac{1}{2} [\frac{B_1}{B_2} + \frac{B_2}{B_1}] S_1 S_2 \qquad \text{Eq. 15}$$

This may be compared readily with U_{no}^+:

$$U_{30}^+ = (1 + \frac{B_o}{B_3}) C_1 C_2 - [\frac{B_1}{B_2} + \frac{B_o}{B_1} \frac{B_2}{B_3}] S_1 S_2 \qquad \text{Eq. 16}$$

Periodicity after two potential steps requires that $\beta_o = \beta_3$ so that one may clearly combine eqs. 15 and 16 to form

$$\cos kc = U_{30}^+/2 \qquad \text{Eq. 17}$$

Given n-1 steps per unit cell Eq. 17 may be generalized to

$$\cos kc = U_{no}^+/2 \qquad \text{Eq. 18}$$

Remembering elementary band theory we note that allowed bands exist only when $\cos kc \leq 1$ and forbidden gaps occur otherwise. Now when $U_{no}^+ = 0$ then a virtual state exists, which may be related via Eq. 18 to the case of $\cos kc = 0$, i.e. the center of the allowed bands. This then agrees well with one's expectations and to that extent supports the conclusions of Pshenichnov for the tunnelling of electrons through periodic barriers.

Algorithm for $U_{no}^{\pm}$ and $V_{no}^{\pm}$

Table 1 shows that in $U_{no}^{\pm}$ only even numbers, m, of S_i occur; further that the number of such terms is $\binom{n-1}{m} = \frac{(n-1)!}{(n-1-m)! \, m!}$ that is, all possible combinations of n-1 positions taken m at a time. The sign in front of a term like $(\frac{B_4}{B_5} + \frac{B_o}{B_4} \frac{B_5}{B_6}) C_1 C_2 C_3 S_4 S_5$ is + if mod (m DIV 2,2) is zero and negative otherwise (where DIV means integer divide). In the β_i ratios, only β_i corresponding to the S_i occur. In the lead β ratio, the first β_i occurs in the numerator, the second in the denominator, and the alteration continues. The second β_i ratio is the reciprocal of the first ratio multiplied by β_o/β_n.

Two differences occur in the case of the $V_{no}^{\pm}$ function. First, m is only odd. The second occurs in the β_i ratios. In the first ratio one always starts with β_o, whereas in the second ratio the first possible one is β_i and the last β_i factor is always β_n.

Case of Identical Barriers

Pschenichnov's use of identical barriers is modified as indicated in Fig. 3. In reducing the general cases of Table I to obtain the U_{no}^{+}, etc., for the particular examples suggested by Fig. 3 it is useful to reference Table III where the numbers of barriers, potential steps, S_i factors in each term, and number of terms is indicated successively. The last column indicates the distribution of m S_i factors (or β_i) between the barriers and wells (barrier, wells) where the number of such terms follows the parentheses. What is needed to obtain the desired relationships but not indicated in Table III is the distribution depending on whether the β_i ratios start with a β_i corresponding to a barrier or well.

Table IV indicates the equations required for the number of barriers to four. With each additional barrier a factor of four more terms must be simplified, as indicated in Table III.

TABLE III

TERMS FOR A SHORT PERIODIC ARRAY OF BARRIERS

No. Barriers	No. Steps	m	No. Terms	β, Distribution of m (For Barriers, For Wells)
1	2	0	1	(0,0)1
2	4	0	1	(0,0)1
		2	3	(2,0)1; (1,1)2
			4	
3	6	0	1	(0,0)1
		2	10	(2,0)3; (1,1)6; (0,2)1
		4	5	(3,1)2; (2,2)3
			16	
4	8	0	1	(0,0)1
		2	21	(2,0)6; (1,1)12; (0,2)3
		4	35	(4,0)1; (3,1)12; (2,2)18; (1,3)4
		6	7	(4,2)3; (3,3)4
			64	
5	10	0	1	(0,0)1
		2	36	(2,0)10; (1,1)20; (0,2)6
		4	126	(4,0)5; (3,1)40; (2,2)60; (1,3)20; (0,4)1
		6	84	(5,1)4; (4,2)30; (3,3)40; (2,4)10
		8	9	(5,3)4; (4,4)5
			256	

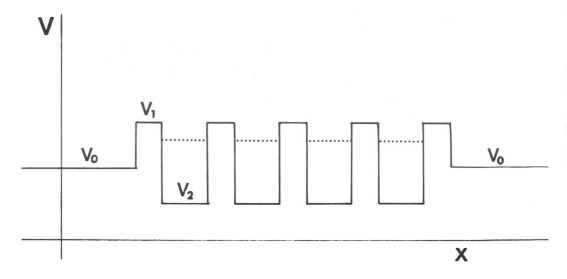

Figure 3. A short array of five barriers.

TABLE IV

SHORT ARRAY OF BARRIERS

Number
Barriers

1       $U_{20}^+/2C_1 = 1$

2       $U_{40}^+/2C_1(C_1C_2) = 1 - (T_1^2 + MT_1T_2)$

3       $U_{60}^+/2C_1(C_1C_2)^2 = 1 - (3T_1^2 + 3MT_1T_2 + T_2^2)$

$$+ MT_1^3T_2 + (M^2-1)T_1^2T_2^2$$

4       $U_{80}^+/2C_1(C_1C_2)^3 = 1-3[2T_1^2 + 2MT_1T_2 + T_2^2]$

$$+ T_1^4 + 6MT_1^3T_2 + (5M^2-6)T_1^2T_2^2 + 2MT_1T_2^3$$

$$- [(M^2-1)T_1^4T_2^2 + (M^3-2M+1)T_1^3T_2^3]$$

$$M = \frac{\beta_1}{\beta_2} + \frac{\beta_2}{\beta_1} \qquad T_i = \tan \beta_i d_i \text{ or } \tanh \beta_i d_i$$

Summary

Using a time independent method the analytic formula for the transmission of an electron through an arbitrary number of step potential changes has been derived. An algorithm has been given for writing down the formula for any number of potential steps. In addition the virtual levels have been identified with the allowed band centers in a corresponding case of n-1 potential step changes per unit cell of a periodic array. Finally, the nature of the solutions for the cases of identical barriers is developed.

The existence of a generalized analytic solution, now available for the first time is important not only in terms of investigating the details of electron tunnelling in one and two dimensional molecular switches but also in terms of electron conduction in polymers. Thus, while eq. 18 is applicable to crystalline or periodic polymers, eq. 14 will be useful for understanding and modeling non-crystalline or non-periodic materials as might occur in multiple co-polymers in the presence or absence of a small electric field.

References

1. F. L. Carter in the NRL Program on Electroactive Polymers; a. First Annual Rept., Ed. Luther B. Lockhart, Jr., NRL Memo. Report 3960, p. 121; b. Second Annual Rept., Ed. Robert B. Fox, NRL Memo Rept. 4335, p. 35.

2. E. A. Pschenichnov, Soviet Physics - Solid State, 4, 819 (1962).

3. P. M. Kuznesof, K. J. Wynne, R. S. Nohr and M. E. Kenney, J.C.S. Chem. Comm. 121 (1980); R. S. Nohr, P. M. Kuznesof, K. J. Wynne, and M. E. Kenney, J. Am. Chem. Soc., 103, 4371 (1981).

4. F. L. Carter, "Solid State Chemistry," Eds. R. S. Roth and S. J. Schneider, Jr., National Bureau of Standards Special Publication No. 364 (1972), p. 515.

5. L. I. Schiff, "Quantum Mechanics," McGraw-Hill Book Co., New York, 1949, p. 92-96.

DISCUSSION

Prof. Code: Xerox, Univ. of Tor. - I just want to make the comment that the matrix method you have used with some exceptions, is very similar to that used for the design of optical interference filters. Many of these problems can be guided by intuition gained in the optical area.

Dr. Carter: Yes, you are right. It also corresponds quite well to the case where you are dealing with arrays of different superconductors, and some of these quantities then become related to the macroscopic phases.

Dr. F. A. Buot: Cornell - My question is have you compared your energy band expression to the usual tight binding energy band expression, with nearest-neighbor interaction? It seems to me that what you have is a periodic array of identical potential wells through which the electron tunnels. An isolated potential well has discrete energy levels; in a periodic array they interact via nearest-neighbor interaction and therefore create energy bands. It looks to me that the energy band expression you have obtained for perfect transmission can be fitted to the usual tight binding energy band expression. My question is have you got a feeling for the nearest-neighbor interaction?

Dr. Carter: (Question not understood at time – the following is an edited answer.) I have not drawn a correspondence between the tight binding energy expression and the one for square well potentials. The tight binding energy expression is a sum of cos $(r_{ij} \cdot \vec{k})$ terms (where r_{ij} is the distance between atoms i and j) and the relationship to the U_{no}^{+} terms is not obvious. However, it is an interesting question since the $\beta_i d_i$ terms can be related to electronegativity terms. In addition I note that there is a fundamental relationship between what happens to the electron density during strong bond formation and the distortion of the unreduced Fermi surface away from sphericity (F. L. Carter in Electronic Density of States, Ed. by L. H. Bennett, Spec. NBS Public. #323, 1971 p. 385).

Dr. Buot: Since there is interaction between potential wells, then one can also start the calculation using a simple tight binding Hamiltonian to obtain the energy bands for perfect electron transmission. To do this kind of calculation however presupposes that one knows enough about the tunnelling interaction between potential wells.

Dr. Carter: The results obtained for $U_{no}^{\pm}$, etc. were derived by matching Ψ and Ψ' at the potential discontinuities so that a term corresponding to an interaction between potential wells is not obvious.

Dr. Buot: The electron wavefunctions overlap between neighboring potential wells and the tunnelling interaction is roughly like $\hbar$, Planck's constant, times frequency of collision against the potential wall, times the probability of tunnelling. I think your calculation is very enlightening; I was hoping it will yield an exact analytical expression for the tunnelling interaction as a function of energy.

Dr. Carter: You are raising some questions worthy of further consideration. We do hope to do some finite-difference time-dependent transmission studies. It would be very nice, for example, to distort some of these potential wells over a long range in a periodic way so as to simulate a phonon and then see how transmission probabilities are affected or how it broadens them or how it cuts them off. Maybe the analogue devices I have proposed will not work as postulated because the phonons will wipe out the pseudo-levels, and hence the coincidence of the energy with the pseudo-levels.

Dr. Buot: I believe this kind of calculation can yield analytical expression for the tunnelling interaction which can perhaps be extended to include phonons.

Dr. Carter: Yes, I hope you are correct.

Dr. Pomerantz: IBM – If you put a potential on the barriers, and you get current flowing even through steady stationary state levels freely, I don't understand why you won't get energy loss. It seems to me if you have a voltage present to tip the barriers and you have a current flowing, that you will have power loss, just the usual V x I.

Dr. Carter: Perhaps the answer is what happens to the electron after it gets through the barrier. The loss probably occurs as the electron slows down or is scattered after tunnelling. I don't think loss generally occurs during tunnelling especially in cases of perfect transmission. While the electron may be gaining energy in the process, and I don't see why Ohm's law should apply at every individual step (meaning barrier, well, or molecular entity).

Prof. Code: Xerox, Univ. of Tor. - I would like to make a comment about losses in tunnelling systems. In the optical case, the reflection from a dielectric mirror is not a loss because it doesn't make the mirror hot. It is only for very high incident laser powers that the mirror breaks down via mechanisms such as stimulated phonon generation, and that energy is thereby dissipated into the mirror. I think that you have to distinguish between loss by reflection (which is recoverable) and irreversible loss associated with dissipation.

Dr. Tsai: Std. Oil - Since you have a regular kind of coherence scattering, you might expect transmission as in band-type situations in the allowed energy ranges.

Dr. Carter: Yes, I think that is a valid viewpoint. Finally I want to thank the attendees for their active participation and while we have encouraged speculation, the basic idea is to start people thinking about switching at the molecular level. I think Hanson's paper among others is a movement in the right direction. As a group, we are now thinking about such devices, and to that extent, at least, the Workshop has fulfilled its purpose. Thank you.

CHAPTER X

SPECIAL ADDED COMMENTARY:

VISUAL PIGMENTS: A NEW TYPE OF MOLECULAR SWITCHING DEVICE

Barry Honig
Department of Physiology and Biophysics
University of Illinois
Champaign, IL 61820

The talks this morning reminded me that there is another type of switching device that has been suggested by recent work on visual pigments, and because it is novel and may have some of the features that may interest you, I thought I would introduce it briefly.

I first want to introduce visual pigments. They exist in the photo-receptor cells in our retinas. They absorb photons and lead to vision by exciting these cells, changing the potential across the plasma membrane.

A related pigment system which is of some interest and has recently been discovered is bacteriorhodopsin. This protein absorbs a photon and uses its energy to pump protons across the membrane, moving them about 40 Angstroms. The proton gradient so generated is used to drive the metabolic processes of the cell. This system is of particular interest because its structure will be known in some detail within two or three years, and we will have for the first time an example of how a proton can move through a biological membrane. It should be of great interest.

Visual pigments all consist of a retinal chromophore. When the retinal binds to different proteins, it can generate blue, green, red pigments and so on. Each protein is different. The chromophore is always 11 cis retinal. Bacteriorhodopsin has an all-trans chromophore, and it forms a pigment absorbing at 570 nanometers.

The generation of color by these pigments is now understood. The chromophore binds to the protein in the form of a protonated Schiff base to the ε-amino group of a lysine. Charged amino acids in the vicinity of the chromophore give rise to different spectra. For bovine rhodopsin, there is a charged group located near carbon 12; for bacteriorhodopsin there is a charge group located near the β-ionone ring. Red, green, and blue pigments have the same chromophore which interacts with charges located in different positions. These charges originate on the protein itself.

The photochemical behavior of these pigments is of interest for this symposium. The visual pigment absorbs a photon, forms its primary photoproduct, bathorhodopsin in a few picoseconds, and this photochemical event in some unknown way leads to vision. The primary photochemical event, rhodopsin to bathorhodopsin is well characterized for the simple reason that the photo-products are stable at 77 degrees kelvin. The photochemistry is completely reversible. You can go back and forth between the two states. The photo-product is always shifted relative to the pigment, so the states can be discriminated by spectral differences.

This is one of the reasons it seems to form the basis of thinking about molecular switching devices. A fair amount of work has gone into characterizing the energetics of the primary photochemistry, and it is really quite remarkable. Rhodopsin absorbs a 55 Kcal/mole photon and bathorhodopsin is generated. This species is known to be 35 kcal/mole higher in energy than rhodopsin itself, so there is a fairly efficient energy storage mechanism involved. The nature of the primary event has been debated in recent years although it turns out to correspond to the original suggestion of Wald and co-workers at Harvard. The primary event is a cis-trans isomerization of the chromophore. In the absence of a protein, cis to trans isomerization does not lead to energy storage. How then does the pigment generate a high energy photoproduct.

There is a fairly well-accepted model for this process and it forms the basis of, I think, a new mechanism for charge separation and perhaps a switching device. The basic idea is very simple. We know that the chromophore is charged in the protein, and it forms a salt bridge with a negatively charged amino acid in the protein. Light isomerizes the chromophore from cis to trans. This leads to a charge separation in a low dielectric medium thus generating a high energy species.

The conclusions then for the purposes of this workshop are: 1) visual pigments employ a novel type of charge separation involving considerable energy storage. 2) The back reaction is prevented by the intrinsic barrier to isomerization about double bonds. Thus you have two states that can be distinguished by their spectral differences and by potential differences. People have now taken bacteriorhodopsin, made thin films, reconstituted the protein into membranes and measured light-induced potential changes presumably generated by this stable (at 77°K) charge separation.

This type of mechanism may provide a basis for thinking about molecular switching devices.

REFERENCES

1. B. Honig, U. Dinur, K. Nakanishi, V. Balogh-Nair, M.A. Gawinowicz, M. Arnaboldi, and M. Motto, "An External Point Charge Model for Wavelength Regulation in Visual Pigments", J. Am. Chem. Soc. 101:7084 (1979).

2. B. Honig, U. Dinur, M. Ottolenghi, T.G. Ebrey, and R. Callender, "Photoisomerization and Salt-Bridge Cleavage: A Model for the Early Events in Visual Pigments and Bacteriorhodopsin", Proc. Nat. Acad. Sci. USA 76:7503 (1979).

DISCUSSION

Dr. Dahlberg: Bell — We have also been looking at small molecules such as triphenylformazan which are photochromic. These molecules are also organic semiconductors, and we can follow this photochromic switching electronically.

Prof. Honig: U. of Ill. — Are you moving the charge as well?

Dr. Dahlberg: Our measurements consist of monitoring the photovoltage, so we are looking at the separation of the photoinjected charge in the surface space charge regions of these samples.

Dr. McAlear: EMV — I have a question with regard to Dr. Ulmer's protein recognition. It seems to me the essential point here, if you will agree that if there are ten groups working on this problem, that either they are very naive, or they are going to resolve the problem or not be funded within ten years.

Prof. Honig: No. I wouldn't want to be misunderstood. I am one of those ten groups. I think it is a great thing to be working on, but I don't want anybody to think that it is solved.

Dr. McAlear: The essential thing is that you anticipate it will be solved?

Prof. Honig: I anticipate it will be solved.

Dr. McAlear: Within the next five to ten years?

Prof. Honig: I anticipate the problem involving five amino acids fixed on a framework of antibodies will be solved in the next five years. In my mind, there is too much conformational flexibility in the chain of 30 amino acids to solve that problem in the foreseeable future, especially since the conformation is so solvent dependent. You can take a polypeptide which has one conformation in water, put it into a membrane, and it changes its conformation. The conformation is pH dependent. It is ionic strength dependent. To think you can predict the structure of a chain of 30 amino acids in the foreseeable future is very optimistic. On the other hand, predicting a loop as Dr. Ulmer was talking about, fixed at both ends and interacting with the rest of the protein as in the case of an antibody, is a definitely soluble problem, and I believe that modifying combining sites, modifying active sites of enzymes, is something people should be working on. At least I am trying to, but I want to make a distinction between an unended chain and a fixed problem on a structure that you already know 90 percent of the structure, and you are trying to get the rest of the 10 percent. That is going to be solved.

SECTION THREE
Materials and Microfabrication

CHAPTER XI

A GENERALIZED APPROACH TO ORGANIC PI-DONOR-ACCEPTOR SYSTEMS

Daniel J. Sandman
GTE Laboratories, Inc.
Waltham, MA 02254

INTRODUCTION

In anticipating the continued expansion of activity in electronic applications of organic and related polymeric materials based on donor-acceptor
interactions, it is instructive at this stage to reflect on the scientific
and technological highlights of the recent past. The pi-complex of poly-(N-
vinylcarbazole) (1a) and 2,4,7-trinitrofluorenone (2a), i.e., PVK-TNF, has
been commercially used in photoelectronic devices (2). Battery applications
include the use of a variety of neutral closed-shell donors complexed with
iodine as cathodes (3), and, recently, the use of oxidized and reduced
polyacetylene, $(CH)_x$, in lightweight rechargeable devices (4). Switching
and memory phenomena have been reported in thin films of the copper salt of
TCNQ (3a) grown on a copper substrate (5). The prototype quasi-one-
dimensional organic metal is the ion-radical solid formed from tetrathiafulvalene (4, TTF) and TCNQ (6,7), and the anticipated (6,8) collective transport in organic ion-radical solids has been realized with the observation
of superconductivity under high pressure in the PF_6 (9) and AsF_6 (10) salts
of tetramethyltetraselenofulvalene (TMTSF, 5) and at atmospheric pressure
in the ClO_4 salt of 5.

While the above discussion points to the truly remarkable strides made
in the last decade in supramolecular devices and phenomena, it is also
apparent that the interactions involved in the formation of the materials
cited in the preceding paragraph comprise a relatively small number of types
of donor-acceptor interactions. The perspective of this discussion regards
the above examples as a small clump of trees which could become a giant
sylvan landscape if the seeds still in the ground are properly cultivated.
This article begins by discussing organic pi-donors and acceptors as multistage redox systems and then proceeds to classify donors and acceptors according to charge and the occupancy of the highest occupied molecular orbital
(HOMO), emphasizing their molecular energy levels. Ground-state complexes
are then classified according to the originating donor and acceptor species
with heavy emphasis on examples reported as crystalline solids. The role of
molecular energy levels and specific experimental conditions as they relate
to pi-complex vs. electron-transferred system formation for donor-acceptor
systems formed from neutral closed-shell molecules (Class 1, vide infra) is
discussed. From a chemical point of view, the approach developed herein

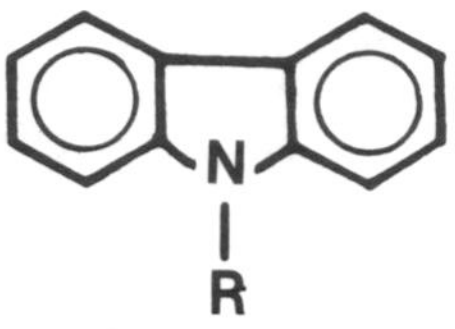

1a   R = CH$_2$ – CH repeat unit

b   R = C$_2$H$_5$

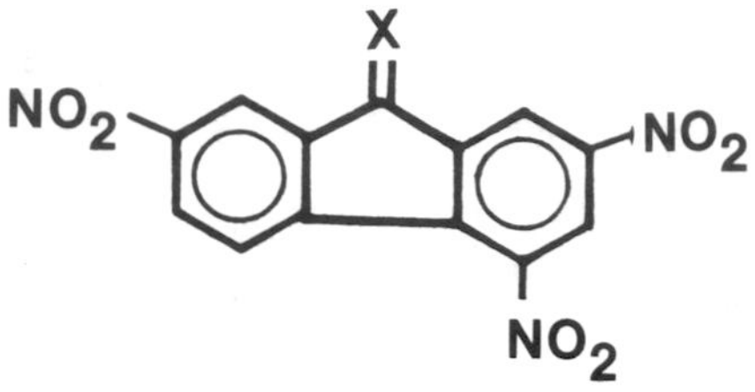

2a, x = 0

b, x = C(CN)$_2$

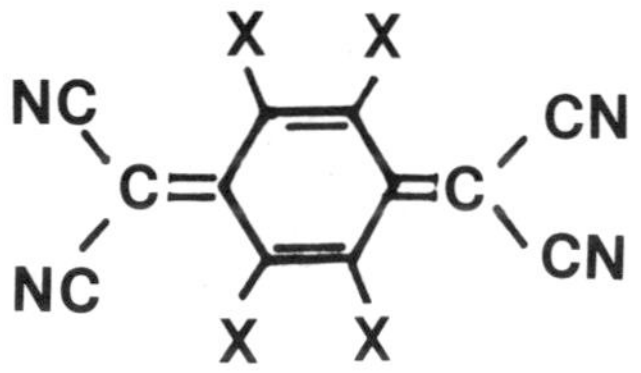

3a,   x = H

b, x = F

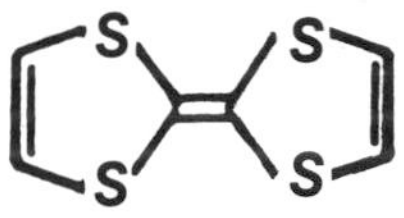

4

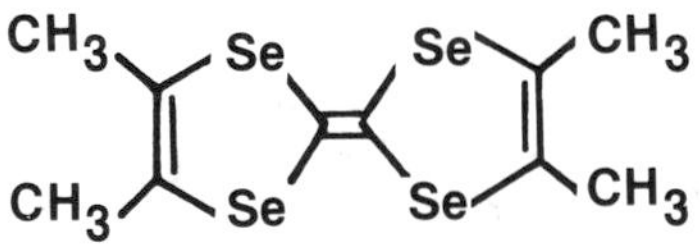

5

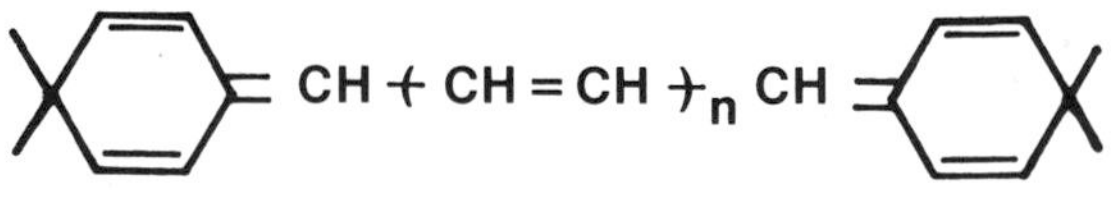

8   n = 1 – 3

anticipates the preparation of new classes of materials ultimately requiring new covalent and noncovalent interactions. From the physical phenomena and applications viewpoints, while the properties of presently unknown materials are also unknown, the results of the preceding decade have shown that judicious investigations of new materials have indeed been very fruitful. While most of the examples discussed herein are organic or organometallic molecular species, the ideas are general, and, in many cases, the extension to polymeric systems is conceptually straightforward.

MULTISTAGE ORGANIC REDOX SYSTEMS

The idea of multistage organic redox systems as a general structural principle was discussed by Deuchert and Hünig (11), and multistage redox phenomena in metal dithiolenes were reviewed by McCleverty (12). In the present work, organic redox systems are regarded as arising from neutral polyradicals. An organic radical with n unpaired electrons gives rise to a multistage redox system of 2n + 1 distinct molecular species by gain and loss of n electrons.

Figure 1 shows a two-stage redox system based on the monoradical N-ethylphenazyl (6a), and includes the redox potentials for reduction to the anion and oxidation to the N-ethylphenazinium (NEP, 7a) cation. All redox potentials quoted herein were measured by cyclic voltammetry in acetonitrile solution relative to a saturated calomel electrode (s.c.e.) using 0.1M tetraethylammonium perchlorate (TEAP) as support electrolyte. Using 6a as an example, Figure 1 also reveals the general principle that any molecular species may be a donor or an acceptor, i.e., pi-amphoteric, depending on the specific experimental conditions under which an interaction takes place.

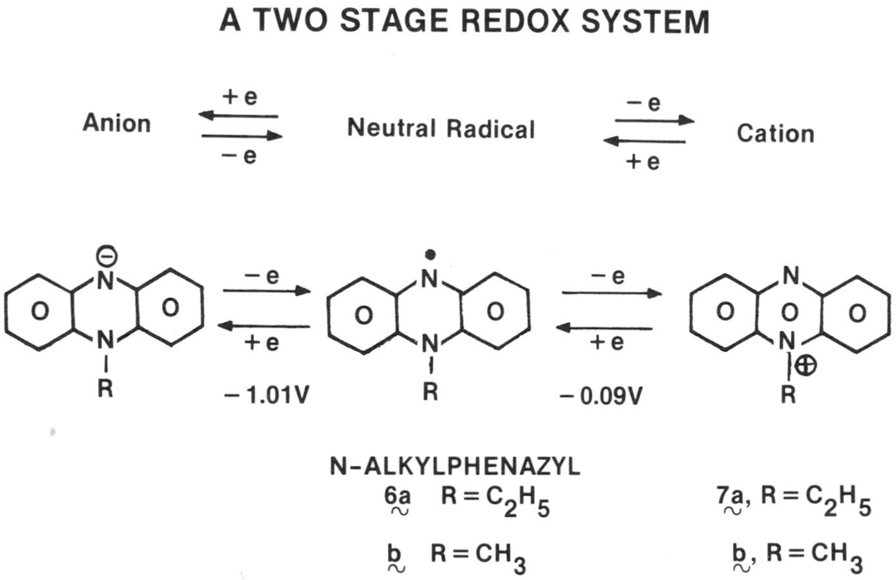

A TWO STAGE REDOX SYSTEM

Figure 1. The N-alkylphenazyl radical as an example of a two stage redox system. The redox potentials are given for 6a.

Figure 2 shows a four stage redox system based on a biradical; the neutral closed-shell molecule is viewed as a special case of the biradical in which the electrons pair in a covalent bond. Figure 2 also reveals that at room temperature, TTF does not undergo all of the steps possible for the four stage system. The four steps of this redox system have been demonstrated for the polyenes 8 in solution by Hünig and collaborators (11).

The six stage redox system is shown in Figure 3. While the triarylmethyl-type triradical in Figure 3 has been found to have a quartet ground state in solution esr studies (13), all of the steps in this redox system do not appear to have been demonstrated to date. Further, in contrast to numerous examples of the molecular species of the redox systems of Figures 1 and 2, relatively few examples of the molecular species in Figure 3 have been characterized to date. Proceeding to contemplate presently unknown polyradicals, the existence of much virgin territory is readily apparent.

A FOUR STAGE REDOX SYSTEM

Dianion $\underset{-e}{\overset{+e}{\rightleftarrows}}$ Anion-radical $\underset{-e}{\overset{+e}{\rightleftarrows}}$ Neutral Molecule or Biradical $\underset{+e}{\overset{-e}{\rightleftarrows}}$ Cation-radical $\underset{+e}{\overset{-e}{\rightleftarrows}}$ Dication

$(TTF)^{\cdot -}$ $\underset{-e}{\overset{+e}{\rightleftarrows}}$ TTF° $\underset{+e}{\overset{-e}{\rightleftarrows}}$ $TTF^{\cdot +}$ $\underset{+e}{\overset{-e}{\rightleftarrows}}$ TTF^{+2}

−1.05V irreversible; 4; +0.33V; +0.68V

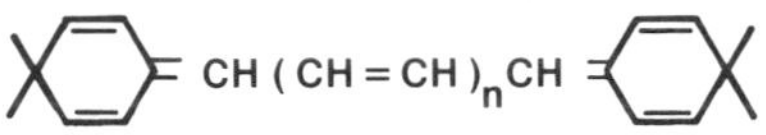

8 n = 1 − 3

Figure 2. Molecular species of the four stage redox system.

A SIX STAGE REDOX SYSTEM

Trianion $\underset{-e}{\overset{+e}{\rightleftarrows}}$ Dianion-radical $\underset{-e}{\overset{+e}{\rightleftarrows}}$ Diradical-anion $\underset{-e}{\overset{+e}{\rightleftarrows}}$ Triradical $\underset{+e}{\overset{-e}{\rightleftarrows}}$ Diradical cation $\underset{+e}{\overset{-e}{\rightleftarrows}}$ Dication-radical $\underset{+e}{\overset{-e}{\rightleftarrows}}$ Trication

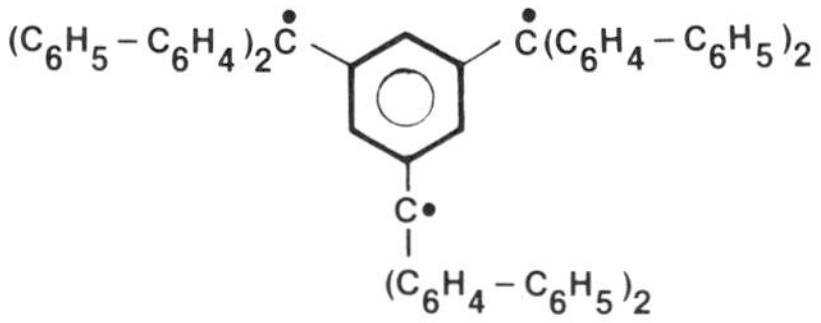

Generalizing, An Organic Radical With n Unpaired Electrons Gives Rise to a 2n Stage Redox System of 2n + 1 Distinct Molecular Species by Gain and Loss of n Electrons.

Figure 3. Molecular species of the six stage redox system and a prototype conjugated triradical.

DONORS AND ACCEPTORS CLASSIFIED ACCORDING TO CHARGE
AND ORBITAL OCCUPANCY; A DONOR-ACCEPTOR MATRIX AND ITS UTILITY (1)

The pi-donor-acceptor classification adopted herein is related to one
used earlier by Mulliken and Person (14) for more general situations. It
begins by using only those molecular species from two and four stage redox
systems and recognizes their pi-amphoteric character. Molecular systems are
designated donors or acceptors according to their most common behavior under
"typical" experimental conditions, e.g., in solution between 273° and 373°K.
Figure 4 lists five classes of representative donors, with abbreviations,
and their energy levels (I_G is the gas phase vertical ionization energy from
ultraviolet photoelectron spectroscopy; I_C is the vertical solid state
ionization energy; E_1 is the first oxidation potential measured by cyclic
voltammetry), and Figure 5 lists five classes of representative acceptors,
and abbreviations, and their energy levels (A_A is the gas phase electron
affinity; E_1 is the first solution reduction potential). A more comprehensive listing and treatment of this approach is in preparation (15).

While the majority of the examples given in Figures 4 and 5 are well-
characterized species, several present interesting physico-chemical situations
worthy of comment. Two electron reduction of 18 and related CSDCs (16), if
achieved, would lead to a biradical. In a similar vein, two electron loss
from CSDA 13 could lead to either a biradical or a three-membered ring.
If a biradical, especially in the triplet state, can be stabilized in solid,
novel magnetic interactions may occur. Thermal isomerization of cis-
polyacetylene (c-(CH)$_x$) to the trans isomer gives rise to the OSNR soliton
species whose redox properties have been probed. The magnetic susceptibility
of t-(CH)$_x$ in the dilute "doping" concentration range with AsF_5 is as
expected for the oxidation of the OSNR species (17). The photoconductivity
of t-(CH)$_x$ observed (18) near 1 eV is also a manifestation of the OSNR
species. In the context of this article, possible complexation of the OSNR
soliton to an adjacent closed-shell neutral polymer chain is uncertain at
present.

REPRESENTATIVE DONORS AND ENERGY LEVELS

- **Neutral Closed-Shell Molecules (NCSD):**

  Tetrathiafulvalene (4, I_G = 6.81 eV, E_1 = + 0.33V) N,N,N´,N´-Tetramethyl-p-Phenylenediamine

  (9, I_G = 6.84 eV, E_1 = + 0.13V); Phthalocyanine (10, I_G = 6.41 eV); N-Ethylcarbazole (16, I_G = 7.29 eV)

- **Closed-Shell Monoanions (CSMA)** p-Tricyanovinylphenyldicyanomethide (11, E_1 = + 0.80V);

  1,1,3,3-Tetracyanopropenide (12)

- **Closed-Shell Dianions (CSDA):**

  $TCNQ^{-2}$ (E_1 = − 0.29V); 2-Dicyanomethylene-1,1,3,3-Tetracyanopropanediide (13)

- **Open-Shell Anion-Radical (OSAR):** $TCNQ^-$ ($I_C \sim$5.0 − 6.0 eV); (p-Chloranil)$^-$ (14)

- **Open-Shell Neutral Radical (OSNR):** Cobaltocene (15, I_G = 5.55 eV); N-Ethylphenazyl (6);

  Soliton in t-(CH)$_x$

Figure 4. Molecular species which function as pi-donors and their energy
levels.

REPRESENTATIVE ACCEPTORS AND ENERGY LEVELS

• **Neutral Closed–Shell Molecules (NCSA):**

  TCNQ (3a, $A_A = 2.8$ eV; $E_1 = +0.17$V) p – Chloranil (14, $A_A = 2.7$ eV; $E_1 = +0.02$V)

  2,4,7-Trinitrofluorenone (2a, $A_A = 2.2$ eV, $E_1 = -0.42$V)

• **Closed–Shell Monocations (CSMC):**

  N–Methylphenazinium (7b, $E_1 = -0.08$V); 2,4,6-Triphenylthiapyrylium (16a, $E_1 = -0.23$V)

• **Closed–Shell Dications (CSDC):**

  TTF^{+2} ($E_1 = +0.68$V); Paraquat (17, $E_1 = -0.26$V); Ditropylium Ether (18)

• **Open–Shell Cation–Radicals (OSCR):** TTF^+; $TMPD^+$ (9)

• **Open–Shell Neutral–Radical (OSNR): Diphenylpicryl Hydrazyl (19)**

Figure 5. Molecular species which function as pi-acceptors and their energy levels.

$(CH_3)_2N$ — O — $N(CH_3)_2$

9

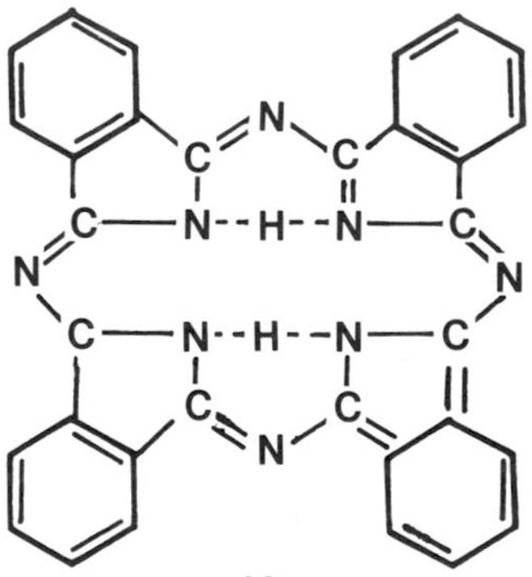

10

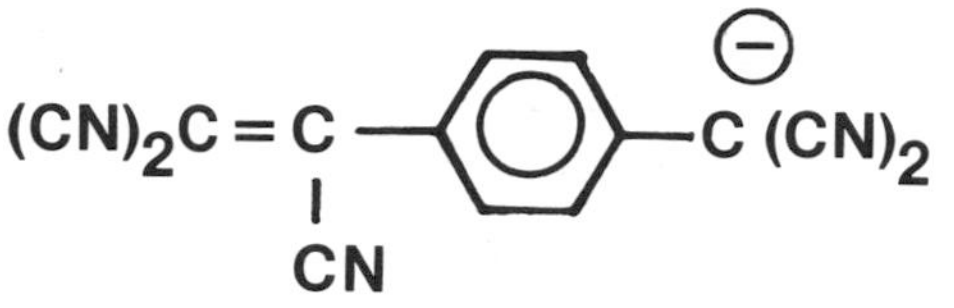

11

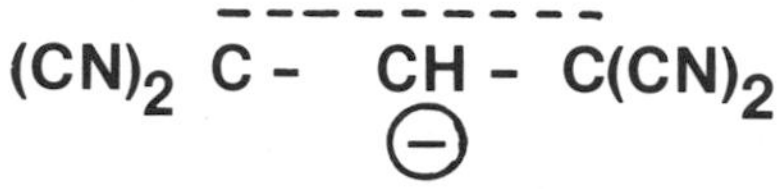

12

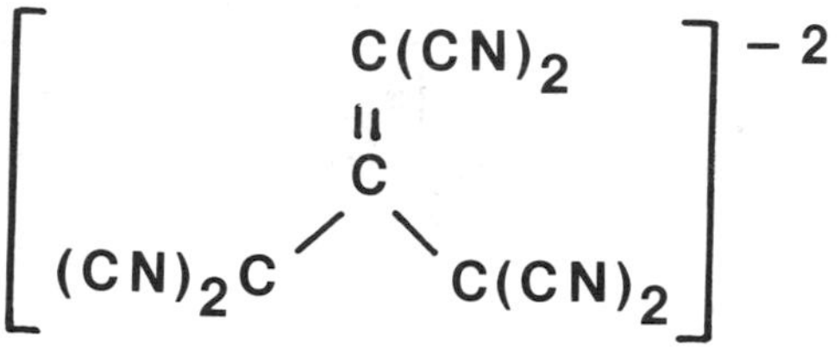

13

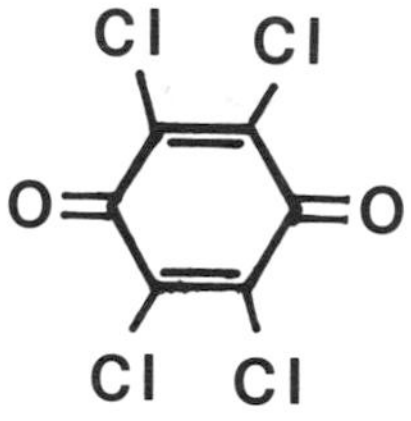

14

15

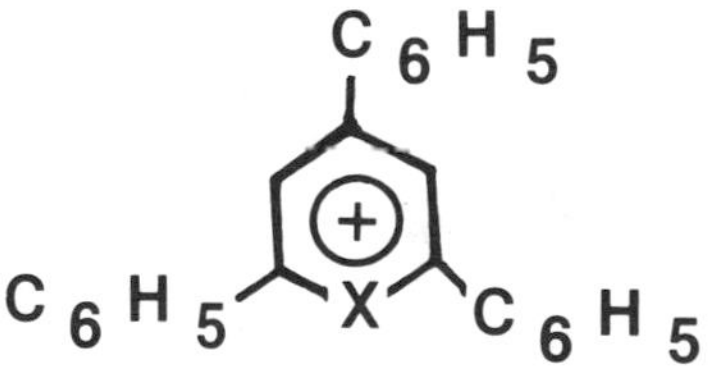

16a, X = S

b, X = O

Using the abbreviations of Figures 4 and 5, Figure 6 shows a donor-acceptor matrix in which classes of donors are placed on a horizontal axis, and classes of acceptors placed on the vertical axis. Since Figures 4 and 5 use only molecules from two and four stage redox systems, the matrix in

17

18

19

20

Figure 6 is a simplified version of a matrix which is effectively infinite
in both horizontal and vertical directions. The numbers in the blocks of the
matrix designate classes of pi-donor-acceptor systems which may involve
either weak complexes or electron-transferred systems depending on the
energy levels involved. A given donor-acceptor system may be placed in a
given class in the matrix depending on the molecular species which interact
to initiate its formation or on the nature of the molecular species in the
final isolated solid complex. In the present discussion, the former
situation, i.e., the kinetic perspective, will be emphasized. This approach
allows a given material to be in more than one class of the matrix depending
on the method of preparation, a potential chemical advantage. The organic
metal TTF-TCNQ is preferably prepared as a Class 1 material, but may also be
prepared (19) from the fluoroborate of TTF^{+} and the 1:2 TCNQ salt of the
triethylammonium cation as a Class 19 solid. TCNQ and dibenztetrathiaful-
valene (DBTTF, 20, I_G = 6.81 eV, E_1 = +0.53 V) interact in acetonitrile
solution or by cosublimation (20) to give the weak Class 1 complex, while
the same complex is formed by electron transfer to $DBTTF^{+}$ from $Li^{+}TCNQ^{-}$.
(Class 19) (21). Examples of the various classes of complexes and ion-
radical solids suggested by the matrix in Figure 6 are presented now with
heavy emphasis on materials for which a crystal structure determination has
been reported.

Class 1. The interaction of neutral planar closed-shell donors and
acceptors may lead to the formation of new covalent bonds, possibly via a
pi-complex intermediate, weak pi-complexes, and ion-radical salts (22). A
detailed review article (23) has described the extensive crystallography of
the weak complexes and the early examples of ion-radical salts with mixed
stack structures, analogous to the complexes, formed from TMPD (9) and
p-chloranil (14) and TCNQ. The segregated stack salt TTF-TCNQ will be
discussed below, and the next section of this article will deal in detail
with Class I systems, especially with the role of molecular energy levels
in determining the details of the donor-acceptor interaction.

DONOR-ACCEPTOR MATRIX

DONORS ⟶

ACCEPTORS ↓	NCSD	CSMA	CSDA	OSAR	OSNR
NCSA	①	②	③	④	⑤
CSMC	⑥	⑦	⑧	⑨	⑩
CSDC	⑪	⑫	⑬	⑭	⑮
OSCR	⑯	⑰	⑱	⑲	⑳
OSNR	㉑	㉒	㉓	㉔	㉕

Figure 6. A donor–acceptor matrix using molecular species from two and four stage redox systems. The abbreviations are given in Figures 4 and 5.

$(CH_3)_2N$—⟨⟩—R

21a, R = $-\overset{\displaystyle |}{\underset{\displaystyle CN}{C}}=C(CN)_2$

b, R = H

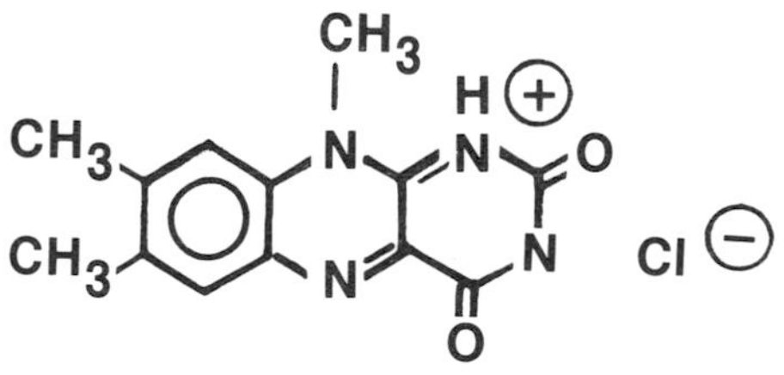

22

Class 2. The only structure reported to date in this class is the complex of the CSMA 11 and TNF (24). The complex is a photosensitive insulator, and several short crystallographic distances were reported in the mixed stack structure.

In the course of that work, it was noted that the electrochemical characteristics of 11 were analogous to those of the neutral molecule p-tricyanovinyldimethylaniline (TCVDMA, 21a). It was subsequently found that TCVDMA behaved as a donor in its 1:1 complex with TNF and as an acceptor with N,N-dimethylaniline (21b) in a 1:4 complex (25), an unusual stoichiometry in weak complexes (23). TCVDMA is the first pi-amphoteric molecule to give crystallographically defined complexes.

Class 4. The earliest structurally established example of this class is $Cs_2(TCNQ^{\bar{\cdot}})_2(TCNQ^\circ)$ (26); the structure contains both neutral TCNQ and its anion-radical. Another reported structure in this class involves $TCNQ^{\bar{\cdot}}$ (with cyanine-dye cation) and 9-dicyanomethylene-2,4,7-trinitrofluorene (2b) in an alternating chain (27). Since this structure was refined to only R = 0.114, the details of the donor-acceptor interaction are uncertain.

Class 5. No crystal structures in this class have been reported as yet. Cobaltocene (15) interacts with tetracyanoethylene (TCNE) to give an electrically insulating solid reported (28) to be a charge-transfer salt.

Class 6. There are numerous examples of this class of complex, including several mixed stack crystal structures of CSMC flavins. The 1:1 complex between lumiflavinium chloride (22) and hydroquinone (23) is an example of this type (29). Early (30) examples of solid complexes in this class are the electrically insulating complexes of the CSMC 7b with aromatic hydro-carbons or 23.

Class 7. The first structurally established member of this class is the photosensitive mixed stack complex of 16b with 12 (31). The complex of 16a with 11 (24) is photosensitive between 4000 and 9500Å with an estimated quantum yield of 0.02. The charge-transfer biradical as a ground-state species is an as yet unreported member of this class.

Class 8. The only reported (32) structure in this class involves the donor 13 and the CSMC quinolinium (24) in a 2:1 stoichiometry.

Class 9. The structure of the mixed chain complex formed from the tropylium ion (25) and the OSAR of the nickel dithiete 26a has been reported (33); the complex is a Curie-Weiss paramagnet between 77 and 300°K. The complex formed between 25 and 26a sharply contrasts with the interaction of 25 and $TCNQ^{\bar{\cdot}}$ where covalent bond formation is observed (34). This difference in behavior is likely due to the better donor behavior of $TCNQ^{\bar{\cdot}}$, manifested in redox potentials (33, 34).

The interaction of 7a and 7b with $TCNQ^{\bar{\cdot}}$ leads to two component crystal-line solids whose structures do not indicate donor-acceptor interaction, even

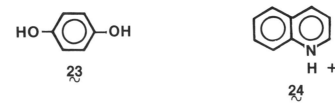

23   24

though redox potentials (22, 34) indicate that some electron transfer should
be possible. The role of assorted impurities in the formation and properties
of the uniform segregated stack structure from 7b, i.e., the conductor
NMP-TCNQ, will be discussed below. The structure (35) of the insulator from
7a, i.e., NEP-TCNQ, reveals two TCNQ anions interacting at a distance of
1.631Å, regarded as a labile sigma bond from esr (36a) and optical (36b)
studies. This crystal chemistry of TCNQ⁻ has also been observed in a
structure with a platinum cation (37), but placed in the more general context
of cyanocarbon chemistry, it is not unusual. TCNQ⁻ may be represented by the
valence bond structure 27, emphasizing radical character, and the dimerization of cyanocarbon radicals, e.g., 28, involves labile sigma bond species
(38). Long carbon-carbon single bonds are characteristics of certain
"dimerized" triarylmethyl systems (39).

Class 11. Many phenols form solid complexes with 17 (40); the crystal
structure (41) of the diiodide of 17 with 23 exhibits the usual alternate
stacking.

Class 13. Interaction of TTF^{+2} with the dianion of 26b involves electron
transfer to give a black semiconducting solid whose esr spectrum in acetone
solution reveals both ion-radicals (42).

Class 14. There have been extensive studies of the phases formed by interaction of TCNQ⁻ with cations such as 17, but there are no strong indications
of a donor-acceptor interaction. In the crystal structure (43) of the 1:3
TCNQ salt of 17, e.g., the CSDC is "included" between chains of triads of
TCNQ anionic species.

25

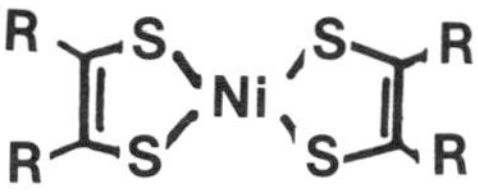

26a, R = CF$_3$

b, R = CN

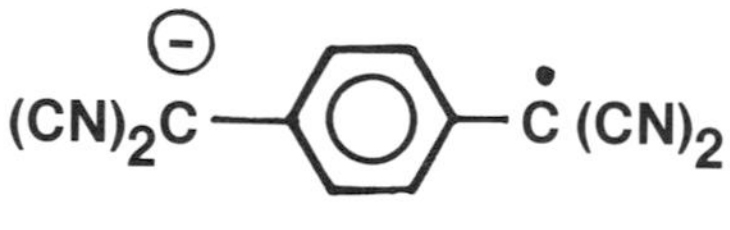

27

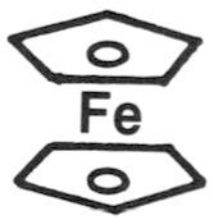

29

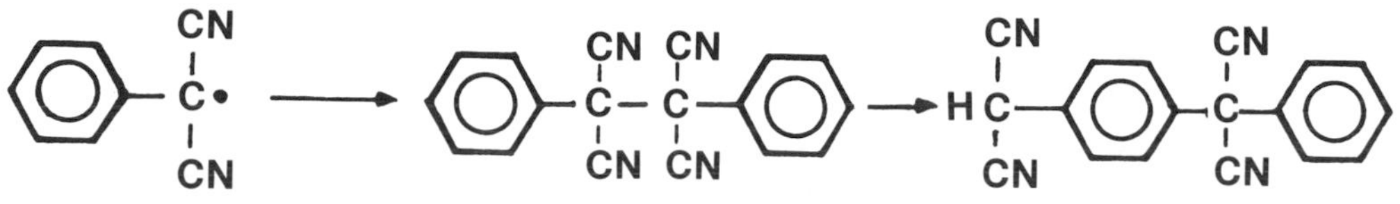

28

Class 18.   The OSCR of 9 interacts with the dianion of 26b to give a paramagnetic solid whose crystal structure consists of alternating flat sheets
of the CSDA and stacked sheets of dimerized chains of TMPD^{+} (44).   No
significant interaction between cation and anion was noted.

Class 19.   TTF-TCNQ and DBTTF-TCNQ were discussed above as examples of this
class.

From the preceding discussion and examples, it is apparent that one
application of the perspective of the matrix in Figure 6 would be the preparation of new classes of complexes which have not yet been characterized
as solids.   It is equally apparent from some of the examples above that
solid phases with two molecular components, known from other studies to
behave as donors or acceptors, may involve only non-selective van der Waals
and Coulombic interactions.   Just as the Periodic Table of the Elements
at its inception by Mendeleev was used to anticipate the existence of
elements unknown at that time, a matrix, such as Figure 6, can play the
same role.   As the Periodic Table with its relationships has been used in
the elaboration of chemical and physical phenomena, the matrix of Figure 6
and its generalization can be used in the same manner.   The fundamental
principles underlying the Periodic Table were not known at its inception;
new fundamental concepts may also underlie this work.

A complex whose formation may be initiated from ferrocene (29) and TCNE
and is described (45) as a complex of the cation-radical of 29 and the
pentacyanopropenide (30) ion poses an interesting classification problem
vis-a-vis the matrix.   Since the complex forms from solution on prolonged
standing from 29 and TCNE, it is a Class 1 material whose formation appears
to involve electron transfer and covalent bond formation.   However, this
complex also forms in a solid state reaction from the ferrocene·TCNE complex,
a situation which the matrix does not deal with from the point of view of
initiation.   From a final state view, the complex as reported would be
Class 17.

Another application of the donor-acceptor matrix is the use of the
variety of interactions suggested by the scheme, along with other nonbonded
interactions, to discuss the initiation (22) of phase formation of certain
1:1 stoichiometry ion-radical salts which exhibit uniform segregated stack
crystal structures.   For the case of Class 1 systems, this approach was
formulated to account for the formation of TTF-TCNQ, since all previously
reported 1:1 salts exhibited the alternating cation-radical-anion-radical
arrangement.   In this approach, phase formation may be intrinsic (prototype
TTF-TCNQ), involving only the donor and acceptor, their redox states, and
their mutual interactions, or extrinsic, involving chemical species other
than those implied by the name of the solid.

The above approach is a kinetic viewpoint which offers qualitative,
at present, answers to the question: "What are the pathways by which 1:1
uniform segregated stack structures form?"   This approach contrasts to the
traditional, very useful, approach which quantitatively assesses the
contributions of various cohesive forces to the binding energy of the solid.
The latter approach has recently been critically reviewed by Metzger (46).

The interactions proposed for the initiation (22) of formation of
TTF-TCNQ are complexes between TTF and its cation-radical (Class 16) and
between TCNQ and TCNQ$^{\cdot}$ (Class 4), possible dimerization of both ion-radicals,
and sulfur-cyano nitrogen attraction.   The chalcogen-cyano and chalcogen-
chalcogen contacts are general features of the uniform segregated stack
organic metals (47, 48) and reveal an explicit crystal chemical role for the

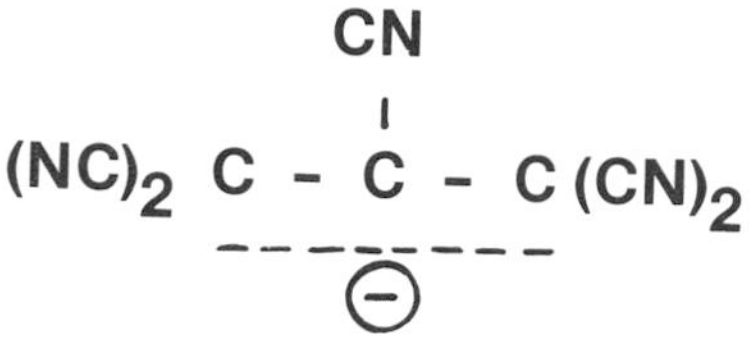

CN
|
(NC)$_2$ C – C – C (CN)$_2$
------ $\ominus$ ------
30

31

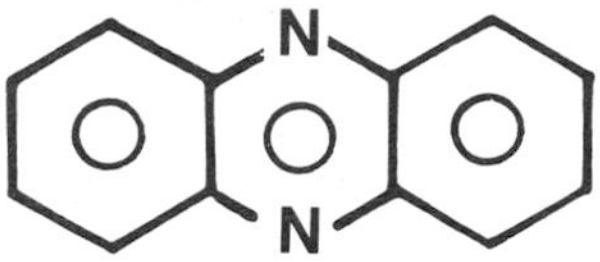

32

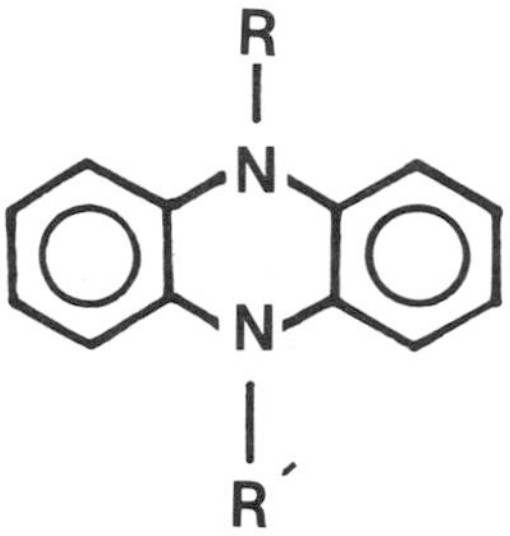

33a,   R = R′ = CH$_3$

b,   R = C$_2$H$_5$,   R′ = H

chalcogen. A short sulfur–cyano contact qualitatively different from that in TTF–TCNQ was observed (49) in the 2:3 semiconducting TCNQ salt of 4,4′-bithiopyranylidene (31).

It was long known that the 1:1 TCNQ salt of 7b (NMP–TCNQ) was unusual among the 1:1 salts of planar closed-shell nitrogen heterocyclic monocations in that it was a uniform segregated stack conductor rather than a non-stacked insulator. Since the chemical reactivity of 7b guarantees that it is always accompanied by a variety of phenazine (32) derivatives, some of which are paramagnetic, it was recognized (22, 50) that the crystal structure, low temperature magnetic susceptibility and specific heat are dominated by impurities, and an impurity model emphasizing donor–acceptor interactions between 7b and 32 (Class 6) was proposed (22, 50) for the formation of the phase.

Impurity-induced phase formation in a 1:1 stoichiometry was demonstrated by the conversion of the insulating TCNQ salt of 7a into a structure analogous to NMP–TCNQ (22, 50). The conductivity of the new phase was enhanced by 10^9 vs. NEP–TCNQ, and the relevant donor–acceptor interactions are 32·7a (Class 6) and TCNQ$\bar{\cdot}$·TCNQ (Class 4). The role of 32 in this experiment is selective in that it could not be replaced by 33a or 33b. The mixed-stack (51) structure from dimethyldihydrophenazine (33a) and TCNQ was also converted (52) into a structure resembling NMP–TCNQ by use of 32. The lattice constants for thse phases are listed in Table 1.

TABLE 1

LATTICE CONSTANTS OF IMPURITY-INDUCED PHASES AND RELATED SYSTEMS

	NEP-TCNQ	CONDUCTING NEP-TCNQ	NMP-TCNQ
a	7.7662 Å	3.817 Å	3.8682 Å
b	8.1151	7.920	7.7807
c	16.397	16.181	15.735
α	87.21°	93.65°	91.67°
β	93.61°	94.94°	92.67°
γ	95.76°	94.25°	95.38°
V	1040Å^3	484.8Å^3	470.7Å^3

	DMPH$^+$ TCNQ$^-$	CONDUCTING DMPH$^+$ TCNQ$^-$
a	11.166Å	3.843Å
b	13.583	7.730
c	6.799	16.028
α	90.00	91.93°
β	92.39°	93.56°
γ	90.00°	94.57°
V	1030.3Å^3	473Å^3

CLASS 1 DONOR-ACCEPTOR COMPLEXES, ION-RADICAL SALTS, AND MOLECULAR ENERGY LEVELS

The systematic use of a donor-acceptor matrix such as Figure 6 requires detailed knowledge of molecular energy levels such as I_G, A_A, and redox potentials, as well as some control of noncovalent interactions. Information of this type is most abundant for neutral closed-shell donors and acceptors, and one function of this section is to show the potential intricacy of the charge transfer problem in that class of materials which is best known. It follows that the intricacy found in Class 1 materials may be found in any other class. Charge transfer between neutral donors and acceptors can be understood in terms of a charge transfer interaction energy, ΔE_{CT}, eq. 1:

$$\Delta E_{CT} = (I_G - A_A) - (E_M + E_{ex} + E_{pol} + \ldots) \qquad (1)$$

In equation 1, charge transfer occurs when the cost of ionizing a donor-acceptor pair (I_G-A_A) is adequately compensated by Madelung forces (E_M), exchange forces (E_{ex}), polarization forces (E_{pol}), etc., (46). Since 4, 9, and 20 have the same value of I_G (ca. 6.8 eV) (20) and interact with TCNQ to give, respectively, a segragated stack metallic salt, a mixed-stack salt, and a neutral complex, it follows that the relationship of E_M, E_{ex}, and E_{pol} to molecular structure is not simple and that phase formation requires a kinetic perspective (22). Since the first oxidation potentials of 4, 9, and 20 are +0.33, +0.13, and +0.53 volts vs. S.C.E., it is apparent that I_G and E_1, both dealing with loss of one electron, do not correlate, a point emphasized by Nelsen (53) in his work in organonitrogen compounds. While one might be tempted to conclude that electron transfer in solution may be readily predicted from solution redox potentials based on the examples of 4, 9, and 20 with TCNQ, such is not the case. The bis-carbomethoxy ester of 2-(thiopyran-4-ylidene)-1,3-dithiole (I_G = 6.83 eV, E_1 = +0.47 V) interacts with TCNQ to give a weak complex (54), while TSeF (I_G = 6.90 eV, E_1 = +0.48 V), the Se analog of 4, interacts with TCNQ to give a segregated stack metallic salt (55).

The possibility of a thermal transition from a neutral complex to an ion-radical salt in a solid was discussed by Soos (56), and other workers (57, 58) have also advanced theoretical models for charge transfer as a function of temperature. On the basis of esr studies, it was suggested (59) that the mixed-stack solid from 33a and TCNQ undergoes a neutral-ionic transition near 390°K. However, infrared studies (60) indicated that this solid was ionic at room temperature. Recent spectral studies (61) of ten neutral complexes including TTF·14 and DBTTF·TCNQ at pressures between 5 and 30 kbar revealed the appearance of the molecular spectra of the ion-radicals indicating a reversible neutral-ionic transition.

DBTTF-TCNQ has been prepared in solution (21) and by cosublimation (20) in efforts to obtain it as an ion-radical solid. The esr spectrum (62) of polycrystalline samples of DBTTF-TCNQ at 1 atmosphere reveals two weak (spin concentrations of 2-3 ppm) signals at room temperature. One signal is broad (ca. 8 gauss) with a g-value of 2.00480, exactly one half of the sum of the g-values of DBTTF$^+_{.}$ and TCNQ$^+_{.}$, and the other is narrow (ca. 1 gauss) with a g-value of TCNQ$^-_{.}$, 2.00279. Temperature dependent esr spectra of DBTTF-TCNQ, shown in Figure 7, reveal that the broad signal disappears on heating (and does not reappear on cooling) above 150°C while the narrow line grows exponentially with T. The role of the metastable species associated with the broad signal in a neutral-ionic transition in DBTTF-TCNQ is uncertain at present. When 1% TCNQF$_4$ (3b) is doped into DBTTF-TCNQ (63), the crystal structure is unchanged, and the esr spectrum (Figure 8) observed for polycrystalline samples is that of a species with anisotropic g-values very similar to those of DBTTF$^+_{.}$ with a spin concentration of ca. 1%. For the present, we associate the narrow line in DBTTF-TCNQ with the mobile

34

35

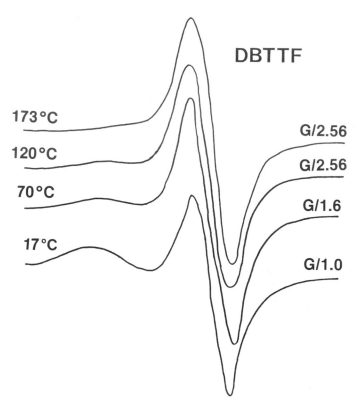

Figure 7. Temperature-dependent esr spectrum of polycrystalline DBTTF-TCNQ.
Spin concentrations, g-values, and linewidths are given in the text.

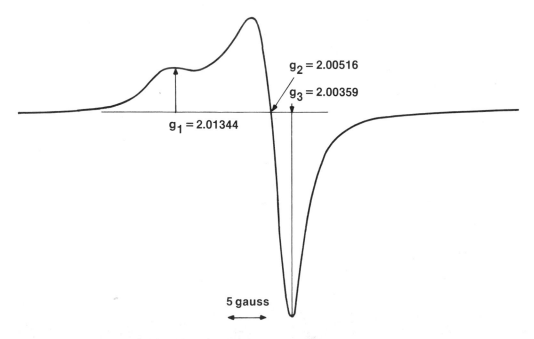

Figure 8. Esr spectrum of polycrystalline DBTTF-TCNQ doped with 1% TCNQF$_4$
at -165°C. Linewidths and g-values are indicated.

triple ion, shown on the left in Figure 9, in which two TCNQ$^-$ sandwich a diamagnetic DBTTF^{+2} in the normal crystal structure of the complex. In an analogous vein, based on its g-values, we associate the resonance in the TCNQF$_4$ doped sample with the mobile triple ion shown in Figure 9 at the right in which two DBTTF^{+} sandwich a diagmagnetic TCNQF$_4^{-2}$. Species such as DBTTF^{+2} in DBTTF-TCNQ and TCNQF$_4^{-2}$ in the doped solid, which involve loss or gain, respectively, of two electrons from the initiating molecular species, are quite rare in organic solids. Based on ESCA sulfur binding energies, it was suggested (64) that ca. two electrons were transferred in the formation of the solid from the tetramethyl derivative of TTF (34) and 2,3-dichloro-5,6-dicyano-p-benzoquinone (35). Gain or loss of two electrons is clearly energetically costly (56), and doubly charged molecular ions are often regarded as "fluctuations" (8) in carrier motion in tight-binding bands. A treatment (65) of the energetics of double charge-transfer has recently appeared.

ANTICIPATED DEVELOPMENTS

While it is easy to project that pursuit of new materials suggested by a matrix such as Figure 6 or its elaborations with molecular systems based on higher polyradicals will lead to interesting scientific and technological developments, it may be more fruitful in the short term to make projections based on the degree of order (66) in assorted organic molecular and polymeric

DOUBLY CHARGED SPECIES ASSOCIATED WITH TRIPLE IONS IN THE WEAK PI-COMPLEX DBTTF-TCNQ

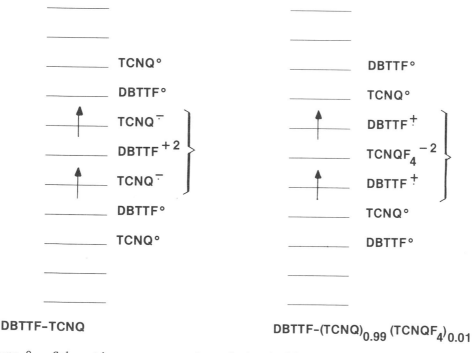

Figure 9. Schematic representation of the doubly charged species associated with triple ions in the normal crystal structure of DBTTF-TCNQ.

solids. From a materials viewpoint, the amorphous or molecularly doped polymers (3, 67) used in current large area photoelectronic devices are a scientifically mature topic. While strides have been made in both fundamental science and applications of highly conducting polymers, e.g., charge-transferred $(CH)_x$, it is important to realize that the forms of $(CH)_x$ currently available (68, 69) are partially crystalline at best. Since the theoretical discussions of the electronic structure of $(CH)_x$ are based on ordered systems, the preparation and characterization of such materials will be the focus of much activity in the near future. While the area of non-stoichiometric and impurity-induced phases holds much promise as an open-ended problem, more specific developments may be anticipated in the area of fully ordered crystals. The stabilization of the organic metallic state to low temperatures has involved progression from organosulfur to selenium donors, and the crystal chemical role of the chalcogen in interchain coupling (22, 47, 48) is recognized. The tellurium analogs of the organo-selenium donors which give the presently known low temperature organic metals and superconductors have not been synthesized to date, but it may be antici-pated that the necessary chemical methodology will be available in the near future. Based on current knowledge, it is expected that organotellurium materials with analogous crystal structures will exhibit enhanced super-conducting transition temperatures and will be less one dimensional when compared to their selenium counterparts. The possibilities of the presently unknown phenomenon triplet superconductivity are also intriguing. Indeed, organic superconductors may hold much promise in the continuing development (69) of Josephson junction devices for ultra-high speed electronic tech-nologies.

ACKNOWLEDGMENT

The author thanks his collaborators named in the references, the principal authors of references 4, 16, 36a, 46 and 71 for preprints of their work, Professor Bruce Foxman for calling reference 45 to his attention, and Joanne McLaughlin for typing this manuscript.

REFERENCES

1. D.J. Sandman, 178th American Chemical Society Meeting, Washington, DC, September, 1979, Abstract ORGN 60.

2. J.W. Weigl, Angew. Chem. Internat. Edit., 16, 374 (1977).

3. J.M. Pearson, S.R. Turner, and A. Ledwith, "The Nature and Applications of Charge-Transfer Phenomena in Polymers and Related Systems", in "Molecular Association", Vol. 2, ed. R. Foster, Academic Press, New York, N.Y., (1979).

4. P.J. Nigrey, D. MacInnes, Jr., D.P. Nairns, A.G. MacDiarmid, and A.J. Heeger, J. Electrochem. Soc., submitted, 1980; Chem. Eng. News, 59 (4), 39 (1981).

5. R.S. Potember, T.O. Poehler, and D.O. Cowan, Appl. Phys. Lett., 34, 405 (1979); R.S. Potember, T.O. Poehler, A. Rappa, D.O. Cowan, and A.N. Bloch, J. Am. Chem. Soc., 102, 3659 (1980).

6. L.B. Coleman, M.J. Cohen, D.J. Sandman, F.G. Yamagishi, A.F. Garito, and A.J. Heeger, Solid State Commun., 12, 1125 (1973).

7. J.P. Ferraris, D.O. Cowan, V. Walatka, and J. Perlstein, J. Am. Chem. Soc., 95, 948 (1973).

8. A.F. Garito and A.J. Heeger, Acc. Chem. Res., 7, 232 (1974).

9. D. Jerome, A. Mazaud, M. Ribault, and K. Bechgaard, Acad. des Sci., Compt. Rend., Ser. B, 290, 27 (1980).

10. M. Ribault, J.-P. Pouget, D. Jerome, and K. Bechgaard, J. Physique, Lett., 41, L607 (1980); K. Bechgaard, K. Carneiro, F.B. Rasmussen, M. Olsen, G. Rindorf, C.S. Jacobsen, H.J. Pedersen, and J.C. Scott, preprint submitted to J. Am. Chem. Soc.

11. K. Deuchert and S. Hunig, Angew. Chem. Internat. Edit., 17, 875 (1978).

12. J.A. McCleverty, Prog. Inorg. Chem., 10, 49 (1968).

13. G. Kothe, E. Ohmes, J. Brickman, and H. Zimmermann, Angew. Chem. Internat. Edit., 10, 938 (1971).

14. R.S. Mulliken and W.B. Person, in "Electron Donor-Acceptor Complexes and Charge Transfer Spectra" in "Physical Chemistry, An Advanced Treatise", Vol. III, ed. D. Henderson, Academic Press, New York, NY, 1969.

15. D.J. Sandman, to be published.

16. P.J. Stang, G. Maas, T.E. Fisk, J. Am. Chem. Soc., 102, 6361 (1980); P.J. Stang, G. Maas, D.L. Smith, and J.A. McCloskey, to be published.

17. S. Ikehata, J. Kaufer, T. Woener, A. Pron, M.A. Druy, A. Sivak, A.J. Heeger, and A.G. MacDiarmid, Phys. Rev. Lett., 45, 1123 (1980).

18. S. Etemad, M. Ozaki, D.L. Peebles, A.J. Heeger, and A.G. MacDiarmid, to be published.

19. F. Wudl, J. Am. Chem. Soc., 97, 1962 (1975).

20. D.J. Sandman, G.P. Ceasar, P. Nielsen, A.J. Epstein, and T.J. Holmes, J. Am. Chem. Soc., 100, 202 (1978).

21. R.N. Lyubovskava, M.Z. Aldoshina, V. Ya. Rodionov, T.A. Chibisova, and M.L. Khidekel', Izv. Akad. Nauk SSSR, Ser. Chem., 168 (1975).

22. D.J. Sandman, Mol. Cryst. Liq. Cryst., 50, 235 (1979).

23. F.H. Herbstein, "Crystalline π-Molecular Compounds: Chemistry, Spectroscopy, and Crystallography", in "Perspectives in Structural Chemistry", Vol. 4, ed. J.D. Dunitz and J.A. Ibers, Wiley, New York, (1971).

24. D.J. Sandman, S.J. Grammatica, T.J. Holmes, and A.F. Richter, Mol. Cryst. Liq. Cryst., 59, 241 (1980).

25. D.J. Sandman and A.F. Richter, J. Am. Chem. Soc., 101, 7079 (1979); D.J. Sandman, A.F. Richter, D.E. Warner, and G.T. Fekete, Mol. Cryst. Liq. Cryst., 60, 21 (1980).

26. C.J. Fritchie, Jr., and P. Arthur, Jr., Acta Cryst., 21, 139 (1966).

27. V.F. Kaminskii, R.P. Shibaeva, and L.O. Atovmyan, J. Struct. Chem., 15, 434 (1974).

28. R.L. Brandon, J.H. Osiecki, and A. Ottenberg, J. Org. Chem., 31, 1214 (1966).

29. R. Karlsson, Acta Cryst., B28, 2358 (1972).

30. H. Inoue, S. Hayashi, and E. Imoto, Bull. Chem. Soc. Japan, 37, 336 (1964).

31. T. Tamamura, T. Yamane, N. Yasuoka, and N. Kasai, Bull. Chem. Soc. Japan, 47, 832 (1974).

32. S. Sakanoue, N. Yasuoka, N. Kasai, M. Kakudo, S. Kusabayashi, and H. Mikawa, Bull. Chem. Soc. Japan, 42, 2408 (1970).

33. R.M. Wing and R.L. Schlupp, Inorg. Chem., 9, 471 (1970).

34. L.R. Melby, R.J. Harder, W.R. Hertler, W. Mahler, R.E. Benson, and W.E. Mochel, J. Am. Chem. Soc., 84, 3374 (1962).

35. B. Morosin, H.J. Plastas, L.B. Coleman, M.M. Stewart, Acta Cryst., B34, 540 (1978).

36. (a) R.H. Harms, H.J. Keller, D. Nothe, M. Werner, D. Gundel, H. Sixl, Z.G. Soos, and R.M. Metzger, to be published; (b) D.B. Tanner and D.J. Sandman, unpublished experiments.

37. Vu Dong, H. Endres, H.J. Keller, W. Moroni, and D. Nothe, Acta Cryst., B33, 2428 (1977).

38. H.D. Hartzler, "Radicals with Cyano Groups" in "The Chemistry of the Cyano Group", Z. Rappoport, ed., Interscience Publishers, New York, NY (1970).

39. W.D. Hounshell, D.A. Dougherty, J.P. Hummel, and K. Mislow, J. Am. Chem. Soc., 99, 1916 (1977); C. Ruchardt and H.-D. Beckhaus, Angew. Chem. Internat. Edit., 19, 429 (1980).

40. A. Ledwith and H.J. Woods, J. Chem. Soc. (C), 1422 (1970).

41. M.M. Mahmoud and S.C. Wallwork, Acta Cryst., B32, 440 (1976).

42. F. Wudl, C.H. Ho, and A. Nagel, J. Chem. Soc., Chem. Comm., 923 (1973).

43. G.J. Ashwell and S.C. Wallwork, Acta Cryst., B35, 1648 (1979).

44. M.J. Hove, B.M. Hoffman, and J.A. Ibers, J. Chem. Phys., 56, 3490 (1972).

45. M. Rosenblum, R.W. Fish, and C. Bennett, J. Am. Chem. Soc., 86, 5166 (1964).

46. R.M. Metzger, "Cohesion and Ionicity in Organic Semiconductors and Metals", in "Cohesive and Conformational Energies", ed. R.M. Metzger, Topics in Current Physics, Springer, Berlin, in press.

47. G.D. Stucky, A.J. Schultz, and J.M. Williams, Ann. Rev. Mat. Sci., 7, 30, (1977).

48. T.J. Kistenmacher, American Institute of Physics Conference Proceedings, Series 53, "Modulated Structures", 1979, p.193 ff.

49. D.J. Sandman, A.J. Epstein, T.J. Holmes, J.-S. Lee, and D.D. Titus, J. Chem. Soc., Perkin Trans. II, 1578 (1980).

50. D.J. Sandman, J. Am. Chem. Soc., 100, 5230 (1978).

51. I. Goldberg and V. Shmueli, Acta Cryst., B29, 421 (1973).

52. H. Endres, H.J. Keller, W. Moroni, and D. Nothe, Acta Cryst., B36, 1435 (1980).

53. S.F. Nelsen, Israel J. Chem., 18, 45 (1979).

54. D.J. Sandman, T.J. Holmes, and D.E. Warner, J. Org. Chem., 44, 880 (1979); D.J. Sandman, G.P. Ceasar, A.D. Baker, and D.D. Titus, to be published.

55. A. Schweig, N. Thon, and E.M. Engler, J. Elect. Spectr. Rel. Phen., 12, 335 (1977).

56. Z.G. Soos, Ann. Rev. Phys. Chem., 25, 121 (1974); Z.G. Soos and S. Mazumdar, Phys. Rev. B, 18, 1991 (1978).

57. R.E. Merrifield, Phys. Rev. Lett., 34, 877 (1975).

58. J.-J. Chang, S. Jafarey, and D.J. Scalapino, J. Chem. Phys., 65, 505 (1976).

59. Z.G. Soos, H.J. Keller, W. Moroni, and D. Nothe, J. Am. Chem. Soc., 99, 5040 (1977).

60. I. Fujita and Y. Matsunaga, Bull. Chem. Soc. Japan, 53, 267 (1980).

61. J.B. Torrance, J.E. Vazquez, J.J. Mayerle, and V.Y. Lee, Phys. Rev. Lett., 46, 253 (1981).

62. M.T. Jones, R. Kellerman, A. Troup, and D.J. Sandman, Chem. Scripta, 1981, in press.

63. M.T. Jones, D.J. Sandman, R. Kellerman, and A. Troup, 181st National American Chemical Society Meeting, Atlanta, Georgia, March 29-April 3, 1981, Paper PHYS 196.

64. M.A. Butler, J.P. Ferraris, A.N. Bloch, and D.O. Cowan, Chem. Phys. Lett., 24, 600 (1974).

65. Y.-N. Chiu and J. Parker, Solid State Commun., 31, 123 (1979).

66. D.J. Sandman, J. Electron. Mater., 10, 173 (1981).

67. J. Mort, Science, 208, 819 (1980).

68. G. Lieser, G. Wegner, W. Muller, and V. Enkelmann, Die Makromol. Chemie., Rapid Commun., 1, 621, 627 (1980).

69. W. Deits, P. Cukor, and M. Rubner, "The Effect of Structural Variables on the Conductivity of Iodine Doped Polyacetylene", in "Conducting Polymers", ed. R. Seymour, Plenum Press, New York, NY, to be published.

70. J. Matisoo, Scientific American, 242, 50 (1980); D.G. McDonald,
     Physics Today, 34 (2), 36 (1981).

DISCUSSION

Dr. Pomerantz: IBM — When you talked about adding impurities
to TTF-TCNQ, you said that you changed the crystal structure, or do you merely
dope it in the sense of a semiconductor that has been doped into conductivity?
Is it clear whether the crystal structure is changed from the original material?

Dr. Sandman: GTE — This experiment is done in the following way.
One takes NEP-TCNQ and dissolves it in solution in the presence of phenazine.
If you have 10 percent phenazine, what crystallizes will be a new phase with
new lattice constants which are markedly different than those of NEP-TCNQ so
it is not a doping. In conventional semiconductors, one considers the dopant
as occupying a site in the normal lattice. Here we have totally changed the
crystal structure. The critical difference is the four Angstrom lattice spacing
which is indicative of a uniform spacing in a TCNQ chain in the modified
system. NEP-TCNQ is a non-stacked structure. One sees isolated dimers of
the TCNQ and the ethylphenazinium which is what I will term a conventional
phase for one to one stoichiometry, nitrogen, planar, closed shell, heterocyclic
cations.

Prof. Ratner: NW Univ. — You mentioned that Jerry Torrance had made
high pressure studies in which at high pressure you get a separated cation and
anion and at lower pressures you get the charge transfer interactions. I
would have thought it would go the other way. Is it clear why it does that?

Dr. Sandman: The two examples—he reported ten examples. Earlier
this year, I believe Phys. Rev. Lett. No. 3, 1981, Dr. Torrance reported
that for TTF-chloranil at about eight kilobars, one sees the spectra of the ion
radicals of TTF and chloranil which are not present in the initial complex.

Prof. Ratner: Is it clear why that happens? I would think if you
increase the pressure, you squash them closer together. You want to delocalize
them. You go from the radicals to the mixed instead of the other way around.

Dr. Sandman: I believe his argument is that you are simply
improving the overlap. He sees this also by lowering the temperature; in
other words, simple thermal contraction in the TTF-chloranil leads to the
phase transformation, which he described in a recent JACS communication.
The question as to why the transition takes place is uncertain. We suggested
to him last August, based on the results we observed in dibenz TTF-TCNQ, that
we would be surprised if the metastable species we see in dibenz TTF-TCNQ are
unique to that system. In fact, we see them in the dimethyl, dibenz TTF-TCNQ,
and we encouraged him to anneal some of his samples, to anneal out the random
paramagnetic species and to see if the transition took place. The mechanism
of the transition is uncertain, and it has not yet been related to the
variety of theoretical models proposed by Soos, Scallapino, and Merrifield
at Dupont, so it is a very open question at this stage, although Torrance's
experiments are certainly consistent with it taking place.

CHAPTER XII

NANOLITHOGRAPHY USING <u>IN SITU</u> ELECTRON BEAM VAPORIZATION OF VERY

LOW MOLECULAR WEIGHT RESISTS

M. Isaacson and A. Muray
School of Applied and Engineering Physics
and
National Research and Resource Facility for Submicron Structures
Cornell University
Ithaca, NY 14853

We have initiated a program of investigation of the suitability of very low molecular weight materials as electron beam resists for the development of structures on the size scale of nanometers. With the advent over the last decade of reliable field emission technology, electron sources can be produced with useful brightnesses several orders of magnitude greater than that achievable with existing thermionic sources. Thus, nanoampere beam currents are attainable in subnanometer diameter beams of electrons of 100keV kinetic energy. The scanning transmission electron microscope (VG Microscopes Ltd. Model HB5) in operation in the National Research and Resource Facility for Submicron Structures at Cornell University can produce up to one nanoampere of current into a beam diameter as small as 0.5 nm. This beam current density of 5×10^5 amps/cm^2 means that it takes only 10μsec to deposit a dose of 5 coulombs/cm^2 in a sample. These high beam current densities thus enable us to explore some of the limits of electron beam lithography, since we can begin to consider materials for use as beam resists that are not necessarily as radiation sensitive as the standard high molecular weight resists that are commonly used (e.g., Polymethylmethacrylate-PMMA requires less than 10^{-4} coul/cm^2 exposure using 100keV electrons).(1)

Our explorations have centered on materials of molecular weight around 100 daltons which could be readily vaporized under the action of a finely formed electron beam with doses from 10^{-3} to 10^3 coul/cm^2. There are several reasons for choosing such materials. First, the in situ vaporization means that the initial pattern writing and development can be done in one step, thus eliminating a processing step. Second, low molecular weight molecules tend to be small and therefore one might expect a smaller "grain size" or resolution than with more conventional high molecular weight polymeric materials. For instance, the "average" molecular radius is roughly proportional to the cube root or square root of the molecular weight. (If the molecule were spherical then $\Gamma_{mol} \sim (MW)^{1/3}$). Thus, since conventional resists have molecular weights around $10^5 - 10^6$ daltons (see e.g.,2), we might expect 100 dalton molecular weight resists to have a grain size one to two orders of magnitude smaller than the higher molecular weight polymers. Third, because we are choosing beam vaporizable materials, the mechanism for vaporization is probably surface desorption, so that beam proximity effects might be minimal.

The two types of materials that we have chosen to initially study are alkali halides and aliphatic amino acids. These materials can easily be vacuum sublimated or evaporated as uniform thin films (some can be solvent evaporated as well) and there is a wealth of information to indicate that they are readily vaporized under the action of electron beams produced in electron microscopes, (e.g., 3,4).

Because we want to directly vaporize the material, the irradiation must be done in a clean, relatively high vacuum. Hydrocarbon contaminants found in some standard conventional transmission and scanning electron microscopes diffuse along the sample surface and tend to be polymerized by the action of the beam (e.g., 5). This results in a build-up of hydrocarbon contamination in the region where the beam has exposed the sample. Broers et al have used this fact to produce "contamination" resists which resulted in an end product of continuous metal lines as small as 8 - 12 nm wide. (6) In our case, such hydrocarbon build-up can act as a competing process to the vaporization and one may never be able to "etch" clear through the material. The vacuum near the sample environment in our instrument was always kept at better than 7×10^{-10} torr. We could focus a 1 namp current beam to 1 nm in diameter and irradiate the same spot for more than 5 minutes and observe no evidence of hydrocarbon contamination build up. This corresponds to a dose in excess of 30×10^6 coul/cm^2, orders of magnitude more than needed for vaporization exposure.

Because of the various signals attainable in a scanning transmission electron microscope, we can make compositional characterizations of the resist materials on a scale limited primarily by the diameter of the incident beam. For example, by monitoring the characteristic energy loss spectra of the transmitted electrons, we can determine the compositional (and electronic) change of the resist during exposure (e.g., 4,7). Video signals are obtained from the beam transmitted through the sample by an annular detector which collects electrons elastically scattered out of the main beam and by a "bright field" detector which collects the remaining transmitted beam that either has not been scattered or only scattered through angles less than 1°. (See figure 1 for a schematic of a general scanning transmission electron microscope). A spectrometer placed between the annular detector and the "bright field" detector allows us to obtain characteristic energy loss spectra. Preliminary results on irradiation of sodium chloride crystals indicate that an intermediate state of sodium metal is formed during the exposure. (8)

We can use the annular detector signal and the bright field detector signal for determining the absolute resist thickness, since the amount of scattering is a function of nσt where n is the molecular density in molecules/ unit volume, σ is the cross section for scattering and t is the film thickness. Measurement of these signals as a function of dose (coul/cm^2 incident on the sample) allow us to directly determine thickness versus dose and thus obtain "contrast" curves in situ for any vaporizable resist. (9) Furthermore, by monitoring these signals, we can directly determine that we have etched clear through the resist to the substrate. This is shown in figure 2, where we show a low dose line scan of the bright field signal as the beam moves across a hole etched through a 300Å thick NaCl single crystal. Note that the signal through the etched hole is the same as the signal from the substrate indicating complete vaporization of the NaCl.

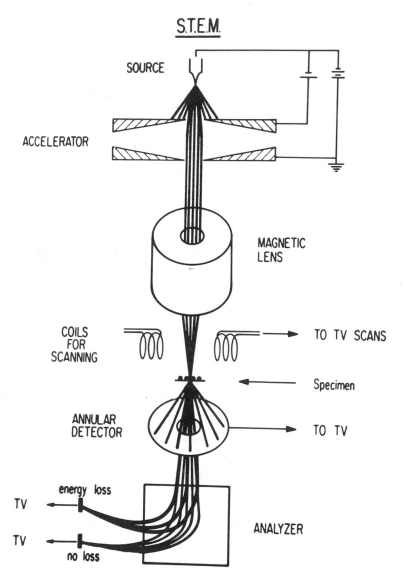

Figure 1. Schematic diagram of a general scanning transmission electron microscope. An electrostatic deflector positioned beneath the electron gun is used to sweep the beam off the sample.

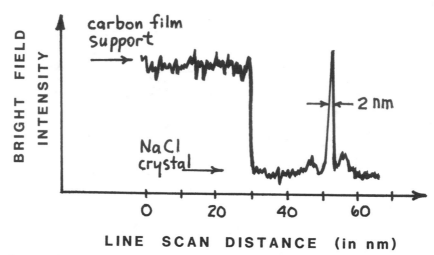

LINE SCAN DISTANCE (in nm)

Figure 2. A plot of the bright field signal intensity as a function of distance along a line as the beam is scanned over a hole etched into an NaCl crystal. The crystal intensity and the substrate intensity are indicated. The higher the intensity, the thinner the sample (or rather, the smaller the mass thickness). Note that the full width at half maximum of the etched hole is 2 nm wide.

Our initial results have been obtained using NaCl evaporated onto 50-100Å thick amorphous carbon substrates. NaCl was chosen since it requires a relatively large dose for vaporization ($\sim 10^2$ coul/cm^2 with 100keV electrons). Thus, we could vaporize a "pattern" and then record a micrograph of the area with a much lower dose, but a dose sufficient enough to allow us to obtain a statistically meaningful picture. Very small indium particles (mean diameters $\sim 1/2 - 1$ nm) were evaporated onto the thin carbon substrate before the NaCl evaporation. This was done to aid the nucleation of the salt crystals and as a means of determining the beam diameter. The NaCl was evaporated over a baffle so that we obtained a continuous variation of crystal thicknesses on the same sample from as small as about 2 nm to a continuous film. (See figure 3).

We find that the "contrast" (as commonly defined in the literature-- e.g., 2) for exposure of NaCl varies between about 1 and 2 depending upon the film thickness. A typical contrast curve is shown in figure 4. The end point dose for complete vaporization depends upon the film thickness, increasing with the thickness of the film. (10) This thickness dependence is consistent with a surface desorption mechanism for the vaporization.

We have been able to etch lines in 20-30 nm thick NaCl crystals that are less than 1.5 nm wide on 4.5 nm centers (figure 5). Simple patterns with 2 nm lines have also been produced using this vaporization technique (e.g., figure 6), although our pattern making ability is limited at the present due to environmental stability problems. Troughs can be etched completely through NaCl crystals with height to width ratios in excess of 20 for 2 nm widths and we are beginning to try direct vaporization of self-supporting NaCl crystals. Such "stencils" could then be transformed into masks for proximity printing.

Although the results we have presented here are very preliminary, and we have not yet transformed the "etchings" into metal structures, we feel our results are encouraging and that we have not yet reached the limits of lithographic methods.

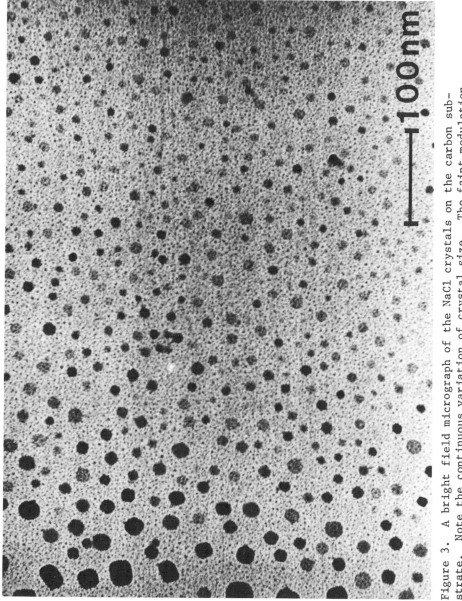

Figure 3. A bright field micrograph of the NaCl crystals on the carbon substrate. Note the continuous variation of crystal size. The faint modulation
in the background is due to the small In particles.

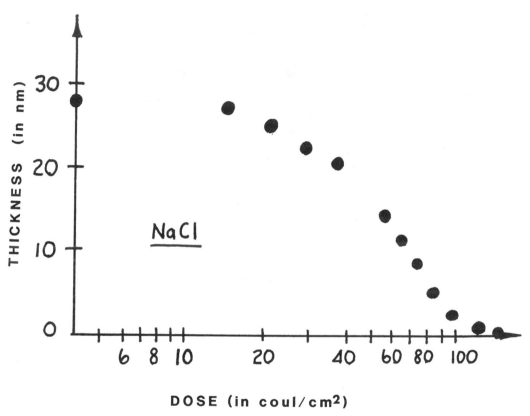

Figure 4. A typical dose response (contrast) curve for a NaCl crystal. The initial thickness (as measured from the electron scattering signals) was about 280Å. The initial electron energy was 100keV.

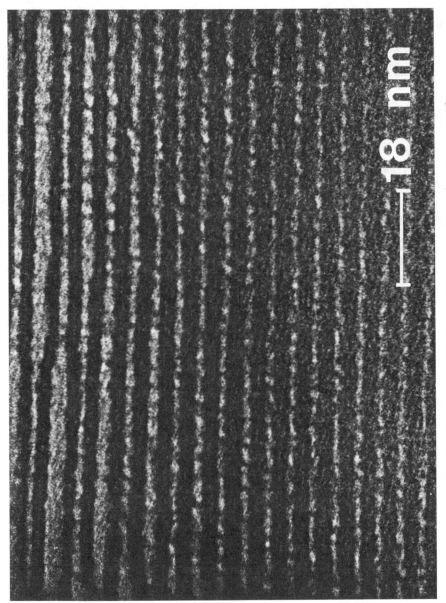

Figure 5. Bright field micrograph of 1.5 nm wide lines etched into an NaCl crystal a few hundred Å thick. The bright lines are the portions etched away. The mottled nature of the lines is due to the small In particles used to determine the beam diameter.

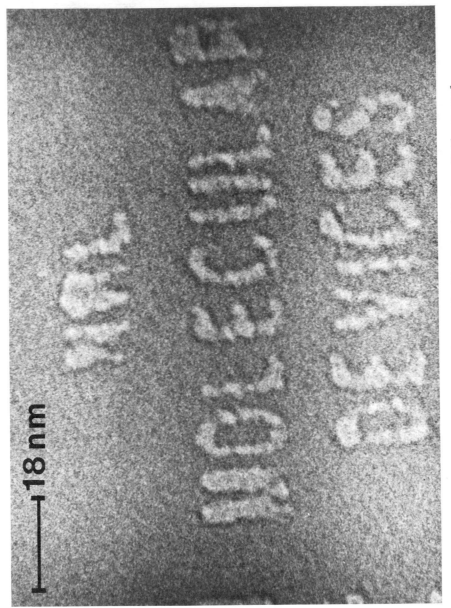

Figure 6.   Bright field micrograph of 2 nm wide lines etched in a NaCl crystal.

ACKNOWLEDGMENT

This work was supported by NSF Grant No. 77-09688 through the National Research
and Resource Facility for Submicron Structures.

REFERENCES

1. Preliminary investigations on unconventional materials have been performed
    by A.N. Broers et al using a scanning transmission electron microscope
    equipped with an LaB_6 thermionic source. (A.N. Broers, J. Cuomo, J.
    Harper, W. Molzen, R. Laibowitz and M. Pomerantz, Electron Microscopy,
    1978, Vol. III, Ninth International Congress on Electron Microscopy,
    Toronto, 1978, p.343).

2. L.F. Thompson and R.E. Kerwin. Ann. Rev. Mat. Sci. 6, 267 (1976).

3. L.W. Hobbs. Ultramicroscopy 3, 381 (1978).

4. M. Isaacson. "Specimen Damage in the Electron Microscope" in Principles
    and Techniques of Electron Microscopy, Vol. 7 (ed. M.A. Hayat) Van-
    Nostrand Reinhold Press, New York (1977) pp. 1-78.

5. J. Hren. "Barriers to AEM: Contamination and Etching" in Analytical
    Electron Microscopy, (eds. J.J. Hren, J.I. Goldstein and D. Joy),
    Plenum Press, New York and London (1979) p. 481.

6. A.N. Broers, W. Molzen, J. Cuomo and N. Wittels, Appl. Phys. Lett. 29,
    596 (1976).

7. M. Isaacson, D. Johnson and A.V. Crewe. Rad. Res. 55, 205 (1973).

8. M. Isaacson, L. Grunes and A. Muray (unpublished).

9. M. Isaacson and A. Muray. Proc. 39th Ann. Meet. EMSA, Atlanta (1981), in
    press.

10. M. Isaacson, A. Muray and I. Adesida. Proc. 16th Symposium on Electron,
    Ion and Photon Beam Technology, Dallas (1981).

DISCUSSION

Dr. Cukor: GTE - The premise of your investigation was better
line definition because of lower molecular weight of the resist. I was
wondering if you would like to comment on that because it is hard to tell from
the photographs if you indeed achieved this.

Prof. Isaacson: Cornell Univ. - At the last pattern, it is 100
Angstroms thick resist, and the lines are about 10 Angstroms wide. That is
10 to 1 ratio.

Dr. Cukor: The lines did not look very straight.

Prof. Isaacson: That problem occurs because we are essentially
using an old oscilloscope for the scanning and handling, and we are in an
unfavorable environment for the next six months. The magnetic field is

really quite high so that the short-term and long-term stability is not very good. A lot of those problems will be relieved when the submicron facility moves into its new building in about six months.

Dr. Cukor: How did you put down the sodium chloride?

Prof. Isaacson: All our resists are vacuum sublimated.

Dr. Siedle: 3M - Would you please say a few words about the facilities at this national laboratory and about who may use them.

Prof. Isaacson: Anyone. If one wishes to propose work or collaborate with people who are there, one should write to Robert Buhrman, School of Applied Engineering Physics, Cornell University, Ithaca, New York, 14850. Send him a paragraph proposal on what you would like to do and he will send you back a very short form, a couple of paragraphs, to see if it is compatible with what we can do. There are certain things that can be done reasonably well and there are other things that can't be done at all, and there are some things that can be done more or less. If one is interested, just simply write or call as it is relatively informal.

CHAPTER XIII

BIOTECHNICAL ELECTRON DEVICES

James H. McAlear and John M. Wehrung
EMV Associates, Inc.
Rockville, MD 20850

The area of biotechnical electron devices has been the subject of interest recently. A 1978 NSF-sponsored meeting (1) provided biologists and device physicists a forum in which to discuss the possibility of using biotechnology for device fabrication or function. This was the same year that the authors received patents (2) for using protein mono- or multilayers in conjunction with biochemical reactions to form molecular subassembled micropatterns which could be used as novel resists, masks and information transfer devices.

The recent advances in biotechnology, coupled with simultaneous scaling down of electronic devices, has created speculation that protein macromolecules of living things may, in nature, function to transfer electrons in a manner analogous to device function. Moreover, these macromolecules in nature are often highly oriented arrays on biomolecular lipid membranes or in helically oriented filaments, subassembling according to specific charge patterns on their surface. Our intention has been to develop means of organizing such molecules on non-biological surfaces for the microfabrication of electron devices.

Our initial efforts during the 1970's involved primarily conceptual phases, the eventual outcome of which were the above-reference patents. Subsequently, in 1980, we were awarded an NSF grant to investigate electron beam lithography of ultrathin, protein monolayer composite resist films. This work, accomplished in conjunction with Dr. J. Hanker of the University of North Carolina, entailed 1) adsorption of a synthetic protein-like material, polylysine, on glass, 2) deposition of polymethyl methacrylate (PMMA) on this film, 3) exposure of the composite to an electron beam pattern, and 4) development of the exposed pattern in absolute ethyl alcohol. This revealed free amino groups of polylysine in the uncovered areas on which an ammoniacal silver stain was precipitated and eventually reduced to metallic silver using thiocarboxy hydrazide (TCH). The TCH also served as a bridging agent to control the amount of silver attached.

The results are shown in Figures 1 and 2 as dense conducting lines of silver. This is to our knowledge the first method to be described for the direct deposition of a conductor only on the pattern specified with no

175

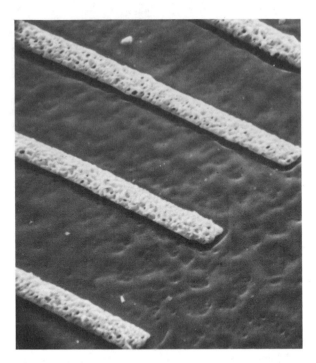

Figure 1 – SEM micrograph of silver lines attached to synthetic protein micropattern. (1000X).

Figure 2 – Silver L X-ray intensity map of region shown in Figure 1. Intensities off lines are background.

requirement for removal of metal from adjacent regions. The greatest
significance, however, is that it opens up the immediate opportunity to deposit
a broad variety of enzymes and proteins with useful characteristics. It makes
available a brand new materials technology with short-term applications to
present device fabrication, including high resolution proximity masks,
superlattices, lateral heterojunctions and sensors.

     Another objective has become much clearer with recent progress in the
identification and characterization of molecular conductors and "switching"
molecules to which this workshop is addressed. Computer modeling of amino
group sequences in an ordered protein film may ultimately provide information
that would allow specific, genetically engineered protein macromolecules to be
subassembled on the protein, producing biological electronic elements in a
functional device configuration such as depicted in Figure 3. This subassembly
is similar to the manner in which proteins associate with the prosthetic
groups of enzymes. These are often organometallic complexes of porphyrin
molecules in association with atoms such as Fe, Cu, Mn, Co, Zn or Mg. The
organization of organic conductors and switching molecules by protein
macromolecules specifically engineered for that purpose is likely to become
a leading technology in the late 1980's.

     The prospect exists for fabricating functional systems by genetic
engineering which can subassemble in three dimensions to produce more complex

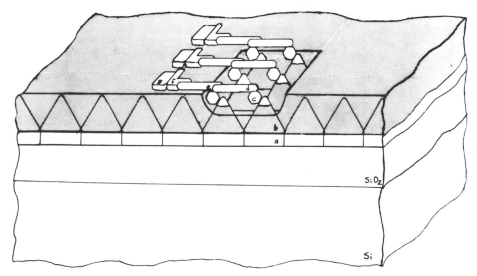

Figure 3 - Model of protein monolayer and basis for an oriented protein/metal
           subassembly sequence (a,b,c,d,e,f,g). Such a sequence could
           resemble that occurring naturally on the membrane of living cells.
           In this case the location of the pattern is determined by the
           specific areas where active protein sites are exposed by electron
           beam lithography. Depending upon the subsequent treatment and the
           nature of the specific protein molecules, a variety of functional
           elements are possible such as conductors, semiconductors,
           insulators and transducers or as superlattices.

and higher density systems. This could lead to an evolution of electronic devices in a manner analogous to living things except that logic may direct such an evolution instead of natural selection.

ACKNOWLEDGMENT

This material is based upon work supported by the National Science Foundation under Award Number DAR 8009745.

REFERENCES

1. J.M. Ballantyne, Editor, NSF Workshop on Opportunities for Microstructures Science and Engineering, Cornell University Press, Ithaca, New York, November 19 - 22, 1978.

2. U.S. Patents No. 4,103,064 and 4,103,073, July 25, 1978.

DISCUSSION

Dr. Nagel: NRL - Does the protein layer remain underneath the metal?

Dr. McAlear: EMV - Yes.

Dr. Nagel: Is it an insulator or conductor? What I am driving at is whether or not the insulating layer can be used to make a field effect transistor?

Dr. McAlear: We don't know the answer to that. We haven't devised any means of making a cross-section to see how far the silver penetrates toward the glass. This protein, this polylysine was put on by adsorption. We can assume that it is more than a monolayer, so again I can't answer that question. We don't know.

Dr. Nagel: It seems as if it would be interesting to put the protein down on a conductor and study its electrical characteristics to see if it could be made into a transistor.

Dr. McAlear: Yes. We have put together some schemes for making devices out of these sorts of things, but that's a good question. Perhaps one should select the proteins very carefully for that purpose even at this crude approximation.

Dr. Sandman: GTE - The highest occupied energy levels in a protein are those on aromatic residues. Do you see any specific function of the groups in proteins in the fabrication of your devices and their behavior? For example, would one find any advantage in going to, instead of a natural protein, a synthetic polypeptide based on a aromatic residue such as tyrosine?

Dr. McAlear: In terms of device function, I won't be able to comment on that. Certainly there might be some advantages in simplicity in producing an oriented monolayer using a peptide which could be synthesized specifically for that function. There are naturally occurring proteins I might mention which are highly desirable for an oriented monolayer. Dr. Paul Muehller has described a group of proteins that exist in biological membranes. They are hydrotropic phase. There is an axial ratio of about three to one, and one end is highly positively charged with a chelated ion, and the other is relatively negatively charged, so these should orient very nicely on an air/water interface without denaturing.

Prof. Marks: NW Univ. - Maybe I missed something in that silver experiment. You adsorbed silver solution, and presumably the silver ions are coordinating to the amino groups. Did you or did you not then reduce the silver metal?

Dr. McAlear: Yes. The reason I didn't go into that in more detail is Dr. Hanker is going to cover that.

Dr. Marks: So chemically the polypeptide absorbs silver ions and they can be subsequently reduced?

Dr. McAlear: Right. There is a difference with an ordinary correlation phenomenon. The stuff is really precipitating on the amino groups.

CHAPTER XIV

SELECTIVE DEPOSITION OF METALS BY BIOCHEMICAL REACTIONS FOR
ELECTRON DEVICE FABRICATION

J. S. Hanker
Dental Research Center
University of North Carolina
Chapel Hill, NC 27514

B. L. Giammara
Department of Anatomy
University of Louisville
School of Medicine
Louisville, KY 40292

INTRODUCTION

The prospect of selectively exposing the active groups of proteins in a
protein-resist composite has been described by J. H. McAlear and J. M. Wehrung
in these proceedings (1). The purpose of this paper is to show how a compatible technology can be derived to deposit electron and X-ray opaque compounds
or electron conductors at the sites of these active groups. This approach
has been developed from the field of modern cytochemistry because, ever since
the study of biological specimens was undertaken with the electron microscope
approximately 30 years ago, a need for a similar methodology has received much
attention. As a result of these studies, generalized chemical approaches have
been developed (2,3) for depositing electron-opaque and electrically-conductive
metal compounds at fixed sites of tissue structural biomacromolecules, enzymes
and antigens. Compounds of silver, uranium or lead, or of the platinum metals
such as osmium, palladium and ruthenium can be linked to various unsaturated
lipid, carbohydrate, complex carbohydrate, acidic (e.g., acid mucopolysaccharide)
or basic (e.g., histone) constituents of cells or their organelles, to extra-
or intercellular substances, or to related synthetic macromolecules.

The metallic compounds deposited on the exposed active groups of a protein
resist composite should have sufficiently high ordinary density (Table 1) to
scatter electrons differentially. The importance of this parameter in
differential electron scattering as a basis for image contrast in transmission
electron microscopy has been discussed by Cosslett (4); specimen thickness is
also an important factor in differential electron scattering. Although atomic
number is a minor factor in the differential elastic scattering of electrons
of the 50 kV beam by atomic nuclei of a solid (Fig. 1), it is the primary
factor in X-ray scattering which depends on interaction with the electrons of
a solid. To summarize, the product of the parameters ordinary density and
thickness is more important than atomic number, in determining electron opacity

TABLE I

COMPARISON OF PROPERTIES RELATING TO ELECTRON OPACITY

	At. No.	At. Wt.	At. Radius	d_4^{19}	σ_s
Iodine	53	126.91	1.33	4.93	3.6 ± 0.5
Osmium	76	190.2	1.35	22.48	
Iron	26	55.85	1.26	7.86	11 ± 1
Lead	82	207.19	1.75	11.34	11 ± 1
Uranium	92	238.03	1.38	19.05	~ 10

Physical constants of atoms considered in predicting relative electron opacity. At. = atomic. σ_s = scattering cross section per atom. Although iodine has a higher atomic number (At. No.) than iron, the latter is more electron opaque, even when iodine is not lost by vaporization from a specimen.

at the usual operating voltages of the electron microscope; these considerations permit the use of the transmission electron microscope (TEM) to estimate electron opacity. For scanning electron microscopy (SEM), where the operating voltages are ordinarily much lower than TEM, interaction of the electron beam with the specimen results in the emission of secondary electrons which are collected for image formation. Therefore, atomic number becomes a more important factor and the electrical conductivity of the metal-coated specimen is responsible for image contrast (5). The electrical conductivity of metal compounds is indirectly indicated by their ability to form conductive coatings for SEM; it also could be directly measured.

Transition metal compounds are less electron-opaque than compounds of silver, lead, uranium and the platinum metals because of their relatively lower ordinary densities. Because of the properties of natural and synthetic transition metal compounds whereby they are useful as heterogeneous catalysts to effect oxidative polymerization reactions (3,6), they have become very important in cytochemical reactions to render contrast for TEM. This approach will be discussed later. Moreover, certain transition metal compounds of elements of the first transition series, whose 3d shells are incompletely filled, can be quite electrically conductive. Cupric ferrocyanide, for example, appears to show similar properties to the enzymatic and nonenzymatic iron porphyrin hemoproteins with respect to semiconduction. This is undoubtedly due to the considerable resonance stabilization of ferrocyanide ion (Fig. 2; 7) which implies electron delocalization and planarity similar to that observed in the resonance stabilized 18π-electron aromatic system of the iron porphyrins (8). It is doubtful, however, that this resonance stabilization of ferrocyanide results in sufficient electron delocalization or mobility as have been postulated for the iron porphyrins (9). Free electrons, resulting from

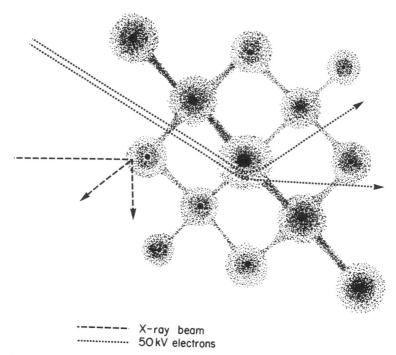

- - - - - -   X-ray beam
.... 50 kV electrons

Fig. 1. Diagram showing how electrons of the 50kV beam are scattered
         elastically, principally by interaction with the nuclei of a solid.
         The closer the electron trajectory to the nucleus, the greater its
         angle of deflection. The X-ray beam, on the other hand, scatters
         principally as a result of interaction with the electrons of the
         solid, accelerating each with a vibratory motion. After Hanker,
         Ref. 3.

extensive delocalization due to the resonance stabilization of the πbond
aromatic system, may be responsible for the conductivity of graphite. In
metals, the delocalization of electrons is apparently complete.

BRIDGING AND POLYMERIZATION REACTIONS FOR INCREASING AMOUNTS OF METALLIC
COMPOUNDS AT DEPOSITION SITES
        Two general methods have been devised to add to the quantity of a
(primary) metal compound that has been deposited at the tissue sites of a
stationary biomacromolecule, related synthetic product, enzyme or antigen.
The first method utilizes a bridging reaction. If the primary metal compound
is one of silver, lead, uranium, a platinum or a transition metal, increased
quantities of electron-opaque or electrically conductive metal may result
from bridging reactions. Secondary metal compounds are linked to the primary
metal compounds already bound to a tissue site (Fig. 3). This may readily
be achieved by employing organic molecules containing more than one functional
group as bridging agents (10). Carbohydrazide, thiocarbohydrazide, tannic
acid, p-phenylenediamine, and gallocyanine are examples of bridging reagents
employed to link the secondary to the primary metal compound. In cytochemistry,
osmium tetroxide and silver proteinate have been extensively used as secondary
metal compounds. Although one bridging cycle usually results in adequate
contrast for TEM, the sequence of reactions, or the cycle, may be repeated as
often as required to achieve sufficient electron or X-ray opacity. The
bridging cycle is usually repeated several times to achieve sufficient
contrast or conductivity for SEM (11).

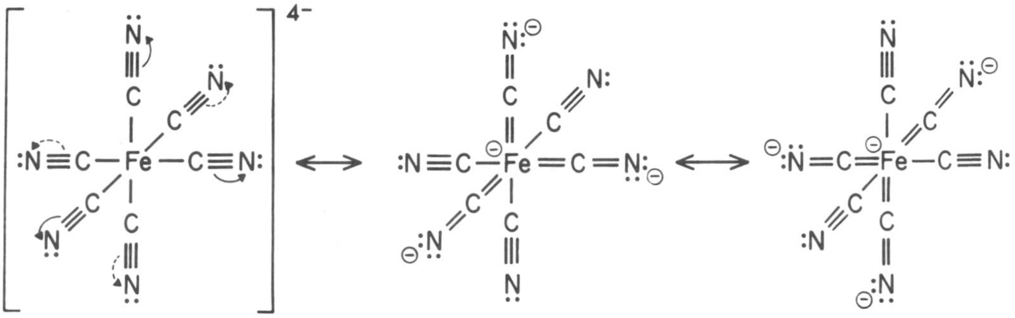

Fig. 2. Resonance stabilization of ferrocyanide ion. The different structures contributing to the resonance hybrid can be derived by alternative electron displacements as shown by the curved solid or dotted arrows. Atoms of transition metals are not restricted to the formation of single covalent bonds but can form multiple covalent bonds with electron-accepting ligands. In this case the hybridized 3d, 4s and 4p orbitals of the iron atom are utilized. After Pauling, "The Nature of the Chemical Bond," Cornell University Press, Ithaca, 1960.

The second general method for increasing the amount of metallic compound at the tissue sites of a stationary or attached biomacromolecule, enzyme or antigen or, alternatively, a biochemical reaction product, employs a polymerization reaction to chemically amplify the primary metallic compound, which is invariably a transition metal compound. The latter may be a nonenzyme hemoprotein such as hemoglobin or an endogenous enzymatic hemoprotein such as cytochrome oxidase, catalase or a peroxidase. It may be an exogenous peroxidase such as horseradish peroxidase transported in a neuron or linked to a tissue antigen. Alternatively, it may be a transition metal compound such as cupric ferrocyanide deposited at the tissue sites of a dehydrogenase or acid hydrolase such as nonspecific esterase, acid phosphatase or arylsulfatase (Fig. 4), or cobaltous ferricyanide deposited at the tissue sites of alkaline phosphatase, adenosine triphosphatase or carbonic anhydrase (3, 6).

In any case, the special properties of these transition metal compounds which have catalytic activities resembling those of artificial oxidases, can be important in chemical amplification reactions via polymerization. The ligand of a transition metal complex is responsible for its ability to function as a catalyst in the oxidation of organic substrates such as the aromatic diamines and phenols (12,15-20). This catalytic activity is related to the tendency for variable valency shown by these metals (21). This results from the small difference in energy levels between orbitals in the outer and penultimate shells of the metals which, in turn, facilitates the promotion of electrons, complexing ability, and catalytic activity in oxidative reactions. Whether arylamines, phenols, or mixtures of the two are employed as substrates, catalytic oxidation of these substrates by transition metal compounds results generally in oxidative coupling and polymerization reactions. The resulting products may be polymers resembling melanin pigments and, like the latter, are generally osmophilic (22). Thus an oxidation product, containing a number of groups which can react with osmium tetroxide, is formed at the sites of a single molecule of insoluble transition metal compound. These products may be highly conductive as well as electron opaque, and may contain metal-to-metal bonds (such as osmium to osmium) or even free osmium metal which may, likewise, be important factors in their high ordinary density and electron opacity.

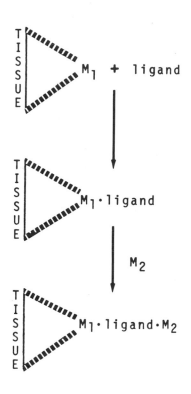

$$\text{ligand} = H_2NNH\overset{\overset{S}{\parallel}}{C}NHNH_2 \text{(TCH)} \quad \text{or} \quad H_2NNH\overset{\overset{S}{\parallel}}{C}NH_2 \text{ (TSC)}$$

M_1 = Primary Metal

M_2 = OsO_4

Fig. 3. Diagram of bridging reaction for ehnancement of sites of a tissue-
bound primary metal cation (M_1) by stepwise treatment with a multiden-
tate ligand, thiocarbohydrazide (TCH), and a secondary metallic compound, M_2, usually OsO_4. The OsO_4 renders the sites of M_1 much more
visible as well as electron opaque by osmium black formation. After
Hanker, Ref. 3.

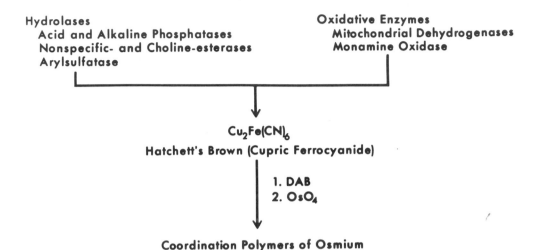

Fig. 4a.   Composite overall reaction sequence for the cytochemical
           demonstration of hydrolytic and oxidative enzymes by catalytic
           osmiophilic polymer generation. In either case, the action of the
           enzyme upon its substrate results in the deposition of a small
           amount of the insoluble cupric ferrocyanide at the subcellular
           sites of the enzyme. The cupric ferrocyanide is "chemically
           amplified" by employing it as a transition metal catalyst in the
           oxidative polymerization of DAB (3,3'- diaminobenzidine).
           Subsequent treatment of the polymer with OsO_4 results in the
           formation of electrically-conductive and electron-opaque osmium
           blacks at the sites of the enzyme.

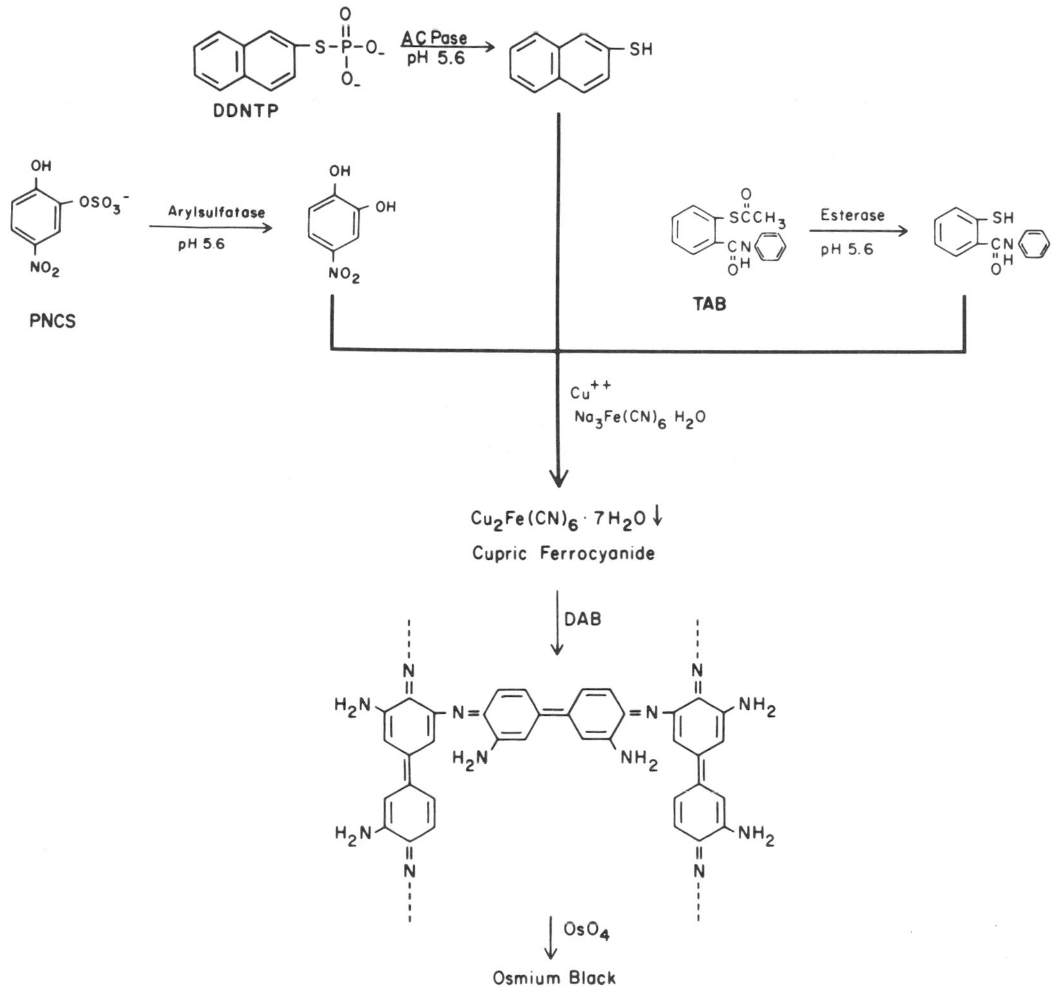

Fig. 4b. For the demonstration of the acid hydrolases, the incubation media are identical with the exception of the synthetic enzyme substrate. The hydrolysis of the appropriate substrate liberates a reducing agent in each case as the primary reaction product. The latter, a thiol in the case of acid phosphatase and nonspecific esterase, or nitrocatechol in the case of arylsulfatase, reduces cupric ferricyanide to cupric ferrocyanide which is precipitated at the sites of enzyme activity. In any case, the deposited transition metal compound, Hatchett's brown or cupric ferrocyanide, is employed as a catalyst to effect the oxidative coupling of DAB. The resulting highly-colored insoluble osmiophilic indamine-type polymer is converted to an electron-opaque and electrically-conductive, as well as highly visible, osmium black at the sites of enzyme activity upon treatment with OsO$_4$. After Hanker, Ref. 3.

One of the most widely employed compounds in cytochemical oxidative polymerization reactions, 3,3'-diaminobenzidine (DAB), was introduced by Graham and Karnovsky (22,23) as a substrate for the demonstration of exogenous horseradish peroxidase in animal tissues. Its oxidation yields a phenazine polymer which has the ability to bind two atoms of metal per monomer unit (Fig. 5). Although copper is very satisfactory for enhancing the visualization of the DAB polymer for light microscopy, the oxidation product is generally reacted with osmium tetroxide resulting in the formation of osmium blacks for electron microscopy. In this case the oxidation product of DAB is an osmiophilic polymer. The cytochemical methods where transition metal compounds are deposited as primary reaction products for subsequent employment as catalysts in DAB oxidation are known as catalytic osmiophilic polymer generation methods.

For the increased deposition of secondary metallic compounds at the sites of antigens, the iron porphyrin transition metal compound horseradish peroxidase is linked to the antigen via antibody to effect the amplification reaction. These catalytic osmiophilic polymer generation reactions are chemical amplification reactions which can be employed to deposit large amounts of electron and X-ray opaque, and electrically-conductive, osmium black end products at the sites of an almost endless variety of hydrolytic as well as oxidative enzymes and antigens. They can also be employed for the demonstration of some organic functional groups.

THE SELECTIVE DEPOSITION OF SILVER AT THE SITES OF POLYLYSINE EXPOSED IN A POLYLYSINE-RESIST COMPOSITE

Several approaches have been undertaken to develop reactions for the selective deposition of metals at the sites of polylysine, exposed by a radiation source, on the surface of a silicon wafer. Preliminary studies were performed on small filter paper discs impregnated with spots of polylysine or on microscope slides on which polylysine has been streaked. These were prepared from a 1% solution of polylysine (MW 30,000-70,000). The most promising approach appears to be one which utilizes a modification of the ammoniacal silver reaction to deposit silver on the polylysine. Additional silver, or other secondary metals, may then be linked to the primary silver atoms initially bound to the polylysine by bridging with thiocarbohydrazide (TCH) as described above.

The ammoniacal silver reaction has been classically used in electron microscopic cytochemistry to demonstrate basic proteins such as the arginine-rich protamines and arginine- and lysine-rich histones of cell nuclei (24). The sequence of chemical reactions employed are shown in Figure 6. Figures 7 and 8 are light micrographs showing silver deposited at the sites of polylysine exposed by irradiation of a polylysine-resist-composite on a glass slide. Scanning electron micrographs of these results have been included in the paper by J. H. McAlear and J. M. Wehrung in these proceedings (1).

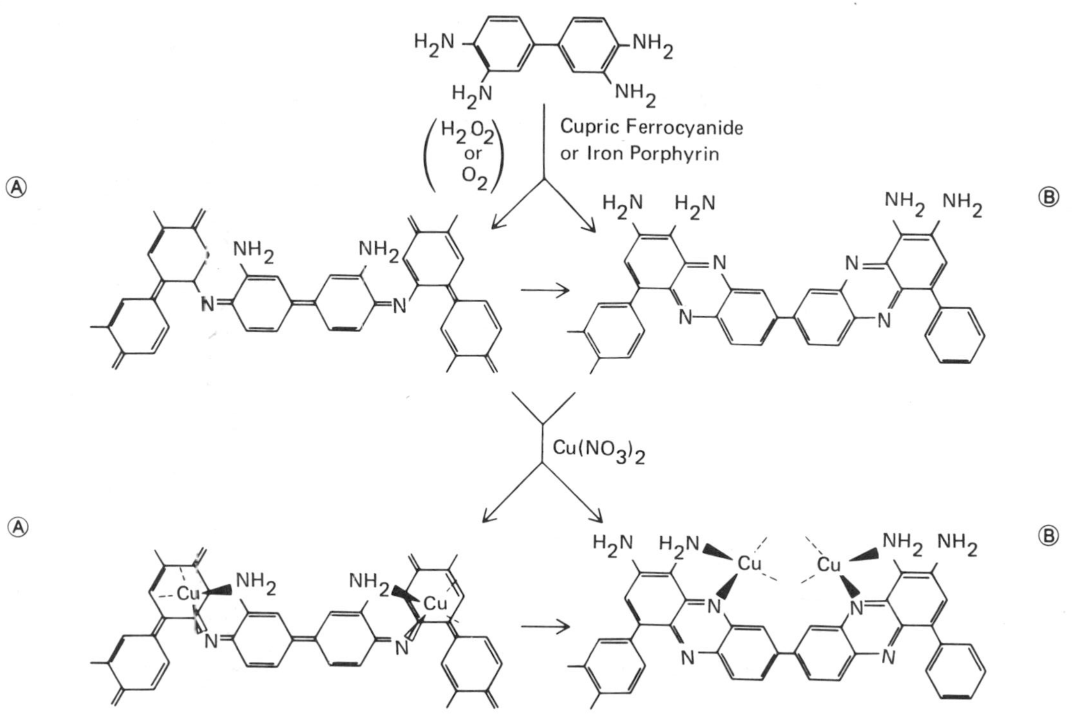

Fig. 5. Hypothetical formulation of the oxidative (or peroxidative) polymerization of DAB, catalyzed cupric ferrocyanide or iron porphyrin hemoproteins, resulting in the formation of indamine or phenazine coupling products. Note that either one of these products can coordinate with cupric ion, principally because of the presence of primary aromatic amino groups. Note also that the indamine polymer (A) may cyclize to form the phenazine polymer (B).

REACTIONS FOR COATING POLYLYSINE
WITH SILVER

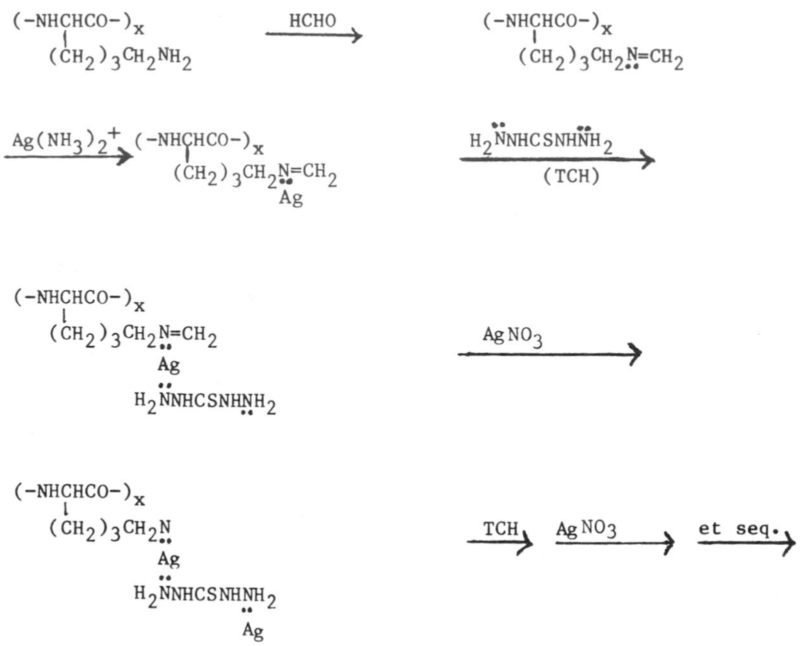

$$(-NHCHCO-)_x \atop (CH_2)_3CH_2NH_2 \qquad \xrightarrow{\text{HCHO}} \qquad (-NHCHCO-)_x \atop (CH_2)_3CH_2\ddot{N}=CH_2$$

$$\xrightarrow{Ag(NH_3)_2^+} \quad (-NHCHCO-)_x \atop (CH_2)_3CH_2\underset{Ag}{\overset{..}{N}}=CH_2 \qquad \xrightarrow[\text{(TCH)}]{H_2\ddot{N}NHCSNH\ddot{N}H_2}$$

$$(-NHCHCO-)_x \atop (CH_2)_3CH_2\underset{\underset{H_2\ddot{N}NHCSNH\ddot{N}H_2}{Ag}}{\overset{..}{N}}=CH_2 \qquad \xrightarrow{AgNO_3}$$

$$(-NHCHCO-)_x \atop (CH_2)_3CH_2\underset{\underset{H_2\ddot{N}NHCSNH\ddot{N}H_2}{Ag}}{\ddot{N}} \qquad \xrightarrow{TCH} \xrightarrow{AgNO_3} \xrightarrow{\text{et seq.}} \atop \overset{..}{Ag}$$

Fig. 6.   Reaction sequence to render polylysine, exposed by irradiation of a
polylysine resist-composite, conductive. The Schiff's base
resulting from formylation of the basic polylysine readily reacts
with ammoniacal silver as shown. Thiocarbohydrazide (TCH) is then
employed as a bridging agent to link more silver to that already
bound to the basic polylysine. The bridging cycle may be repeated,
as required, to achieve sufficient conductivity.

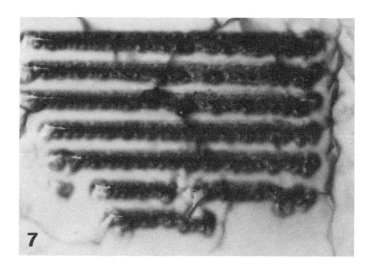

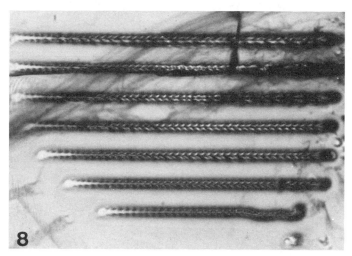

Figs. 7,8 Light micrographs of a polylysine-resist-composite, in which
           polylysine exposed by irradiation lithography, was treated by the
           reactions described in Fig. 6. The bridging cycle was repeated
           one time resulting in the staining shown. Magnification, X 600.

ACKNOWLEDGMENT

These studies were supported by USPHS Research Grants DE 02668, RR 05333 and NSF grant DAR8009745.

REFERENCES

1. J. H. McAlear and J. M. Wehrung, These proceedings.

2. J. S. Hanker, A. R. Seaman, L. P. Weiss, H. Ueno, R. A. Bergman and A. M. Seligman, Science, 146, 1039-1043 (1964).

3. J. S. Hanker, Prog. Histochem. Cytochem., 12, 1-85 (1979).

4. V. E. Cosslett, J. R. Micro. Soc., 78, 1-17 (1959).

5. M. A. Hayat, Introduction to Biological Scanning Electron Microscopy, University Park Press, Baltimore, 1978.

6. J. S. Hanker, W. A. Anderson and F. D. Bloom, Science, 175, 991-993 (1972).

7. L. Pauling, "The Nature of the Chemical Bond," Cornell Univ. Press, Ithaca, N. Y., 3rd Ed., 1960.

8. M. N. Hughes, "The Inorganic Chemistry of Biological Processes," John Wiley and Sons, London and New York, 1972.

9. J. F. Gibson and D. J. E. Ingram, Nature, 178, 871-872 (1956).

10. J. S. Hanker, C. Deb and A. M. Seligman, Science, 152, 1631-1634 (1966).

11. R. O. Kelley, R. A. F. Dekker and J. G. Bluemink, J. Ultrastruct. Res., 45, 254-258 (1973).

12. K. Kinoshita, Bull. Chem. Soc. Jap., 32, 772-780 (1959).

13. J. P. Candlin, R. A. Taylor, and D. T. Thompson, "Reactions of Transition Metal Complexes," Elsevier Publ. Co., Amsterdam, 1968.

14. A. P. Terentev and D. Ya. Mogelyansky, J. Gen. Chem. USSR, 28, 1959-1962 (1958).

15. H. C. Bach and W. B. Black, J. Polymer Sci. Part C, 22, 799-811 (1969).

16. H. C. Bach and W. B. Black, Adv. in Chem. Series, 91, 679-691 (1969).

17. P. D. McDonald and G. A. Hamilton, in "Oxidation in Organic Chemistry Part B," Ed. W. S. Trahanovsky, Academic Press, New York and London, 1973.

18. W. G. Nigh, in "Oxidation in Organic Chemistry Part B," Ed. W. S. Trahanovsky, Academic Press, New York and London, 1973.

19. A. I. Scott, Quart. Rev. (London), 19, 1-35 (1965).

20. D. G. Cooper, "The Periodic Table," Plenum Press, New York and London, 1968.

21. P. Drochmans, Int. Rev. Exp. Path., 2, 357–422 (1963).

22. R. C. Graham, Jr. and M. J. Karnovsky, J. Histochem. Cytochem., 14, 291–302 (1966).

23. R. C. Graham, Jr. and M. J. Karnovsky, J. Exp. Med., 124, 1123–1149 (1966).

24. M. M. Black and H. R. Ansley, Science, 143, 693–695 (1964).

DISCUSSION

Dr. Siedle: 3M – What color is the polydiaminobenzidine? Is it a photoconductor? Does anyone know about the electronic properties of that polymer?

Prof. Hanker: The diaminobenzidine (DAB) polymer is brownish-red in color. It is not, as far as I know, a particularly good conductor. Nor have its electronic or photoconductive properties been studied. Its coordination compounds, like its copper and osmium complexes, however, can be used instead of gold coating to render biological specimens conductive for scanning EM. This implies some ability to conduct electrons.

Mr. Cukor: GTE – I understand your comments about using these techniques for diagnostic purposes, but the materials you have discussed such as osmium and diaminobenzidine are extremely poisonous. Would you explain how can you use them for treatment?

Prof. Hanker: These chemical reactions don't have to be used in the way we showed them here. They could be confined entirely to an implanted diagnostic or prosthetic device. The device would be activated by a biochemical or physiologic stimulus at the device/tissue interface. These reactions, within the device, could be utilized to deposit a conductive metal compound which would act like an artificial nerve, sensory or motor.

Dr. Sandman: GTE – I'm fascinated by your suggestion of the diaminobenzidine coming up to the active site of the metal in the protein. It is easy to accept that it would have to come to the active site to have the electron transfer to initiate the polymerization to take place, but it doesn't necessarily follow that the diaminobenzidine would not diffuse away from the active site. Could you comment on that and whether or not it is important?

Prof. Hanker: The polymerization of DAB is a very fast reaction which has been used in many cytochemical reactions to demonstrate the sites of various enzymes even at the level of cell organelles. It is known, for example, that the enzyme cytochrome oxidase is located in the inner membrane of the mitochondrion. When DAB is used as a reagent for the demonstration of this enzyme, only the inner mitochondrial membrane is stained. Therefore, its polymerization apparently occurs with sufficient rapidity to avoid diffusion artifact.

Dr. Greyber: NSF – If you just had a main nerve cut, could you imagine depositing substances on it which could then lead to an artificial device?

Prof. Hanker: Yes, I could. There are, for example, many cholinesterase-positive nerves. If one of these nerves is cut,

acetycholinesterase is released and can be used to deposit a conductive metal
compound within a device in the vicinity of, or apposed to, the severed nerve.
The metal compound within the device could, of course, complete a circuit.

CHAPTER XV

RATIONAL CONTROL OF ELECTRONIC STRUCTURE AND LATTICE ARCHITECTURE IN
ELECTRICALLY CONDUCTING MOLECULAR/MACROMOLECULAR ASSEMBLIES

Tobin J. Marks, Carl W. Dirk, and Karl F. Schoch, Jr.
Department of Chemistry and the Materials Research Center
Northwestern University
Evanston, IL 60201

Joseph W. Lyding
Department of Electrical Engineering and Computer Science
and the Materials Research Center
Northwestern University
Evanston, IL 60201

INTRODUCTION

The past several years have witnessed the advent of advanced new types of
organic, metal-organic, and inorganic materials with unusual, highly anisotropic, and potentially tailorable electrical, optical, and magnetic properties
(1-5). Such materials have stimulated much activity in the chemistry and
physics communities. As a result, there have been advances in chemical
synthetic strategy and methodology, in spectroscopic and charge transport
measurement techniques, and in condensed matter theory. Furthermore, applications of this new knowledge to sensors (6), rectifiers (7), switching devices
(8), photoresists (9), fuel cells (10), chemoselective electrodes (11), solar
energy conversion elements (12), and electrophotographic devices (13) have been
the subject of much discussion. Of course, to develop such technology there
must be an intimate understanding at the molecular level of those structural
and electronic variables which govern collective properties. A refined
synthetic chemistry for constructing desired molecular assemblies and
optimizing performance charcteristics is also required. Despite the advances
which have been achieved, our understanding of and our ability to exert
chemical control over the above factors is at a primitive level, thus representing a major barrier to progress.

Research in this Laboratory has focused on the evolution of rational,
flexible syntheses of new low-dimensional electronic materials and on
understanding the physical properties of the products which result (14,15).
In this article we review our recent work on constructing molecular arrays
composed of cofacially linked, partially oxidized metallomacrocycles. By
beginning with chemically-versatile and well-characterized molecular precursors, this strategy capitalizes upon a great deal of accumulated chemical and
physical information about the component subunits. Our strategy offers the
possibility of constructing robust new conductive assemblies with well-defined

partial oxidation enhances charge mobility by creating numerous electronic
vacancies. An analogous description can be generated for partial reduction.

Our initial approach to synthesizing low-dimensional mixed-valent arrays
was to cocrystallize planar, conjugated metallomacrocyclic donor molecules
such as glyoximates (A,B) (17-19), phthalocyanines (C) (20,21), and tetraazan-
nulenes (D) (22) having an MN_4 core structure, with bromine or iodine oxi-

dants (A), as shown in eq. (1). When successful, the result is a crystal
composed of segregated (i.e., donors and acceptors in separate columns), partially oxidized metallomacrocyclic stacks and parallel arrays of halide or

$$\text{(1)}$$

polyhalide counterions. We also demonstrated that the form of the halogen
(even if disordered) could be determined in a straightforward fashion by resonance Raman and iodine Mössbauer spectroscopic techniques (15,19,23,24). The
degree of partial oxidation ($\delta+$) follows from this information and the
stoichiometry. As an example, nickel phthalocyanine iodide, $[Ni(Pc)]I_{1.0}$,
crystallizes in stacks of staggered $Ni(Pc)^{+0.33}$ units arrayed at 3.244(2) Å
intervals and surrounded by parallel chains of I_3^- counterions. The 300°K
conductivity of this material in the molecular stacking direction is 300-700
Ω^{-1} cm^{-1} and the temperature dependence is "metal-like" ($\rho \sim T^{1.9}$) down to
60°K (21). The conductivity is predominantly a ligand-centered phenomenon,
and carrier mean free paths are comparable to some of the most conductive
"molecular metals."

The molecule/halogen cocrystallization approach to the synthesis of mixed
valent, low-dimensional, metal-like materials is often effective.
Nevertheless, all strategies that rely upon molecular stacking suffer from the
weakness that the lattice architecture is totally dependent upon the unpredic-
table and largely uncontrollable forces that dictate the stacking pattern, the
and easily-manipulated microstructures. The covalent bonds which hold such
arrays together are far stronger than packing, van der Waals, and band formation forces. As a result, it has been possible to delve into those factors
which stabilize the metallic state without fear of a breakdown in stacking, to
control lattice microstructure, and to deliberately perturb bandwidth and
phonon dynamics.

REQUIREMENTS FOR HIGHLY CONDUCTIVE MOLECULAR SOLIDS

Two features are now generally recognized as necessary for transforming an unorganized collection of molecules into an electrically conductive molecular array. First, the component molecules must be positioned in close spatial proximity, and in crystallographically similar environments, with sufficient intermolecular orbital overlap to provide a continuous electronic pathway for carrier delocalization. With the molecules positioned in this manner, the conduction pathway has a minimum of energetic "hills" and "valleys." Second, the arrayed molecules must be in formal fractional oxidation states ("mixed valence," "partial oxidation," "incomplete charge transfer"). That is, the molecular entities to be connected in series must have fractionally occupied electronic valence shells. Within the framework of a simple one-dimensional Hubbard model, this prerequisite reflects the relatively narrow bandwidths (4t) and large on-site coulomb repulsions (U) in such systems (16). A simplified, valence bond picture of this situation is depicted in Figure 1; donor-acceptor orientations, and the stacking repeat distances. There are numerous conceivable donor-acceptor crystallization patterns which do not involve segregated stacking of the components (25-28). Indeed, a common pitfall in the design of new materials is that segregated stacks do not form, and that the elegant effort expended in donor or acceptor design is for naught. This problem severely limits the ability to design and tailor microstructures which lead reliably to electroactive molecular assemblies.

THE COFACIAL ASSEMBLY APPROACH

Our approach to controlling molecular stacking involves the assembly of macro-molecules in which arrays of metallomacrocycles are rigidly locked into a

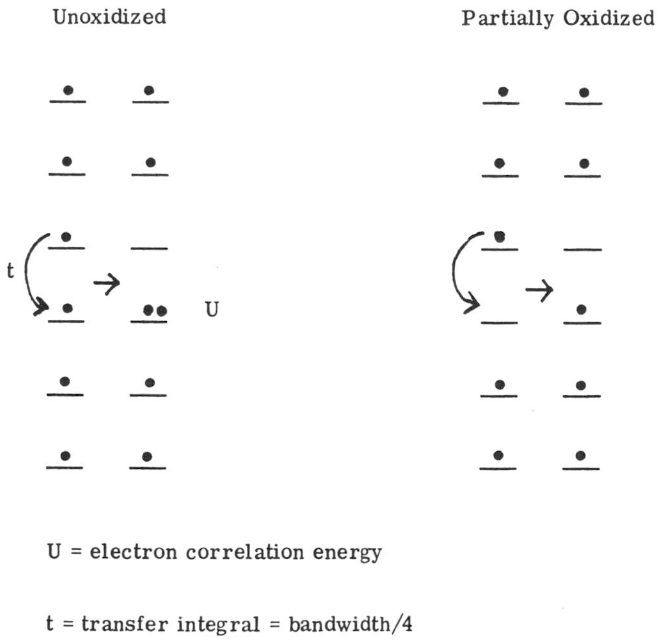

Unoxidized   Partially Oxidized

U = electron correlation energy

t = transfer integral = bandwidth/4

Fig. 1. Schematic diagram of how partial oxidation enhances charge transport in a simple molecular stack.

$$\text{(2)}$$

"face-to-face" configuration by strong, covalent bonds (eq.(2)) (29-31). The architecture of the stack can be varied by suitable modification of the macro-cycle, the metal (M), and the connecting linkage (X). Our first studies have capitalized on pioneering chemistry of Kenney (32) and involve phthalocyanine systems where M = Si, Ge, Sn and X = O. Thus, $Si(Pc)(OH)_2$, $Ge(Pc)(OH)_2$, and $Sn(Pc)(OH)_2$ can be condensed at $300-400°C/10^{-3}$ torr to form "face-to-face" phthalocyanine polymers (Figure 2). As a prelude to doping and transport measurements, we first investigated the properties of these compounds as poly-mers. The $[M(Pc)O]_n$ materials have high chemical and thermal stability; moreover, they are not significantly degraded by oxygen or moisture. We find that the polysiloxane polymer can be recovered unchanged from concentrated sulfuric acid (typical of phthalocyanines containing non-electropositive metals (33)). A rough estimate of the minimum average chain length of $[Si(Pc)O]_n$ produced in the condensation polymerization can be obtained by Fourier transform infrared spectrophotometric analysis of the Si-O stretching region. For a typical sample, the degree of polymerization is estimated to be on the order of ca. 100 subunits or more (31). This result is in agreement with preliminary light scattering data from sulfuric acid solutions (34) and measurements of the amount of water evolved during polymerization (35). Infrared analyses of the germanium and tin analogues (considerably more dif-ficult measurements) yield minimum average chain lengths on the order of 30 or more subunits (36).

Structural information on the face-to-face polymers has been derived from several lines of evidence. X-ray powder diffraction data can be indexed in the tetragonal crystal system using iterative computer techniques. Data are very similar to those from the columnar crystal structures of $[Ni(Pc)]I_{1.0}$ (21) and $Ni(dpg)_2I_{1.0}$ (17). The interplanar spacings ($c/2$) in these latter tetragonal structures, determined in single crystal studies, are 3.244(2) Å and 3.271(1) Å, respectively. The corresponding separations derived for the $[M(Pc)O]_n$ materials from the powder diffraction data are a function of the metal ionic radius and vary from 3.32(2) Å (Si-O-Si) to 3.51(2) Å (Ge-O-Ge) to 3.95(2) Å (Sn-O-Sn). The reliability of these metrical parameters is further supported by single crystal diffraction results on the model trimer $[(CH_3)_3SiO]_2(CH_3)SiO[Si(Pc)O]_3Si(CH_3)[OSi(CH_3)_3]_2$ which contains three cofa-cial Si(Pc)O units linked by linear Si-O-Si connections at a distance of 3.324(2) Å (37). Furthermore, the $[Ge(Pc)O]_n$ and $[Sn(Pc)O]_n$ interplanar spa-cings obtained from diffraction data agree with values estimated from standard ionic radii (38) assuming linear Ge-O-Ge and Sn-O-Sn vectors, i.e., 3.58 Å for $[Ge(Pc)O]_n$ and 3.90 Å for $[Sn(Pc)O]_n$. There is good precedent for molecules with linear Si-O-Si, Ge-O-Ge, and Sn-O-Sn linkages (39). Importantly, then, we have achieved a means to manipulate the interplanar spacings of electri-cally conductive subunits in a metallomacrocyclic system where the transport properties are relatively insensitive to the identity of the metal ion.

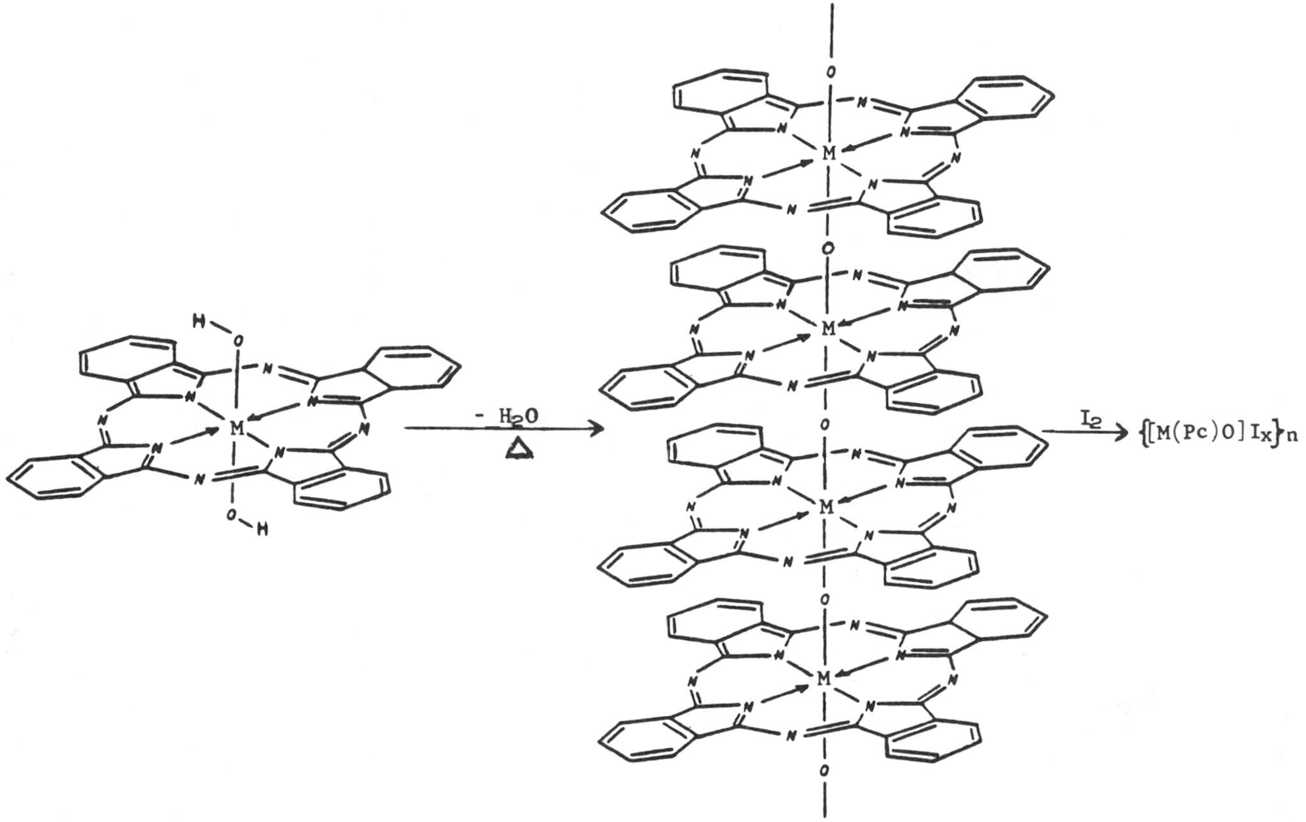

M = Si, Ge, Sn

Fig. 2. Polymerization reaction to produce cofacial arrays of Group IVA metallophthalocyanines.

PARTIAL OXIDATION WITH HALOGENS

Following assembly of the metallophthalocyanines into cofacial arrays, doping experiments were conducted using the halogenation procedure (14,15) developed in this Laboratory for simple, stacked metallomacrocyclic systems. Stirring the powdered polymers with solutions of iodine in organic solvents or exposing the powders to iodine vapor results in substantial iodine uptake. Alternatively, $[Si(Pc)O]_n$ can be doped by dissolving in sulfuric acid and precipitating with an aqueous I_3^- solution. The stoichiometries which can be obtained depend upon the reaction conditions; examples of these materials are listed in Table 1. A survey experiment also indicated that bromine-doped materials could be prepared. That oxidation of the cofacial array has indeed occurred was confirmed by resonance Raman scattering spectroscopy in the polyiodide region. Powder ESR data confirm that the oxidation is ligand centered, producing arrays of π cation radicals (g = 2.002) (31).

Table 1. Physical Properties of Polycrystalline Samples of Halogen-Doped $[M(Pc)O]_n$ Polymers and $[Ni(Pc)]I_{1.0}$.

Compound	$\sigma(\Omega^{-1}cm^{-1})300°K$	Activation Energy (eV)	Interplanar Spacing (Å)
$[Si(Pc)O]_n$	3×10^{-8}		3.33(2)
$\{[Si(Pc)O]I_{0.50}\}_n$	2×10^{-2}		
$\{[Si(Pc)O]I_{1.55}\}_n$	1.4	0.04±0.001	3.33(2)
$\{[Si(Pc)O]I_{4.60}\}_n$	1×10^{-2}		
$\{[Si(Pc)O]Br_{1.00}\}_n$	6×10^{-2}		
$[Ge(Pc)O]_n$	$<10^{-8}$		3.51(2)
$\{[Ge(Pc)O]I_{0.31}\}_n$	7×10^{-4}	0.08±0.001	
$\{[Ge(Pc)O]I_{0.62}\}_n$	1×10^{-2}	0.05±0.001	
$\{[Ge(Pc)O]I_{1.94}\}_n$	6×10^{-2}	0.05±0.007	
$\{[Ge(Pc)O]I_{2.0}\}_n$	1×10^{-1}		
$[Sn(Pc)O]_n$	$<10^{-8}$		3.95(2)
$\{[Sn(Pc)O]I_{1.2}\}_n$	1×10^{-6}		3.95(2)
$\{[Sn(Pc)O]I_{5.5}\}_n$	2×10^{-4}	0.68±0.01	
$[Ni(Pc)]I_{1.0}$[a]	7×10^{-1}	0.036±0.001	3.244(2)

[a] Reference 20.

    Four-probe van der Pauw (40) electrical conductivity measurements on
compacted $[M(Pc)O]_n$ powders show them to be insulators. However, iodine or
bromine doping results in substantial increases in electrical conductivity
(Table 1). The general trend in conductivity as a function of metal is
$\sigma_{Si} > \sigma_{Ge} > \sigma_{Sn}$. Since it is known that the transport characteristics of
iodine-oxidized metallophthalocyanines are largely ligand-dominated and relatively insensitive to the identity of the metal (20,21), the metal dependence
of the conductivity observed in the face-to-face polymers is logically
ascribed to microstructural differences such as how the interplanar separation
is influenced by metal ionic radius. Indeed, the $\{[Si(Pc)O]I_x\}_n$ interplanar
separation is within 0.1 Å of that in the aforementioned "molecular metal"
$[Ni(Pc)]_{1.0}$ and the room temperature powder conductivities of the two
materials are quite comparable (Table 1). Variable temperature studies indicate that the $\{[M(Pc)O]I_x\}_n$ powder conductivities are thermally activated
(Figure 3) and least-squares fits to eq.(3) yield the activation energies compiled in Table 1. Powder conductivity measurements are, of course, influenced

$$\sigma = \sigma_0 \exp(-\Delta/kT) \qquad (3)$$

by interparticle contact resistance and random crystallographic orientations.
For low-dimensional compounds such as $[Ni(Pc)]I_{1.0}$, powder conductivities are
typically 10^2-10^3 less than single crystal conductivities in the stacking
direction and exhibit thermally activated temperature dependences. Thus,

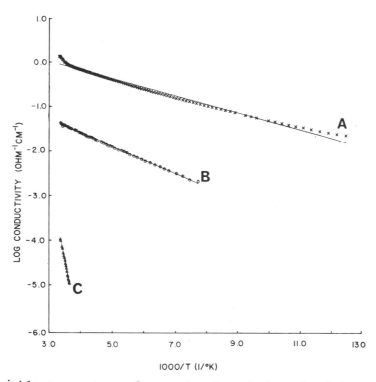

Fig. 3. Variable temperature, four-probe electrical conductivity data for
         compacted powders of A. $\{[Si(Pc)O]I_{1.55}\}_n$ B. $\{[Ge(Pc)O]I_{2.0}\}_n$
         C. $\{[Sn(Pc)O]I_{5.5}\}_n$. The straight lines indicate least-squares fits
         to eq.(3).

"metal-like" temperature dependence (dσ/dT < 0) is usually masked. However, from the magnitudes of the powder conductivities of the $\{[M(Pc)O]I_x\}_n$ materials it is possible to anticipate that "metal-like" charge transport will be observed in the chain direction for the M = Si and perhaps M = Ge materials. Further information on this question is provided by voltage shorted compaction (VSC) measurements (41). This technique offers a qualitative means to ascertain anisotropic transport properties in pressed powder samples by deliberately shorting out sources of interparticle resistance. As can be seen in Figure 4, this measurement (42) reveals metal-like (dσ/dT < 0) behavior at higher temperatures, a relatively broad maximum, and a transition to a less conducting state at low temperatures. The results of the variable temperature conductivity measurements also underscore the robust thermal character of the cofacially arrayed polymers. $\{[Si(Pc)O]I_x\}_n$ samples could be cycled to 300°C with only minor deterioration in room temperature conductivity (apparently due to vaporization of the iodine).

Weak, relatively temperature independent paramagnetism is another characteristic of highly conductive materials with appreciable bandwidths (1-5). Static susceptibility measurements on the $\{[Si(Pc)O]I_x\}_n$ and $\{[Ge(Pc)O]I_x\}_n$ materials by the Faraday method reveal weak ($\chi_m = 300-500 \times 10^{-6}$ emu after corrections for diamagnetism) paramagnetism which varies only modestly with temperature from 300-77°K. Again, there is evidence for a "metal-like" material.

WHAT CONSTITUTES AN EFFECTIVE DOPANT?

Halogens are known to be especially effective acceptors for stabilizing low-dimensional mixed valent arrays of a great many organic and metal-organic donors (15), with the present systems being only a small subset. In attempting to understand why halogens are so effective at partially oxidizing

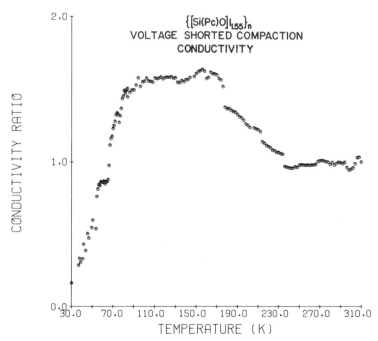

Fig. 4. Voltage shorted compaction conductivity measurement on $\{[Si(Pc)O]I_{1.55}\}_n$.

metallomacrocycles, it is first instructive to consider those factors which stabilize a donor-acceptor lattice. For a charge-transferred material, the crystal binding energy (E_C^{ρ}) can be expressed approximately as in eq.(4),

$$E_C \cong \rho(I-A) + \rho^2 E_M + \rho^2 E_{ex} + \rho^2 E_{pol} + E_B^{\rho} + E_{vdW}^{\rho} + E_{CR}^{\rho} \qquad (4)$$

where ρ is the degree of incomplete charge transfer, I is the gas-phase ionization potential of the neutral donor molecule, A is the gas phase electron affinity of the neutral acceptor, E_M is the Madelung energy, E_{ex} is the exchange energy, E_{pol} is the polarization energy gained by interaction with dipoles induced on neighboring sites, E_B^{ρ} is the energy gained by band formation, E_{vdW}^{ρ} is the van der Waals energy, and E_{CR}^{ρ} is the core repulsion energy (43). Although such a relationship at first appears intractable for predicting which systems will form low-dimensional mixed valent lattices, holding the acceptor constant leads to an interesting empirical result. In Table 2 are collected gas phase ionization potentials (44) of molecular donor systems known to form low-dimensional mixed valent solids with iodine. The surprising observation is that for a wide spectrum of donors, including phthalocyanines and porphyrins, the ionization potentials fall within a narrow range (especially when the perylene complex, which is marginally stable, is excluded). Conjugated donors with higher or lower ionization potentials generally appear not to form mixed valent salts (15). These observations suggest that the I-A term in eq.(4) plays a dominant role, and that the other terms remain nearly constant for the classes of donors presently under consideration.

Halogens are not the only acceptors that form mixed valent materials with organic donors. Organic oxidants such as the high potential quinones shown below form a wide range of partially oxidized conductive salts (1-5). For this reason, it was of interest to explore the response of molecular metallo-macrocycles (e.g., metallophthalocyanines) to quinone oxidants. In all cases investigated to date, and in striking contrast to halogen dopants, only poorly conductive materials were produced (42). This result raises the interesting question of whether, in addition to electron affinity (I-A in eq.(4)), halogens may play some other role, e.g., structure-forming, in stabilizing the mixed valent lattice. There is some evidence that quinones may promote the formation of integrated stack crystal structures (28).

Table 2. Gas Phase Ionization Potentials of Molecular Donors Forming Mixed Valent Salts with Iodine.[a]

Donor	Ionization Potential (eV)
Perylene	6.97
TMPD	6.84
TTF	6.83
TMTTF	6.40
TTT	6.50
M(Pc)	6.36-6.41
M(OEP)	6.31-6.39

[a]TMPD = N,N,N',N'-tetramethylphenylenediamine; TTF = tetrathiafulvalene: TMTTF = tetramethyltetrathiafulvalene; TTT = tetrathiatetracene; M(OEP) = 2,3,7,8,12,13,17,18-octaethylporphyrin.

TCNQ   fluoranil   chloranil

bromanil   DDQ   DHB

The availability of the face-to-face polymer system with enforced metallo-macrocycle stacking suggests an intriguing experiment to begin to differentiate the redox and structure-forming properties of the dopants. Would conductive, mixed valent metallomacrocyclic arrays be produced by quinone oxidants if segregated stacking were inviolably guaranteed? Doping experiments with the $[Si(Pc)O]_n$ polymers were thus carried out by stirring these materials with solutions of the above quinones. The products were characterized by elemental analysis and vibrational specroscopy. That reduction of the quinone occurs, with concurrent oxidation of the metallomacrocyclic array, is demonstrated by infrared specroscopy. As exemplified by Figure 5, the reduced quinone anions (45) (along with neutral quinone) can be readily detected. As can be seen in Table 3, large increases in elecrical conductivity accompany quinone doping of the face-to-face phthalocyanine polymers (but not the molecular phthalocyanine) (42). Indeed, the DDQ-doped materials are nearly as conductive as those doped with halogens. Variable temperature transport data are shown in Figure 6 for several samples. The temperature dependences are thermally activated and activation energies derived from least-squares fits to eq.(3) are compiled in Table 3. Clearly, if the stacked donor microstructure can be preserved, mixed valent conductive assemblies can in fact be produced with quinone or probably many other oxidants. This adds a new dimension to the types of conductive materials which can be fabricated and the range of properties which can be incorporated.

It would also seem possible to produce conductive materials by donor rather than acceptor doping. A number of attempts have been made in this Laboratory to partially reduce metallophthalocyanines using alkali metals (36). In all cases, the resulting materials were insulators, and it was conjectured that nonstacked materials were being produced. A preliminary experiment was conducted in which $[Si(Pc)O]_n$ was reacted with potassium vapor in a sealed tube. The product was collected and handled at all times under an inert atmosphere. As can be seen in Table 3, a significant increase in electrical conductivity accompanies the potassium doping. Further efforts to refine the reductive doping procedure are in progress.

INFRARED SPECTRA

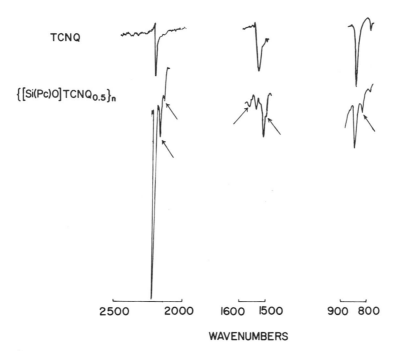

Fig. 5. Solid state infrared spectra of TCNQ and $[Si(Pc)O]_n$ doped with TCNQ. The arrows indicate normal modes assignable to $TCNQ^-$.

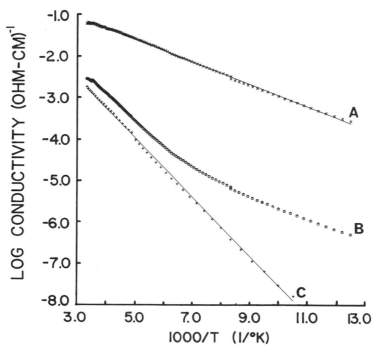

Fig. 6. Variable temperature powder conductivity data for A. $\{[Si(Pc)O]DDQ_{0.35}\}_n$ B. $\{[Si(Pc)O]TCNQ_{0.50}\}_n$ C. $\{[Si(Pc)O]ClA_{0.14}\}_n$.

Table 3.   Charge Transport for Polycrystalline Samples of Molecular
           Phthalocyanines and Cofacial Phthalocyanine Polymers with Various
           Dopants

Dopant[a]	Empirical Formula	$G(\Omega^{-1}\ cm^{-1})300°K$	Activation Energy(eV)
none	$[Si(Pc)O]_n$	3×10^{-8}	
I	$\{[Si(Pc)O]I_{1.55}\}_n$	1.4	$0.04 \pm .001$
Br	$\{[Si(Pc)O]Br_{1.00}\}_n$	6×10^{-2}	
K	$\{[Si(Pc)O]K_{1.0}\}_n$	2×10^{-5}	
DDQ	$\{[Si(Pc)O]DDQ_{1.00}\}_n$	2.1×10^{-2}	
DDQ	$\{[Si(Pc)O]DDQ_{0.35}\}_n$	6.2×10^{-2}	$0.05 \pm .001$
TCNQ	$\{[Si(Pc)O]TCNQ_{0.50}\}_n$	2.8×10^{-3}	
ClA	$\{[Si(Pc)O]ClA_{0.14}\}_n$	1.8×10^{-3}	$0.11 \pm .001$
Flr	$\{[Si(Pc)O]Flr_{0.23}\}_n$	7.2×10^{-4}	$0.13 \pm .001$
Chl	$\{[Si(Pc)O]Chl_{.037}\}_n$	6.9×10^{-4}	$0.13 \pm .002$
Brl	$\{[Si(Pc)O]Brl_{0.84}\}_n$	5.8×10^{-4}	$0.15 \pm .001$
DHB	$\{[Si(Pc)O]DHB_{0.13}\}_n$	3.8×10^{-5}	$0.19 \pm .005$
DDQ	$Ni(Pc)DDQ_{0.11}$	2.5×10^{-7}	0.43 ± 0.004
ClA	$Ni(Pc)ClA_{0.91}$	8.4×10^{-7}	0.16 ± 0.002

a
 Flr = fluoranil; Chl = chloranil; Brl = bromanil; DDQ =
 dichlorodicyanoquinone; ClA = chloranilic acid; DHB = dihydroxy-
 benzoquinone.

CONCLUSIONS

     The cofacial metallomacrocycle assembly strategy represents what is likely
the most powerful approach yet devised for controlling molecular microstructure
in low dimensional, electroactive materials. In regard to fundamental
understanding, we already have learned a great deal about bandwidth-
conductivity and donor-acceptor relationships in conductive materials composed
of molecular stacks. However, the surface has only been barely scratched in
terms of the opportunities which await exploitation in this area. Further
synthetic work offers the opportunity to make drastic changes in metallomacro-
cycle identity and electronic structure, stacking distance and bandwidth,
interplanar relationships and phonon dynamics, and to correlate these chemical
and structural modifications with physical observables. Already, new macro-
cycles (46), metal ions (47,48) and bridging functionalities (49) have been
introduced. We have also learned that it is possible to produce films of
$[Si(Pc)O]_n$ and that halogen doping results in substantial increases in
electrical conductivity (50).

ACKNOWLEDGMENTS

This research was generously supported by the Office of Naval Research and by the NSF-MRL program through the Materials Research Center of Northwestern University (grants DMR79-23573). We thank our colleagues Prof. C.R. Kannewurf and Dr. E.A. Mintz for stimulating discussions.

REFERENCES

1. J.T. Devreese, V.E. Evrard, and V.E. Van Doren, eds., "Highly Conducting One-Dimensional Solids," Plenum Press, New York (1979).

2. W.E. Hatfield, ed., "Molecular Metals", Plenum Press, New York (1979).

3. J.B. Torrance, Accts. Chem. Res., 12, 79 (1979).

4. J.S. Miller and A.J. Epstein, eds., "Synthesis and Properties of Low-Dimensional Materials", Ann. NY Acad. Sci., 313 (1979).

5. H.J. Keller, eds., "Chemistry and Physics of One-Dimensional Metals", Plenum Press, New York (1977).

6. (a) S. Yoshimura and M. Murakami, "Solid State Reactions in Organic Conductors and Their Technological Applications", in reference 4, p. 269; (b) S.D. Senturia, C.M. Sechen, J.A. Wishneusky, Appl. Phys. Lett., 30, 106 (1977).

7. A. Aviram and M.A. Ratner, Chem. Phys. Lett., 29, 27 (1974).

8. R.S. Potember, T.O. Poehler, H. Rappa, D.O. Cowan, and A.N. Bloch, J. Am. Chem. Soc. 102, 3659 (1980).

9. Y. Tomkiewicz, E.M. Engler, J.D. Kuptsis, R.G. Shad, V.V. Patel, and M. Hatzakis, "Organic Conductors as Electron Beam Resist Materials", Extended Abstracts, Electrochemical Society Spring Meeting, St. Louis, May, 1980, No. 63.

10. A.G. MacDiarmid, private communication.

11. (a) S. Yoshimura, "Potential Applications of Molecular Metals", in reference 2, p. 471, and references therein; (b) C.D. Jaeger and A.J. Bard, J. Am. Chem. Soc., 102, 5435 (1980).

12. (a) C.K. Chiang, S.C. Gau, C.R. Fincher, Jr., Y.W. Park, A.G. MacDiarmid, and A.J. Heeger, Appl. Phys. Lett. 33, 78 (1978); (b) M. Ozaki, D. Peebles, B.R. Weinberger, A.J. Heeger, and A.G. MacDiarmid, J. Appl. Phys., 51, 4252 (1980).

13. E.M. Engler, W.B. Fox, L.V. Interrante, J.S. Miller, F. Wudl, S. Yoshimura, A. Heeger, and R.H. Baughman, in reference 2, p. 541.

14. T.J. Marks and D.W. Kalina, "Highly Conductive Halogenated Low-Dimensional Materials", in "Extended Linear Chain Compounds", J.S. Miller, ed., Plenum Press, New York, in press.

15. T.J. Marks, Ann. NY Acad. Sci., 313, 594 (1978).

16. (a) J. Hubbard, Proc. Roy. Soc. London Ser. A., 276, 238 (1963); (b) Proc. Roy. Soc. London Ser. A., 277, 237 (1964); (c) Proc. Roy. Soc. London Ser. A., 281, 401 (1964).

17. M.A. Cowie, A. Gleizes, G.W. Grynkewich, D.W. Kalina, M.S. McClure, R.P. Scaringe, R.C. Teitelbaum, S.L. Ruby, J.A. Ibers, C.R. Kannewurf, and T.J. Marks, J. Am. Chem. Soc., 101, 2921 (1979), and references therein.

18. T.J. Marks, D.F. Webster, S.L. Ruby, S. Schutz, J. Chem. Soc., Chem. Commun. 444 (1976).

19. L.D. Brown, D.W. Kalina, M.S. McClure, S.L. Ruby, S. Schultz, J.A. Ibers, C.R. Kannewurf, and T.J. Marks, J. Am. Chem. Soc., 101, 2937 (1979).

20. J.L. Petersen, C.S. Schramm, D.R. Stojakovic, B.M. Hoffman, and T.J. Marks, J. Am. Chem. Soc., 99, 286 (1977).

21. C.S. Schramm, R.P. Scaringe, D.R. Stojakovic, B.M. Hoffman, J.A. Ibers, and T.J. Marks, J. Am. Chem. Soc., 102, 6702 (1980).

22. L.-S. Lin, M.S. McClure, J.W. Lyding, M.T. Ratajack, T.-C. Wang, C.R. Kannewurf, and T.J. Marks, J. Chem. Soc. Chem. Commun., 954 (1980).

23. R.C. Teitelbaum, S.L. Ruby, and T.J. Marks, J. Am. Chem. Soc., 102 3322 (1980).

24. R.C. Teitelbaum, S.L. Ruby, and T.J. Marks, J. Am. Chem. Soc., 101, 7568 (1979).

25. T.J. Kistenmacher, "Structural Relationships in the Heterofulvalene-TCNQ Family of Organic Conductors", in reference 4, p. 333.

26. S. Metgert, J.P. Pougent, and R. Comes, "X-ray Scattering Studies from One-D Conductors", in reference 4, p. 234.

27. G.D. Stucky, A.J. Schultz, and J.M. Williams, Ann. Rev. Mat. Sci., 7, 301 (1977).

28. F.H. Herbstein, Perspect. Struct. Chem., IV, 166 (1971).

29. K.F. Schoch, Jr., B.R. Kundalkar, and T.J. Marks, J. Am. Chem. Soc., 101, 7071 (1979).

30. C.W. Dirk, J.W. Lyding, K.F. Schoch, Jr., C.R. Kannewurf, and T.J. Marks, Organic Coatings and Plastic Chem., 43, 646 (1980).

31. C.W. Dirk, E.A. Mintz, K.F. Schoch, Jr., and T.J. Marks, "Strategies for Control of Lattice Architecture in Low-Dimensional Molecular Metals: Assembly of Partially-Oxidized Face-to-Face Linked Arrays of Metallomacro- cycles", in "Organometallic Polymers: Perspectives", C.E. Carraher and J.E. Sheats, eds., Marcel Dekker, New York and J. Macromol. Science-Chem., in press.

32. (a) R.D. Joyner and M.E. Kenney, J. Am. Chem. Soc., 82, 5790 (1960); (b) M.K. Lowery, A.J. Starshak, S.J., J.N. Esposito, P.C. Krueger, and M.E. Kenney, Inorg. Chem., 4, 128 (1965); (c) W.K. Kroenke, L.E. Sutton, R.D. Joyner, and M.E. Kenney, Inorg. Chem., 2, 1064 (1963).

33. F.A. Moser and A.L. Thomas, "Phthalocyanine Compounds", Reinhold Pub. Co., New York (1963).

34. G.C. Berry, private communication.

35. R.D. Joyner and M.E. Kenney, Inorg. Chem., 1, 717 (1962).

36. K.F. Shoch, Jr. and T.J. Marks, unpublished results.

37. D.R. Swift, "Crystal Structures of Two Transition Metal Complexes, Cis-(methylsulfonato)-2, 2'-bipyridine-tricarbonylmanganese(I) and Bis(p-dithiocumato)-platinum(II)methyldiphenylphosphine", Ph.D. Thesis, Case-Western Reserve University, 1970.

38. R.D. Shannon, Acta Cryst., A32, 751 (1976).

39. (a) C. Glidewell and D.C. Liles, J. Chem. Soc. Chem. Commun., 93 (1979); (b) C. Glidewell and D.C. Liles, Acta Cryst., B34, 119 (1978); (c) C. Glidewell and D.C. Liles, Acta Cryst. B34, 124 (1978); (d) C. Glidewell and D.C. Liles, Acta Cryst., B34, 129 (1978).

40. (a) L.J. van der Pauw, Philips Technical Review, 20, 220 (1958/59); (b) F.M. Smits, Bell Syst. Tech. J., 711 (1958).

41. L.B. Coleman, Rev. Sci. Instrum., 49, 58 (1978).

42. K.F. Schoch, Jr., J.W. Lyding, C.R. Kannewurf, and T.J. Marks, unpublished results.

43. (a) A.J. Epstein, N.O. Lipari, D.J. Sandman, P. Nielsen, Phys. Rev. B. 13, 1569 (1976); (b) J.B. Torrance, B.D. Silverman, Phys. Rev. B, 15, 788 (1977); (c) R.M. Metzger, A.N. Bloch, J. Chem. Phys., 63, 5098 (1975).

44. (a) Perylene: E. Clair, W. Schmidt, Tetrahedron, 32, 2563 (1976); (b) TMPDA: R. Egdell, J.C. Green, C.N.R. Rao, Chem. Phys. Lett., 33, 600 (1975);

    (b) TMPDA: R. Egdell, J. C. Green, C. N. R. Rao, "Photoelectron Spectra of Substituted Benzenes," Chem. Phys. Lett., 33, 600 (1975).

    (c) TTF, TMTTF: R. Gleiter, M. Kobayashi, J. Spanget-Larsen, J. P. Ferraris, A. N. Bloch, K. Bechgaard, D. O. Cowan, "Photoelectron and Electronic Absorption Spectra of Tetrathiafulvalene and Related Compounds," Ber. Bunseng. Phys. Chem., 79, 1218 (1975).

    (d) TTT: D. J. Sandman, G. P. Ceasar, P. Nielsen, A. J. Epstein, T. J. Holmes, "Electronic Structure of the π Donor Naphthalene 1,8-disulfide," J. Am. Chem. Soc., 100, 202 (1978).

    (e) J. Berkowitz, "Photoelectron Spectroscopy of Phthalocyanine Vapors," J. Chem. Phys., 70, 2819 (1979).

    (f) S. Kitagawa, I. Morishma, T. Yonezawa, N. Sata, "Photoelectron Spectroscopic Study on Metallooctaethylporphyrins," Inorg. Chem., 18, 1345 (1979).

45. (a) R. Bozio, A. Girlando, and C. Pecile, "Vibrational Analysis of Quinoid Molecular Ions," J. Chem. Soc. Farad. Trans. II, 71, 1237 (1975)

    (b) B. Lunelli and C. Pecile, "Polarized Infrared Spectra of TCNQ and $TCNQ-d_4$ Single Crystals," J. Chem. Phys., 52, 2375 (1970).

46. C. W. Dirk, C. M. Fendrick, K. F. Schoch, Jr., and T. J. Marks, unpublished results.

47. P. M. Kuznesof, K. J. Wynne, R. S. Nohr, and M. E. Kenney, "Highly Conducting Iodinated Fluoroaluminum and Fluorogallium Phthalocyanine Polymers," J. Chem. Soc., Chem. Commun., 121 (1980).

48. R. S. Nohr, K. J. Wynne, and M. E. Kenney, "Iodine-Doped Phthalocyanine Chromium Fluoride: Easily Accessible, Highly Conducting Compositions," Polymer Preprints, in press. We thank these authors for a preprint.

49. C. W. Dirk and T. J. Marks, unpublished results.

50. J. W. Lyding, M. S. McCLure, C. R. Kannewurf, and T. J. Marks, unpublished results.

DISCUSSION

Dr. Sandman: GTE - The polymers in which you go from silicon to germanium to tin and watch the conductivity decrease is a very fascinating example, and possibly the best indication available of that particular phenomenon. There is, I believe, another example of that in the literature; in what I will call a contact driven structure, in the context of my talk earlier this afternoon, is the system characterized by Fred Wudl at Bell where he takes one, four, five, eight-tetrathianaphthalene and TCNQ. He finds a conductivity at room temperature on an order of magnitude lower than TTF-TCNQ. The structure exhibits the normal sulfur intermolecular spacing of about 3.47Å and a somewhat longer interplanar spacing in the TCNQ chain than in TTF-TCNQ, effectively giving a one band system instead of the two-band structure. (Note added: The trend from metallic to semiconducting behavior in organic solids as a function of crystal packing analogous to a Mott transition has been discussed: D. J. Sandman, Mol. Cryst. Liq. Cryst., 50, 235 (1979)).

Prof. Marks: Within the constraints of a molecular system, he has done some very nice things. Of course, the chemistry is both difficult and serendipitous since there is so little control over structure and packing. In contrast, to control architecture in our systems, bond energies on the order of 100 kilocalories per mole are holding the stack together. Furthermore, we can make our polymers in very large quantities.

Dr. Sandman: You described the polymers as being highly crystalline, which is a fascinating situation since the molecular weights at 100 repeat units is relatively high. Do you see any amorphous characteristics in your X-ray diffraction studies?

Prof. Marks: They are somewhat broadened. If you think about what the architecture of this polymer must be like, Dan, it is unlike less rigid polymers. The face-to-face polymers must have very still chains. The material must be highly crystalline. One thing this implies, or at least might be fun to explore, is that some of the characteristics of this material may turn out to be a lot like Kevlar. Kevlar is rod-like, stiff, you can only process it in an acid, but on the other hand, you can make fibers that are stronger than steel. You can make bullet-proof vests out of it. Maybe we could make blue bullet-proof vests or tire cords! Phthalocyanines are blue, if you didn't know it. In regard to characterization of our polymers, we are collaborating with Guy Berry at Carnegie-Mellon in getting solution molecular weight information by light scattering. We are also studying the degree of polymerization in the solid state by FTIR. We are still working on the powder diffraction. At this point the material appears to be quite crystalline. The electron micrographs we have taken indicate that the particles have well-defined edges and corners-- that we are really dealing with small crystallites. In fact, we want to obtain larger crystallites and measure the conductivity of the oriented crystallites.

Dr. Sandman: The remaining question I would ask is do you have any indication in your X-ray data of precisely how the molecular acceptors such as TCNQ go into the polymer?

Prof. Marks: We haven't done any diffraction work on those polymers yet. The halogenated materials are very easy because the diffraction patterns look very much like nickel phthalocyanine iodide, that is, metallomacrocyle stacks and parallel chains of acceptor molecules. The diffraction patterns look very, very similar. Furthermore, the only way the face-to-face polymers differ is that on going from silicon to germanium to tin (you can index them in the tetragonal crystal system) is in the c spacing. That is, the inter-planar repeat distance becomes larger and larger and larger. The rest of the pattern stays pretty much the same.

Prof. Code: Xerox, Univ. of Tor. - Would you have any comment to make on the relative thermal stability of the doped phthalocyanine polymers, in particular, those doped with iodine versus those doped with DDQ.

Prof. Marks: Yes. All that seems to happen upon heating--we have conductivity measurements on the silicon polymer doped with iodine up to 350 degrees centigrade--is that the iodine starts vaporizing out. That doesn't happen as readily with the quinone-doped polymers. These are very, very thermally stable kinds of materials. Of course this type of stability is intrinsic to phthalocyanines. For example, copper phthalocyanine can be sublimed, unchanged, at 1100 degrees centigrade, and can be dissolved concentrated in sulphuric acid and precipitated without change. In fact, this is a good way to purify phthalocyanines. These are very, very stable kinds of building blocks that we are starting with, and siloxane polymers are also very, very stable.

Dr. Shipman: ANL - Do these powers indicate photoconductivity in the absence of donors?

Prof. Marks: Yes, but the numbers we have at present are so qualitative that I can't really tell you much more about photoconductivity at present. The answer is a positive photoresponse. From what one knows about the phthalocyanines, there are a number of papers on phthalocyanine photovoltaics and related devices, it would not be surprising. The fascinating thing is whether or not-- most phthalocyanines, of course, have a slipped structure rather than a one on top of the other structure--the face-to-face architecture brings about something different, and we are certainly anxious to find out. We are also working on making films of this stuff, fibers of it, things like that.

Dr. Haddon: Bell - I seem to remember with the molecular compounds that you had some hysteresis associated with the conductivity. Does that also apply in the case of the polymers?

Prof. Marks: No. First of all, in regard to the molecular compounds, we have checked the transition very carefully. Not all of the crystals showed hysteresis (effort in collaboration with Brian Hoffman and Jim Ibers). Some of the effect seems to be mechanical, and Ted Poehler made some microwave

measurements for us to verify this.   There is definitely a phase transition
there, and we are going to have to do low temperature X-ray work which is just
getting started, to verify this.   I would bet it is a Peierls transition, but
that in itself raises a fascinating question.   When we put the spacers in
between the rings, as you saw in the voltage shorted compaction data, it looks
as if we did something to that transition, and that is exciting.   We want to
figure out what has happened.

CHAPTER XVI

BIOLOGICAL ASSEMBLY OF MOLECULAR ULTRACIRCUITS

K. M. Ulmer
Genex Corporation
12300 Washington Avenue
Rockville, MD 20852

INTRODUCTION

There are two fundamentally different approaches for the fabrication of microelectronic devices. The first of these is exemplified by the current state-of-the-art lithographic techniques. These methods are based on control of physical and chemical parameters at a macroscopic scale in order to produce features with microscopic dimensions. Although these techniques have been developed to a high art and offer potential for further reduction in device size, they have inherent limitations which are perhaps best illustrated by analogy to the problem of trying to write smaller and smaller letters on a piece of paper. The pencil must be sharpened to a finer and finer point, just as electron beams with spot sizes a few nanometers across must be used to produce a submicron circuit pattern. A very steady hand is needed in order to make the characters legible. At a fine enough scale we run into the "shaky" hand of the uncertainty principle. Problems may also be encountered with the paper, particularly when the size of the letters approaches that of the cellulose fibers which make up the paper. Similarly, the heterogeneity of materials at a molecular scale becomes a major problem for submicron device fabrication. Lastly, our written page is only two dimensional and problems may be encountered in trying to neatly stack more than a few sheets at a time. The registration problems associated with submicron lithography are particularly problematical.

At the molecular scale, a radically different approach to device fabrication based upon self-assembly may be possible. Here devices are constructed molecule by molecule, driven by thermodynamics and by the unique chemical properties of the individual molecules. The existence proof for self-assembly of extremely complex functional systems is life. The biochemical organization of living cells is very different from what would be desirable in a molecular electronic device, but molecular biology and biochemistry offer a model upon which to base the development of self-organizing systems. Furthermore, the new techniques of recombinant DNA and genetic engineering now offer the tools required to fabricate self-assembling molecular "devices" with electronic properties.

213

MOLECULAR SELF-ASSEMBLY

Self-assembly is characteristic of biomolecules. All of the genetic information required to produce any organism is encoded in deoxyribonucleic acid or DNA. The DNA molecule is a linear polymer of four nucleotides or bases: adenine (A), cytosine (C), guanine (G), and thymine (T). The genome or complete DNA sequence of a small virus contains several thousand bases in a single linear molecule, while the genomes of higher organisms such as man contain several billion bases. DNA is actually a double-stranded polymer composed of two strands running in opposite directions and whose sequences are self-complementary. A base in one strand is able to form hydrogen bonds with the base opposite it in the other strand according to a pairing rule where A pairs with T and C pairs with G. A short stretch of double stranded DNA could be schematically represented as follows:

5'.......ACCTTGATGCTCCTGGCACAGATGAGGAAAATCTCTCTTTTCTCCTGCTTGAAGGACAGA......3'
3'.......TGGAACTACGAGGACCGTGTCTACTCCTTTTAGAGAGAAAAGAGGACGAACTTCCTGTCT......5'

If the two strands of a DNA molecule are physically separated and then mixed back together in solution under appropriate conditions, they will perfectly reestablish the original pairing for their entire length. This is thermo-dynamically the most stable conformation and therefore arises spontaneously. This is what is meant by self-assembly.

Similar pairing rules are used by the enzyme RNA polymerase in order to copy the information from one DNA strand into another nucleic acid polymer called ribonucleic acid or RNA. RNA contains the base uracil (U) in place of thymine but follows the same pairing rule: U with A. It is the RNA copy of the information in DNA which is used to direct the synthesis of proteins on complex structures called ribosomes. The messenger RNA (mRNA) molecule is "recognized" by the ribosome with the aid of the same nucleic acid pairing rules. The ribosome contains a molecule of ribosomal RNA (rRNA) as part of its structure. The complement of part of the sequence of this rRNA is found near the beginning of each mRNA molecule in a region called the Shine -Dalgarno or SD sequence. After the mRNA has bound to the ribosome in this fashion protein synthesis is initiated. The ribosome moves along the mRNA molecule and extracts the genetic information with the aid of a third type of RNA called transfer or tRNA. Each tRNA molecule is "charged" or bound to an amino acid which is specific for its sequence. Three of the bases in another region of the tRNA molecule pair with three bases in the mRNA on the ribosome. This nucleotide triplet or codon is specific for the amino acid carried by that tRNA. Enzymatic components of the ribosome then remove the amino acid from the tRNA and incorporate it into the growing protein by forming a peptide bond. The ribosome then moves three bases further down the mRNA and the process is repeated. Eventually, one of the three possible codons which code for "stop," rather than for an amino acid, terminates the synthesis and releases the protein from the ribosome. All of the functions carried out by the ribosome including recognition of SD sequences and binding of mRNA, decoding of the genetic information and binding of the appropriate tRNA's, and synthesis and release of the encoded protein are packed into a structure only 18 nm long. The ribosome is truly an impressive molecular "device", which is also self-assembling.

The ribosome is composed to two subunits. The smaller 30S subunit is made up of about twenty proteins and a single rRNA molecule. All of the individual components have been separated and purified. When mixed together under appropriate conditions, they reassemble spontaneously to form functional 30S subunits. In addition, one of the components can be replaced with a molecule isolated from a different species of organism and the subunit will still assemble and function properly even though the foreign molecule has a different sequence. There is a good bit of "flexibility" in the self-assembly process while at the same time maintaining a self-correcting quality. Molecules with a grossly incorrect sequence will not fold up into the proper three dimensional geometry and will therefore not be recognized and assembled into the final structure.

A more complex method of assembly is utilized by the viruses or bacteriophage which infect bacteria. The phage is basically a shell of proteins which surrounds the genetic material of the virus, either RNA or DNA. Infection is initiated by insertion of the phage genome into the host cell. The phage genome codes for specific enzymes and structural proteins required to replicate the genetic material and package it into new phage particles. Some of the biochemical machinery of the host cell is subverted to this end, and other host functions are simply turned off. During phage morphogenesis the genetic material of the virus is copied by polymerases and the various components of the protein shell are produced on the host cell's ribosomes. Some of the proteins in the capsid or coat assemble spontaneously in a manner similar to that described for the ribosome above. Some stages of the phage assembly require the catalytic action of specific enzymes in order to modify the proteins or actually link them together. These enzymes usually do not appear as part of the finished phage particle, but they are often coded on the phage genome. The actual process of phage morphogenesis is far more complex than outlined here, involving the precisely coordinated expression of many genes. Not everything is synthesized at once, but instead there is a temporal sequence of events, orchestrated by the interaction of DNA, RNA and protein, which leads from infection to release of the progeny phage.

BIOMOLECULES IN ELECTRONIC DEVICES

The total diversity of living organisms is based upon exactly the same biochemistry involving DNA, RNA and proteins. Only five different bases in nucleic acids and twenty amino acids in proteins are required. It is the universality of molecular biology and the extraordinary range of organic compounds which can be synthesized by living cells which offers the potential for genetically engineering systems for the production of molecular electronic devices. The biochemicals which are found in living cells today have evolved to play scientific roles in the life cycle of the organism. It is not likely that we will find naturally occurring compounds or macromolecular assemblages which can serve as diodes, transistors, conductors, and resistors. Living cells would have little use for such molecules. Until now, biologists and biochemists have only been able to point at existing structures such as ribosomes and viruses and say, "See what elegant molecular devices we are made of!" They had no idea how to turn them into electronically useful devices. With the advent of recombinant DNA technology, we now have the ability to biologically produce any protein we desire. We are presently limited by not knowing what proteins to make. Conceivably we can custom design proteins to serve as catalysts for the metabolic production of organic compounds with electronic properties such as conduction or switching. Carter (1,2) has described several theoretical organic compounds which might possess such properties. More importantly, however, proteins could provide the structural backbone for molecular electronic devices. Proteins could be designed to recognize and bind electronically functional molecules in the same manner that enzymes recognize and specifically bind their substrates. Different proteins bearing different functional molecules could then self-assemble to bring these molecules together in precise orientation and covalently link them where necessary. This process could be repeated with a diverse array of functional proteins, building up a two-dimensional organic crystal containing a complex electronic circuit.

It may be possible to "borrow" the structure of existing biomolecules which can be modified to function electronically. For example, there are many biomolecules which chelate specific metal ions and incorporate them into their structure. Certain porphyrins can bind a single atom of iron, magnesium, zinc, nickel, cobalt, or copper. These porphyrins can in turn be bound to proteins as in hemoglobin. Using this basic strategy, it may be possible to design a protein which would assemble into a long tubular structure with many metal-containing porphyrin groups stacked along the axis of the tube. With the proper molecular structure it might be possible to overlap the orbitals of adjacent metal atoms and thereby form a linear conductor with a cross-section of only one atom.

GENETIC ENGINEERING

Newly developed techniques in molecular biology, specifically recombinant DNA technology, DNA sequencing, and oligonucleotide synthesis now make it possible to precisely engineer the genetic information of living cells. We can combine genes from widely different organisms into a single host cell and manipulate the regulatory sequences in the DNA to control the expression of the encoded protein products. By de novo chemical synthesis we can create totally artificial DNA sequences for proteins not found in nature or for novel regulatory elements. It is this technology which will allow us to produce any protein sequence desired.

The basic requirements for cloning a foreign gene are a suitable vector or cloning vehicle and a method of introducing the hybrid DNA molecule into a host cell. The vectors most commonly used are plasmids. Plasmids are covalently closed circular DNA molecules which can range in size from a few thousand bases to several hundred thousand bases. The plasmids are self-replicating and exist inside the cell as independent molecules from the chromosomal DNA of the host cell. Each plasmid thus possesses at least one origin of replication which can function in the host cell. Vectors which are designed to function in more than one host frequently contain different origins for each host type. Another important characteristic of a vector is the presence of a DNA sequence which codes for a selectable marker. This means that the plasmid will express a specific protein or set of proteins which enable the investigator to identify those host cells which have the vector in them. Frequently the selectable marker is a gene which codes for resistance to an antibiotic. When a population of host cells is treated with the antibiotic, only those cells containing the plasmid vector and expressing the antibiotic resistance factor will survive.

Specific cloning sites must also be present in the vector. This means that there must be specific locations in the sequence of the plasmid DNA which can be uniquely cut by special enzymes called restriction endonucleases. The restriction enzymes are proteins with the ability to recognize specific short sequences in DNA and then make a cut through both strands of the DNA. When a circular plasmid DNA molecule is cut at a unique restriction enzyme site, it is converted into a linear molecule with two ends. For example

the restriction endonuclease EcoRI recognizes the following hexanucleotide
sequence in DNA:

$$5'.....GAATTC.....3'$$
$$3'.....CTTAAG.....5'$$

This hexanucleotide is a palindrome, which is a sequence that is identical
on both strands when each is read in the 5' to 3' direction. Many of the
recognition sites for restriction enzymes are palindromes. If a plasmid is
treated with EcoRI, every site like the one shown above will be cut by the
enzyme to produce ends with single-strand extensions:

$$5'.....G \qquad\qquad AATTC.....3'$$
$$3'.....CTTAA \qquad\qquad G.....5'$$

These are known as "sticky ends" because the single-strand extension on one
end is complementary to the other. Under appropriate conditions, such ends
can recognize each other and reestablish the hydrogen bonds between the
complementary bases. This brings the two ends back together again. If the
enzyme DNA ligase is added, the covalent bonds between the bases which were
cleaved by the restriction enzyme are reformed and the molecule is again
intact. Several hundred different restriction enzymes have been identified.
Among these over seventy different recognition patterns occur and many
different types of ends are produced by their cleavage.

Restriction enzymes and DNA ligase are the "scissors" and "glue" used
by molecular biologists to "cut and paste" DNA molecules. By appropriate
choice of enzyme(s) a gene or sequence fragment of interest can be cut out
of one DNA molecule and then inserted into a plasmid vector which has been
cut with the same enzyme(s). DNA ligase is then used to glue the hybrid
vector molecule back together.

The "splicing" of DNA molecules can be followed experimentally by the
use of DNA sequencing techniques. Rapid methods are now available to determine the exact sequence of DNA at the nucleotide level. It is thus possible
to perform all of these operations "with our eyes open". The sequence of
every molecular construction can be verified if desired by sequencing. In
addition, DNA sequencing is an invaluable tool for deciphering more of the
genetic code. At present we understand the "genetic code" to the extent that
we can translate DNA into protein and we are able to recognize a few of the
"control signals" which regulate the expression of genes. It is in this
latter area that we are in fact woefully ignorant. We will need to better
understand the regulation of gene expression at the sequence level in order
to engineer complex, coordinately regulated artificial sequences. The number
of bases which have been sequenced to date is approaching 500,000. As this
sequence library grows, we will be better able to recognize patterns in the
sequences which have biological significance. We will also have an extensive
catalog of natural sequences from which to choose "parts" which would be
useful in the construction of engineered sequences.

Once such a recombinant molecule has been created, it must be introduced
into a host cell in order to replicate and amplify the number of copies of the
newly inserted fragment. This process is known as transformation. At present,
the most commonly used host cell is the bacterium Escherichia coli. More
is known about the genetics of this bacterium than any other living thing
on earth, and we have developed the greatest facility for manipulating the

genetics of this organism. Cloning is not limited to E. coli, however, and
has been demonstrated in at least rudimentary fashion in other bacteria, fungi,
and yeast as well as in plant and animal cells. With sufficient effort it
should be possible to use almost any type of cell as a host for cloning.

We are not limited to naturally occurring DNA sequences as a source of
genetic material for cloning. DNA can be chemically synthesized with any
sequence desired. Oligonucleotide synthesis is still a slow and expensive
task, but recent advances in the chemistry, combined with solid phase supports
for the growing oligonucleotide chain have made possible the development of
automated instruments for DNA synthesis. An instrument based on phosphite
chemistry is claimed to add one base every 30 minutes. Although no one has
yet attempted synthesizing a DNA molecule longer than a few hundred base
pairs, with these new machines it should be possible to synthesize a thousand
bases, which is about the size of an average gene. Further improvements in
the rate of DNA synthesis will be critically important for any attempt to
design and build novel proteins for use in molecular electronic devices.

<h2 style="text-align:center">PROTEIN DESIGN</h2>

The basic premise of this approach to the fabrication of molecular
electronic devices is that proteins can be designed with the required catalytic
and/or structural properties. This in turn rests on our ability to predict
the three dimensional folding of a protein from the primary sequence of amino
acids. As a protein is synthesized, thermodynamics favors very specific
folding of the peptide backbone. Some regions of the protein will twist into
helices while others will fold into pleated sheets. Hydrophobic amino acids
will fold inward together, away from the aqueous solvent, and polar side groups
will become hydrated and extend outward from the protein. Specific cysteine
residues may form covalent disulfide bonds to cross-link the folded molecule.
In the final stages of folding, distinct domains in the protein may fold
together due to ionic forces or hydrophobic interactions at their surfaces.
It is this specific pattern of spontaneous folding which we need to be able to
predict with a high degree of accuracy. Active research is in progress in
several areas which are critical for the development of this capability.

In order to devise an algorithm for predicting the three dimensional
folding of a protein from the amino acid sequence we need data from existing
proteins. There are several proteins whose structures have been determined
to a high degree of resolution by X-ray crystallographic techniques. The
most useful among these are the immunoglobulins or antibody molecules. They
are somewhat unique among proteins in that they are composed of subunits
which contain specific regions of identical amino acid sequence as well as
regions of highly variable sequence. The basic backbone of the immunoglobulin
molecule is similar enough among members of a given class, that the structure
of the variable region can be predicted by computer calculation of energies
for all possible combinations of bond stretching and rotation in the variable
region. A real-time color graphic display of the antibody molecule can then
be generated on a computer terminal to be rotated and examined at will. This
capability already exists in several research laboratories (3,4). Thus, it
is now possible to "redesign" small sections of immunoglobulin molecules by
computer.

Although the structures of several other proteins have been determined,
we can not as yet calculate the complete structure entirely from sequence
data. Short stretches of amino acid sequence which comprise domains of the
protein can be predicted with accuracy (5-9), but the higher order folding

of the molecule cannot. What is needed to improve the algorithms and extend
the ability to predict structure are model proteins with specific alterations
in their sequence. Determination of the actual structure of the model proteins
by X-ray crystallography would then provide the data necessary to refine the
algorithms. Recombinant DNA techniques combined with synthetic oligonucleotide capabilities now make possible the generation of such specific model
proteins and peptides. The type of predictive capability which is currently
possible for the immunoglobulins could thereby be extended to other proteins.

The X-ray crystallography is likely to be a limiting step in this process.
One of the most difficult tasks is the actual crystallization of the protein
in order to subject it to analysis. There is more art than science involved
at this stage and indeed many proteins have proved impossible to crystallize.
Recent advances have been made in the ability to collect and analyze X-ray
data, however. Multiwire area detectors have replaced photographic film and
scattering events can now be collected directly by a computer. More rapid
fast-Fourier transforms have reduced the time necessary to calculate the
electron density profiles. Importantly, the very models we wish to improve
allow us to more rapidly derive structures from the data. Rules for protein
folding developed from short peptides can be used to eliminate certain
structures from consideration and guide the model building (3). This
synergistic effect should result in even more rapid data analysis and structure
determination as the models are improved.

Once we can predict the structure of single proteins from sequence data,
we will need to extend the models to predict the interaction of several
molecules. This capability already exists for binding of small substrates
by enzymes (4), and a 34 amino acid peptide has been designed and synthesized
which will bind to single-stranded DNA (10). In addition, researchers have
achieved some degree of success in designing "synthetic" enzymes (11, 12).
Modifications can be made to critical amino acid residues in the active site
of an enzyme, which do not affect the binding of the substrate, but which
alter the type of chemical reaction which is catalyzed by the enzyme. It thus
appears to be possible to utilize the existing peptide backbone of a protein
and by directed modification to alter its functional properties in a
predictable manner. Similarly it may be possible to alter the structure of
existing proteins to serve as components of molecular electronic devices.

BIOLOGICAL DEVICE ASSEMBLY

The ultimate scenario for the biological fabrication of a molecular
computer would be based upon developing a "genome" for the computer. This
genome would function in a manner quite similar to that of a virus, only
instead of producing more virus, it would assemble a functional computer
inside of a cell. A large DNA molecule would be constructed from naturally
occurring regulatory sequences and numerous custom genes produced by oligonucleotide synthesis. These genes would encode proteins which would serve
as enzymes for the biosynthesis of precursor molecules for the circuit. The
raw materials for the entire molecular computer might be as simple and
inexpensive as a solution of mineral salts and sugar. Intermediates of
cellular metabolism would be converted into organic components for the
molecular devices. Other custom genes would encode the structural proteins
which would assemble the circuit. Device molecules would bind in precise
orientations and additional enzymes might form appropriate bonds to "solder"
the components together. A highly structured organic crystal would begin to
form, and full advantage would be made of the three dimensional architecture.
The assembly would be largely self-correcting. One component could not

assemble out of place or out of turn because it would lack the necessary
binding sites required of the correct molecules. The yield of "perfect"
devices by this form of assembly could approach 100%. As the molecular
computer grows, some genes might be turned off and others turned on to provide
new types of molecules for later stages in the assembly. The final layers
added to the outside of the molecular circuitry would provide the necessary
contacts for connection to more conventional microcircuits. The final
"mounting" of the completed molecular computer would be mediated by adhesive
proteins which would bond to the substrate after precise, spontaneous
alignment.

Modifications to the design of the circuit would only require changing
the DNA sequence using standard recombinant DNA techniques. Indeed, a great
amount of flexibility might be designed into the sequence initially which
would permit the same genome to assemble many different types of devices.
By simply adding certain chemicals to the cells it might be possible to
"reprogram" the morphological development of the circuit.

The number of circuits which could be produced by this approach is
essentially unlimited since the DNA which codes for the computer can be
replicated just like any other DNA molecule and passed on to daughter cells
during cell division. The actual production of the molecular devices would
probably require only very simple equipment.

CONCLUSION

Obviously the mastery of the genetic code with this degree of sophistication is still a long way off. The basic tools required in order to pursue
this approach for the fabrication of molecular devices are available today,
and they are already being applied to the development of novel enzymes and
proteins. The potential for harnessing the biochemical machinery of the cell
in order to structure matter at the molecular scale awaits those daring
enough to undertake this radically new form of engineering.

REFERENCES

1. F.L. Carter, "Problems and Prospects of Future Electroactive Polymers and
    "Molecular" Electronic Devices", in "The NRL Program on Electroactive
    Polymers - First Annual Report", L.B. Lockhart, Jr., ed., NRL Memorandum
    Report 3960, Naval Research Laboratory, Washington, D.C. (1979).

2. F.L. Carter, "Further Considerations on "Molecular" Electronic Devices",
    in "The NRL Program on Electroactive Polymers - Second Annual Report,"
    R.B. Fox, ed., NRL Memorandum Report 4335, Naval Research Laboratory,
    Washington, D.C. (1980).

3. J.L. Fox, Chemical and Engineering News 57, 22 (April 2, 1979).

4. R. Langridge, T.E. Ferrin, I.D. Kuntz and M.L. Connolly, Science 211, 661
    (1981).

5. M. Levitt, Biochemistry 17, 4277 (1978).

6. P.Y. Chou and G.D. Fasman, Biochemistry 13 211 (1974).

7. P.Y. Chou and G.D. Fasman, Journal of Molecular Biology 115, 135 (1977).

8. P.Y. Chou, A.J. Adler and G.D. Fasman, <u>Journal of Molecular Biology</u> <u>96</u>, 29 (1975).

9. D. Kotelchuck and H.A. Scheraga, <u>Proceedings of the National Academy of Sciences</u> <u>62</u>, 14 (1969).

10. B. Guttz, M. Daumigen and E. Wittscheiber, <u>Nature</u> <u>281</u>, 650 (1979).

11. Editor, "Researchers Close in on Synthetic Enzyme", <u>Chemical</u> <u>and</u> <u>Engineering News</u> <u>57</u>, 26 (April 9, 1979).

12. P.K. Chakravarty, K.B. Mathur and M.M. Dhar, <u>Experimentia</u> <u>29</u>, 786 (1973). 14 (1969).

DISCUSSION

Dr. Haddon: Bell - It is a fascinating and enticing picture that you have painted. How much flexibility do we have in the sort of molecular components that we are able to incorporate into this organism? Are we restricted to amino acids, for example?

Dr. Ulmer: I am not proposing that the proteins themselves play the functional role. It could very well be that it is quinones or porphyrins or molecules of that sort. The role of proteins would be as enzymes to produce those compounds in the cell, and as structural molecules to bring them into the proper orientation.

Dr. Haddon: How much would the presence of such groups interfere with the assembly of the macromolecules?

Dr. Ulmer: We would be working with the analogy of an enzyme recognizing its substrate. There are people who are presently taking existing enzymes, and changing the structure of the active site. By changing functional groups around, the same substrate fits in, but the enzyme now catalyzes a different reaction, or by changing the shape of the pocket, a new substrate specificity can be conferred on the enzyme. If you are engineering proteins to fit unusual substrates, I don't think that would be a real problem.

Prof. Honig: Univ. of Ill. - I think your statements about the ability to predict protein conformation are simply incorrect. There are a number of groups around the country trying to do it, but I don't think anyone dreams of being able to predict the structure of even 20 or 30 amino acids, and nobody has succeeded in predicting the structures of antibody combining sites. I would like to know the basis of that statement. It is an area of active interest, but nobody has succeeded.

Dr. Ulmer: There have been proteins designed from scratch--short peptides, not proteins, for example, with the ability to bind DNA molecules. I have a paper I can show you afterwards where a 34 residue peptide was designed specifically for that purpose and it functions as designed. For very short peptides, I think the predictability is pretty good.

Prof. Honig: To my knowledge nobody has succeeded in doing it. There are about ten groups trying to work on this problem involving antibody combining sites. Nobody has published a paper where they claim any success in predicting an unknown.

Dr. Ulmer: Mike Potter's group at NIH has the computer system and programs for antibodies I was just discussing.

Dr. Greyber: NSF - If you are creating a polymer and the proteins are directing this, to what extent can you be hurt by heavy metals and components with high Z components. Can the proteins exist in the same milieu and still function?

Dr. Ulmer: Proteins bind small molecules containing high Z number atoms without any apparent problem. They are integral components of many protein complexes. I don't think that would be a problem.

Dr. Greyber: There is no poisoning effect?

Dr. Ulmer: You can poison certain catalytic functions of enzymes by certain heavy metals, but if you were specifically designing a protein structure simply to hold metal atoms in a certain organization, I don't think that would be a problem.

CHAPTER XVII

SPECIAL ADDED COMMENTARY:

SURFACE POTENTIALS AS A MEASURE OF ORIENTATION
AND ANISOTROPY IN MONOMOLECULAR FILMS

Barbara J. Kinzig
Optical Sciences Division
Naval Research Laboratory
Washington, DC 20375

Scientists who work with monolayers and submonolayers know that they are very difficult to form, even more difficult to characterize, and are anisotropic as well.

I would like to discuss the contact potential and the related techniques which we have used to characterize monolayers and submonolayers of organic absorbates. In departing from prior practice, we have introduced the anisotropic shape of the molecule in the theoretical calculations. This permits one to predict the orientation of the molecules in ordered monolayers and to discuss their behavior and polarizability.

Figure 1 illustrates simply the approach that is used for a contact potential difference or a surface potential measurement. Essentially the whole experiment is a Helmholtz capacitor with a substrate. We looked at organic absorbates on mercury. The upper plate is slightly radioactive and it produces a small current path through the absorbate layer from the metal surface to the mercury surface. The electrometer measures the associated voltage as a function of the presence and the orientation of molecules in the layer, (note that we are only going to detect electrical properties which are normal to the surface). For organic layers we have adapted the McDonald and Barlow representation of work function or surface potential changes arising from absorption on a metallic surface:

$$\Delta V = \frac{4\pi\Gamma(\alpha F + \mu)}{\varepsilon_{eff}} \quad \text{in which} \quad \varepsilon = f(\Theta^{1/2}) \qquad \text{Eq. 1}$$

Note that the dielectric term is a function of the coverage to the one-half power.

In this experiment one is putting organic materials into the natural field that exists above the metal surface. However, properties can also be studied as a function of an applied external field. Essentially one measures changes from electrons above the Fermi level of the metal surface.

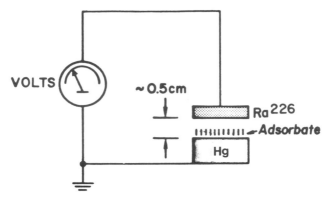

Figure 1. The contact potential measurement equipment is indicated.

    The degree of accuracy of these measurements is illustrated by Fig. 2 as
a function of film density for the case of benzil on mercury; it indicates
reproducibility even at the lowest submonolayer coverage. At the point marked
ESV, another kind of measurement was made separately for an equilibrium
close-packed monolayer film. At this point $\Theta = 1$ for the flat film. An
orientation change occurs when the film is too crowded to be further
compressed. Plotting this data vs molecules per square centimeter as opposed
to area/molecule shows the expected linear extrapolation to zero at low
coverage.

    The calculated surface potential is a function of several variables,
including the field strength, the polarizability, the dipole moment, and a
surface dielectric coefficient (not the bulk coefficient). The bulk
dielectric values, even at full monolayer coverage, do not apply, and
something closer to the refractive index is applicable.

    The anisotropy of the molecular absorbates was introduced via the
anisotropic polarizability tensor for the molecules and their bonds, introducing
only the components that would be normal to the surface for the molecules in
various limiting orientations (e.g. flat on the mercury surface). This approach
gives quite good agreement with the experimental data.

    Figure 3 shows the reduced surface potential as a function of J, the
polarizability per unit volume of adsorbate. Notice that the shape of the
curve varies as the coverage and hence the polarizability per unit volume varies.
This is useful because data for anisotropic molecules can be plotted in the same
way on a reduced curve. Several things are revealed: First of all, some
molecules do not reorient in a submonolayer as the coverage is increased. They
follow the shape of a curve which is consistent with that in Fig. 2. However,
some rigid molecules tend to reorient at a reorientation point. One can think
of these as simply going from a curve with one J or polarizability per unit
volume value to another, sometimes dramatically, and at crosspoints which are
consistent with molecular size and shape.

    For a series of benzene derivatives like benzoic acid the experimental
ESV(ΔV of a film in equilibrium with its bulk, where Θ is assumed to be 1)
values and the calculated $\Gamma\mu$ values all fall on a line with a fairly good fit,
Fig. 4, where $\Gamma\mu_{total}$ is $\Gamma(dF+N)$ from eq. 1. The effective dielectric
coefficient calculated from the slope of this line is 2.36 for all these
compounds whereas the bulk coefficients are as high as 13.0. The monolayer
films, even at full monolayer coverage, do not have properties that are the
same as the bulk values.

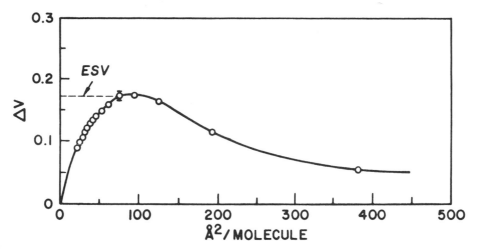

Figure 2. The monolayer surface potential is shown as a function of area per molecule for benzil on mercury.

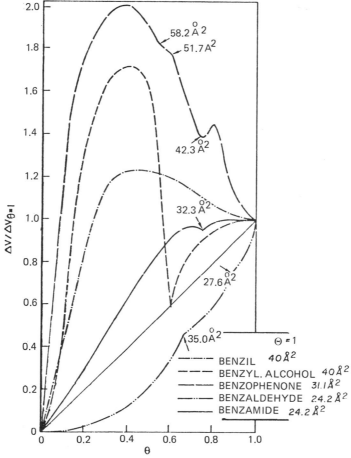

Figure 3. The reduced surface potential <u>vs</u> fractional monolayer coverage is shown for various benzene derivatives on mercury. Local maxima and minima are possible orienting points. The curve for benzil resembles closely the ideal curve and is characteristic of compounds with ΔV and ESV coincidence.

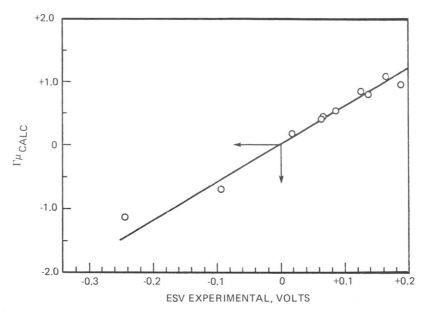

Figure 4. Calculated $\Gamma\mu_{total}$ vs experimental ESV for benzene derivatives on mercury. Each data point is for a different molecule. The least-squares fitted line shown has r = 0.98, and ε_{eff} from its slope is 2.36.

In short, the simple classical measurement technique of the contact potential, which need not necessarily be made in a high vacuum, when combined with calculations involving the orientation of anisotropic molecule in limiting cases, permits one to accurately predict the orientation in the film at monolayer coverage. Alternatively, one can create a film with a desired orientation by impressing the calculated conditions and potential value. I reemphasize that the bulk values are not appropriate for monolayers and submonolayers. This is true in optical experiments as well, where the dielectric coefficient or index of refraction varies with coverage. Finally, I note again that simple techniques like the contact potential can be used for very, very thin films and films at much lower coverage than monolayer.

DISCUSSION

Dr. Pomerantz (IBM): I have two questions. First, how do you spread the molecules on the mercury?

Dr. Kinzig: There are two situations. First, a crystalline material will spread spontaneously on a very, very clean surface of high surface tension to an equilibrium monolayer film. By simply touching a very small crystal of the material to the surface and allowing it to spread, the potential goes instantly and reproducibly to the same value, one which I call the equilibrium spreading potential (ESV). The other density-dependent data were obtained with a spreading solvent which was allowed to evaporate, with the solution added in microliter increments. These values also agree with a film balance experiment done on mercury where the film is prepared at some low coverage and gradually compressed to higher coverage.

Dr. Pomerantz: The other question was about the last viewgraph. The reduced potential seemed to go through zero, is that right? I don't understand why that happens.

Dr. Kinzig: It doesn't pass through zero. The $\Gamma\mu$ is a collection of all the dispolar terms including the polarizability, the permanent dipole moment of the molecule and the charge effects, if present. $\Gamma\mu$ actually crosses below zero because some of the dipole values are negative. Here I haven't shown everything, but the α (polarizability term) is always positive, and the permanent dipole in the molecular components normal to the field is of either sign. The sum of these two is what gives you the net effect. That accounts for some of the systems having a net negative dipole moment and also a net negative surface potential when measured by this contact potential method.

SECTION FOUR
Forefront Technology

CHAPTER XVIII

MICROFABRICATION TECHNIQUES: CURRENT AND FUTURE

Hank Wohltjen
Naval Research Laboratory
Washington, DC 20375

INTRODUCTION

The quest for electronic devices having ever increasing switching speed and ever decreasing size and power consumption has led to the concept of "molecular" electronic devices. Previous and present devices (e.g., transistors and integrated circuits) have exhibited performance limitations which are largely due to intrinsic material limitations and device geometry limitations imposed by the microfabrication process. There is little doubt that molecular electronic devices will experience the same constraints. For this reason it is valuable to review existing and emerging microfabrication technologies from the point of view of one eager to design and build molecular electronic devices.

MOLECULAR ELECTRONIC DEVICE MICROFABRICATION GOALS

The task of developing a suitable "molecular" fabrication technology is complicated by the fact that no particular device structure has yet emerged as the "best" starting point. Thus, the microfabrication technology must be general enough to accomodate a variety of potential candidate devices. Indeed, the early successes and failures of attempts to fabricate molecular electronic devices will shape the subsequent development of microfabrication technology. Fortunately, there are enough common characteristics of proposed molecular electronic devices so that a rough set of guidelines can be drawn. As described by Carter (1,2) many conceivable molecular devices would be approximately 50Å to 500Å in size in each of three dimensions. To provide a useful system, each memory, switching, or signal transport device would have to be interconnected in a fashion determined by the designer (human or otherwise) which would ultimately define the system's function. Finally, a means of providing access to the devices from the outside world (for power, I/O, etc.) would be essential. Thus, it is possible to specify that the desired microfabrication technology should have a spatial resolution of about 10Å (to allow for process variations, etc.), it should be able to define structures ˙ as large as 100,000Å (to permit the connection of macroscopic interface wires

or optical fibers) it should be possible to define any arbitrary interconnection
of one device element to another (within logical constraints), and of course
it should do all of this in three dimensions and in a reasonably short time.
While these requirements are obviously beyond any existing or emerging
technology, one should be aware that preliminary experiments with molecular
electronic devices will have more modest requirements. Specifically, a
spatial resolution of 1000Å would probably be small enough to make connections
to clusters of devices. (This would provide the additional advantage of
making it less likely that the devices would be burned out when connected to
macroscopic measuring instruments). Three dimensional structures would not be
required for early investigations and certainly fabrication speed is not a key
issue.

With these microfabrication goals in mind it is now appropriate to consider
the applicability of existing electronic microfabrication technologies, all
of which are based upon the technique of lithography.

LITHOGRAPHIC TECHNIQUES AND LIMITATIONS

Basic Principles of Lithography

"Lithography" (literally, writing on stone) is an old technique first
developed over 100 years ago by the graphic arts industry and improved
(nearly to the physical limits of perfection) by the modern semiconductor
electronics industry. Transistors and integrated circuits consist of
patterned thin films of metals, dielectrics, and semiconductors on a substrate
(usually silicon). The patterns are defined in the thin film by a process
shown in Fig. 1. A radiation sensitive "resist" layer (usually a sensitized
organic polymer) is coated on top of the thin film to be patterned. Radiation
(visible, UV, or X-ray photons, E-beams, or ion beams) is permitted to strike
the resist wherever a thin film pattern is (or is not) desired. After this
"mask" exposure, the resist is "developed" in an appropriate solvent which
leaves some areas of the thin film still coated with resist and other areas
bare. The unprotected areas of the thin film are then easily etched away
(in acidic media, for example) to yield the desired pattern. The resist
layer can then be stripped with a solvent and the processing of new thin
film levels continued. Clearly, the image forming process in the resist
layer is the key step in the production of very small, complex, multilayer
structures. For this reason a comparison of the resolutions of the various
image forming techniques will define the ultimate capabilities of the
individual technologies.

Resolution is not the only criterion of importance in a lithographic
system, however. Usually, it is necessary to fabricate a second (or third,
or fourth, or fifth, etc.) thin film layer on top of a previously fabricated
layer. This requires that the second level be accurately "registered" to the
first level otherwise necessary contacts will not be made. Obviously, as the
minimum feature size (i.e., resolution) of a system gets smaller, so do the
maximum allowable registration errors. Finally some consideration should be
given to the speed of a particular lithographic system for the intended
application. While this constraint is not nearly as important in research as
it is in production, the extreme demands of molecular electronic devices make
lithographic speed a legitimate concern.

LITHOGRAPHY

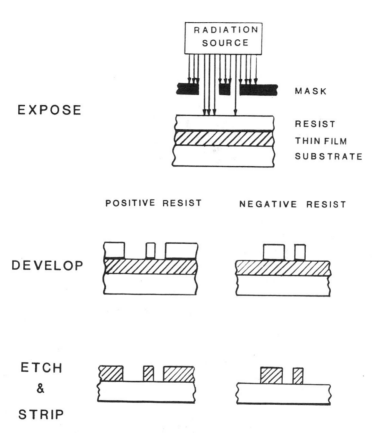

Figure 1. Typical lithographic processing steps.

Optical Lithography

The wide range of available high power radiation sources and precise optical systems for the visible region makes optical lithography the workhorse of the microfabrication industry. Numerous systems exist which will align and image the pattern of an optical mask onto a photoresist coated substrate. The mask can be in contact with the substrate, near the substrate (proximity printing) or the mask image can be projected onto the substrate. Each technique has its own advantages and disadvantages. Contact printing, while simple and very precise, results in severely degraded mask life and reduced device yield. Proximity printing improves this situation at the expense of greater system complexity and reduced resolution that varies with mask-substrate gap size. Projection printers require elaborate optical systems, have poor depth of field ($\sim$2 microns) and lower resolution than contact or proximity printing but it has high throughput (i.e., wafers/hour) and very high device yield. The semiconductor industry relies heavily on projection printers.

The resolution obtainable with an optical system is primarily determined by the wavelength of the incident radiation. Highest resolutions are obtained with the contact printing scheme and here the resolution is set by degradation of the image due to Fresnel diffraction between the mask and the bottom of the resist layer. The maximum resolution obtainable for visible light systems will be approximately 0.75 microns. By using UV light sources the maximum resolution can be pushed to a limit of about 0.5 microns. From this it is clear that optical techniques will have great difficulty contributing to the microfabrication of molecular electronic devices, since 0.1 micron and smaller features would be required.

X-ray Lithography

An X-ray lithographic system is similar to an optical contact printer or proximity printer in terms of its operating principle. The radiation source, mask, and alignment system are significantly different. X-Ray lithographic systems offer the promise of very high resolution due to the small wavelength (λ = 0.4 - 5.0 nm) of the radiation source. Considerable work is being done to develop new X-ray sources for lithographic applications which have the necessary energy and intensity characteristics. X-Rays from laser generated plasmas and synchrotron radiation are promising candidates. The masks for an X-ray system are quite different from those in an optical system.

A common approach is to prepare a thin membrane of silicon, mylar or polyimide (almost transparent to X-radiation) and to form the desired pattern in a gold film (opaque to X-radiation) which is on top of the membrane. The patterns must be prepared using an electron beam or ion beam lithography system since an X-ray cannot be focused and deflected to "draw" the desired pattern on the mask. Thus, the resolution of X-ray lithography will never be better than the resolution of the E-beam or ion beam system which makes the mask. Overlay registration is also a problem with X-rays since submicron accuracies are required. Several schemes are being evaluated. One popular technique involves monitoring the optical interference pattern produced by two overlapping gratings, one of which is on the mask, the other of which is on the substrate. A problem which is particularly relevant to molecular electronic devices is concerned with the relative dimensional stability of the masks and substrates. Processing will distort the substrates and use will distort the masks making overlay difficult. It is doubtful that substrates and masks can be held stable to better than one part in a million. This means it will be very difficult to overlay with an accuracy better than $\pm$50Å if the

distance between registration marks is 5 cm, even if a perfect alignment system
is available. In addition to the diffraction limits and mask imposed limits
on X-ray lithographic resolution one other limit deserves mention. When X-rays
are absorbed in a resist layer, photoelectrons are generated which can expose
the resist a short distance away from the X-ray exposed site. While the effect
is small it limits the minimum feature size to about 50Å.

     X-Ray lithography therefore, offers the potential advantages of high speed,
high resolution and high aspect ratio resist profiles. While these considerations are of paramount concern in a production environment, there are presently
no clear cut advantages to using X-ray lithography (as compared with E-beam
or ion beam lithography) in fundamental research of molecular electronic devices.

Electron Beam Lithography

     E-Beam lithography represents a significant departure from classical
lithographic concepts. The apparatus (shown in Fig. 2) is similar in principle
to an electron microscope. Electrons from a high brightness source are
accelerated and formed into an extremely fine beam which can be focused on a

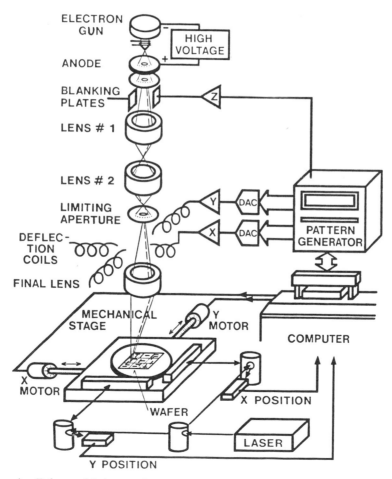

Figure 2. An E-beam lithography system.

substrate and deflected under computer control in the X and Y directions. Thus, there is no longer a physical mask involved in the lithographic process. Pattern information is stored as digital data in the control computer's memory. (E-Beam proximity printers do use a physical mask but these will not be considered here). Ordinarily, the electron beam can only be deflected over a distance of a few millimeters before deflection distortions become severe. To cover larger areas, therefore, it is necessary to move the substrate periodically or continuously under the beam using a laser interferometer to measure the absolute substrate position (typically with an accuracy of a few hundred angstroms).

The electron beam probe can have a spot size as small as 5Å. Unfortunately, the resolution of an E-beam lithographic process is limited by electron scattering in the resist layer and backscattering from the substrate. This phenomenon is referred to as the "Proximity Effect" since it frequently plagues patterns which are written in close proximity to each other on the substrate. The amount of electron charge per unit area (i.e., the DOSE expressed in Coulombs/cm^2) deposited into a resist layer in the presence of scattering is described by two superimposed Gaussian distributions (Fig. 3) with one corresponding to the incident beam and the other corresponding to the back-scattered electrons. If one realizes that different exposure doses will result in varying edge profiles in the resist layer (Fig. 4), then it is easy to see that if one attempts to fabricate the structure shown in Fig. 5 then the small isolated shapes will be underexposed and all shapes in close proximity to each other will be overexposed. The overexposure results when electrons back-scattered from the writing of a shape are integrated into the dose of an adjacent shape. The effect becomes severe when shapes are separated by less than one micron. The problem can be minimized by using very thin resist layers, very thin substrates (e.g., membranes), high contrast resist materials or correction of the E-beam exposure dose when shapes are very close. Devices having minimum feature sizes of 80Å have been fabricated under near optimal conditions (5). Registration of new levels to previously defined levels is accomplished by scanning a registration mark on the substrate with the E-beam and detecting backscattered electrons as is customary in a scanning electron

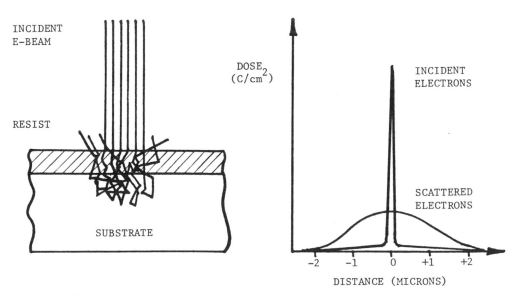

Figure 3. The electron scattering process.

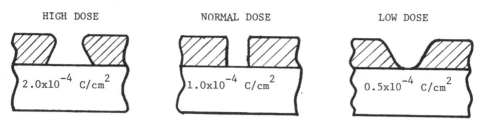

Figure 4. Resist edge profiles obtained in PMMA (polymethylmethacrylate) for various E-beam exposure doses.

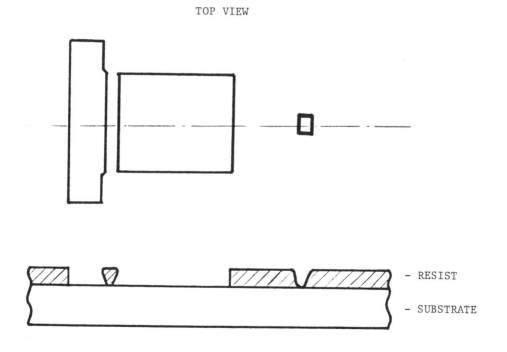

Figure 5. The proximity effect. Large shapes which are close to each other experience an overdose at the neighboring edges causing widening of pattern and undercut resist profile. A small isolated shape receives insufficient dose since there are no nearby exposed areas contributing scattered electrons to its exposure.

microscope. Registration accuracies of $\pm 1000\text{Å}$ are readily accomplished on today's E-beam lithography tools which have a probe spot size of about 1000Å. Smaller probe sizes will permit proportionately smaller registration errors, however, a point will be reached where process induced variations in the substrate material will make overlay very difficult. From the point of view of microfabricating molecular electronic devices it is clear that present E-beam lithography tools can provide resolutions at or below the 1000Å level required to make metallic contacts to clusters of devices. Future improvements in resolution are anticipated in E-beam lithography but problems with the proximity effect, and overlay registration will make it difficult to extend this technique to the ultimately desired three dimensional structures.

Ion Beam Lithography

Ion beam lithography is an emerging technology which is very similar in principle to E-beam lithography. The fundamental difference is found at the radiation source which of course, generates ions instead of electrons. The primary advantage of using a microfocused ion beam is that ions are absorbed more efficiently by the resist material thus greatly reducing proximity effect problems and increasing the "writing" speed of the lithographic system (i.e., for a given beam current, the beam can be deflected faster in an ion beam system than in an E-beam system, due to the higher effective resist sensitivity). Perhaps the most exciting prospect of the ion beam technique is "resistless" processing in which the reactive ion beam is used directly to etch the patterns into the substrate without the usual formation of a resist stencil followed by wet (or dry) chemical etching. By using an appropriate ion beam, localized doping of the substrate through ion implantation is readily achieved. Numerous ions are already available and more are expected. The development of new and brighter ion sources for lithographic purposes is an active area of research.

The resolution of existing ion beam lithography tools is in the range of 1000Å and steady improvements are anticipated. Ultimately, ion beam resolution should approach that of electron beam systems. This fact, coupled with the reduced proximity problem and versatile etching and implanting capabilities will undoubtedly make ion beam lithography the method of choice for future high resolution microfabrication. Overlay registration will be subject to the same limitations as in E-beam lithography.

Reducing the number of processing steps (through direct etching and local ion implantation) could be of great value in the microfabrication of molecular electronic devices since it would reduce the number of process variations.

THE APPLICATION OF EXISTING TECHNIQUES TO MOLECULAR ELECTRONIC DEVICE FABRICATION

A summary of the relevant performance characteristics of existing lithographic techniques is presented in Table 1. The values shown are representative of what is available in existing lithographic systems. Also included are projections of system performance available in 1990. Considering the previously stated design goals for molecular electronic devices it is evident that visible and U.V. lithography will have little to offer in terms of resolution towards meeting these goals. X-Ray lithography, while potentially very attractive in production environments will offer little if

TABLE I

LITHOGRAPHY SYSTEM	RESOLUTION		REGISTRATION	
	PRESENT	FUTURE	PRESENT	FUTURE
OPTICAL	1.5 μm	0.75 μm	± 0.5 μm	± 0.1 μm
UV	0.5 μm	0.25 μm	± 0.25 μm	± 0.1 μm
X-RAY	1000 Å[1]	100 Å[1]	±1000 Å	± 50 Å[2]
SCANNED E BEAM	1000 Å (10 Å)[3]	5 Å	±1000 Å	± 50 Å[2]
SCANNED ION BEAM	1000 Å	10 Å	±1000 Å	± 50 Å[2]

NOTE: 1. LIMITED BY MASK RESOLUTION.
2. LIMITED BY SUBSTRATE STABILITY.
3. DIAMETER OF SMALLEST PROBE FORMED. NOT YET INCORPORATED IN A COMPLETE LITHOGRAPHY SYSTEM WITH OVERLAY CAPABILITY.
4. 0.1 = 1000 Å

TABLE II

	PRESENT ION BEAM	ULTIMATE ION BEAM
RESOLUTION	1000 $\overset{\circ}{A}$	10 $\overset{\circ}{A}$
REGISTRATION ERROR	$\pm$ 1000 $\overset{\circ}{A}$	$\pm$ 50 $\overset{\circ}{A}$
BEAM STEPPING RATE	10 MHz	100 MHz
WRITING TIME (5mm x 5mm Chip 10%)	25 sec	6.9 hours
* PATTERN DATA (estimated)	2.0×10^7 bytes	2.0×10^{11} bytes

* Assuming 8 bytes/shape and avg shape = 100 beam steps

any advantage over E-beam and ion beam techniques with regard to versatility or resolution in the research environment. E-Beam technology is available today which is capable of fabricating microstructures having dimensions less than 1000Å. Such structures could be very valuable for creating electrical connections to clusters of devices and providing spatial definition of the device geometry itself. Ion beam technology, while not readily available today will offer capabilities similar to E-beam and more, in the very near future.

Once a number of molecular electronic devices have been fabricated and their performance characteristics fully investigated it will be desirable to build three dimensional structures having extremely high device densities. Existing lithographic methods will be of little use in such a program. While it is possible to build layered structures using overlay registration methods, this approach will prove to be far too slow and overlay errors will accumulate far too quickly to permit more than 10 or 20 levels to be built. Furthermore, as device sizes shrink it will be increasingly difficult to fabricate delicate structures less than 100Å on a side by blasting a continuous layer of material with a beam that is at best about 10Å in size. Physical barriers have been broken before and perhaps these technological barriers too will fall. However, a new kind of barrier begins to cast its shadow as one considers the construction of extremely large numbers of devices; namely the information barrier. As stated previously E-beam and ion beam techniques store the pattern data as digital information in the control computer's tape or disk memory system. If one attempts to use a 10Å beam to describe a pattern which covers 10% of a five by five centimeter chip, and an average shape takes 100 beam steps (i.e., 10 beam steps on a side) with the pattern computer requiring an average of eight bytes of data per shape, then 2×10^{11} bytes of pattern data would be required. This is an enormous volume of information and transmitting it through the lithography system to the resist on the substrate without many errors is highly unlikely. The symmetry and regularity of large device arrays could permit considerable data compression, however, this would greatly complicate the interconnect process. Table II compares present day limits with projected ultimate capabilities in the year 1990.

It is safe to conclude that existing technology will permit many exciting preliminary investigations of molecular electronic phenomena. The ultimate exploitation of the resulting devices will require a radical departure from existing techniques. Perhaps the recent rapid advances in the field of genetic engineering will result in the microfabrication of large systems using molecular self assembly. Alternatively, one can imagine a system in which chemically active foundation sites are spatially defined by lithography. Subsequent chemical synthesis would then permit devices to be "grown" from these sites.

REFERENCES

1. F.L. Carter, "Problems and Prospects of Future Electroactive Polymers and 'Molecular' Electronic Devices," in the NRL Program on Electroactive Polymers, First Annual Report, Ed. by L. B. Lockhart, Jr., NRL Memorandum Report 3960, March 30, 1979, pg. 121 ff.

2. F.L. Carter, "Further Considerations on 'Molecular' Electronic Devices," in the NRL Program on Electroactive Polymers, Second Annual Report, Ed. by Robert B. Fox, NRL Memorandum Report 4335, September 15, 1980, pg. 35 ff.

3. A. N. Broers, "Resolution, Overlay, and Field Size for Lithography Systems,"
    International Electron Devices Meeting; Technical Program, New York,
    Institute of Electrical and Electronics Engineers, 1980, pg. 2 ff.

4. "Microstructure Science, Engineering, and Technology," Panel on Thin
    Film Microstructure Science and Technology, National Academy of Sciences,
    Washington, DC, 1979.

5. W.W. Molzen, A.N. Broers, J.J. Cuomo, J.M.E. Harper, R.B. Laibowitz,
    J. Vac. Sci. Technol. 16(2), Mar./Apr. 1979.

DISCUSSION

Dr. Beneking: A. T. Univ. - I would like to comment on your table
where you compare different systems. I think it was very nice to see this
comparison. However, irrespective of resolution, the data shown on E-beam
lithography are conservative by about a factor of five as you have shown it.
Using an automated alignment procedure the overlay accuracy continuously
achievable is better than 200 Angstroms, so indeed today one can make manmade
structures down to 0.1 μm which is a factor of about five in respect to the
data presented.

Dr. Wohltjen: NRL - You are saying that you have an instrument which
has a registration accuracy of $\pm$ 200 $\overset{o}{A}$ and a probe size of less than 1000 $\overset{o}{A}$?

Dr. Beneking: Yes.

Dr. Wohltjen: Wow! Do you think that a registration accuracy of
$\pm$ 50 $\overset{o}{A}$ is achievable within this decade?

Dr. Beneking: I think it can be reached. If you use thinned
substrates, and higher beam voltages you will come down to smaller structures.
I guess we could get about 10 to 15 $\overset{o}{A}$ overlay accuracy leading to 10 μm
structures.

Dr. Wohltjen: 10 to 15 $\overset{o}{A}$, that's impressive.

Dr. Aller: NSF - Do you have any feelings for whether long-term
yield rates, or what amounts to the same thing, their reliability, are different
with the different techniques? You didn't include that as one of the parameters.

Dr. Wohltjen: Well, there is some evidence that with the scanned ion
beam you do considerable damage to the substrate material as you irradiate, and
subsequent laser or thermal annealing is necessary to anneal out some of the
damage. The experience with ion beam lithography is not very extensive because
there are few machines in operation. With regard to electron beam techniques,
a number of one micron and submicron devices have been fabricated and the
radiation induced damage has not been a significant problem in the programs
that I am familiar with.

Dr. Flanders: MIT - Another correction on your table; X-ray
lithography at 200 $\overset{o}{A}$ resolution has been demonstrated with carbon k X-rays
and registration has also been demonstrated at better than 200 $\overset{o}{A}$ superposition
precision with interferometric techniques.

Dr. Wohltjen: I am aware of demonstrated overlay accuracies of $\pm$ 100 Å on instruments using grating structures for overlay registration. The figures presented in the table reflect what you could expect on a day-to-day basis from a practical process. In many cases, it may be possible to obtain better short-term performance by pushing the machine to the ultimate. Admittedly, these numbers are highly conservative. I also have noted that the resolution in X-ray lithography is strictly mask limited.

Dr. Beneking: I would like to comment on the yield problem. You have to take into account that E beam and ion beam systems don't use masks. That is a large advantage, so that from that point of view, the yield will be better using the E beam or ion beam. Furthermore no mask alignment is needed contrary to the X-ray systems where you have to adjust the mechanical mask always exactly to the wafer.

Dr. Wohltjen: It is a rather elegant approach; using computers to design new computers and build new computers.

CHAPTER XIX

TRANSPORT IN SUBMICRON DEVICES*

D. K. Ferry
Department of Electrical Engineering
Colorado State University
Fort Collins, CO 80523

H. L. Grubin
Scientific Research Associates
Glastonbury, CT 06033

J. R. Barker
Warwick University
Coventry CV4 7AL, U.K.

INTRODUCTION

Over the last two decades, the electronics industry has been involved in
an ongoing revolution in digital large-scale integration (LSI). This digital
revolution, spawned in the late 1960's, is leaving a permanent imprint on
all aspects of life today, especially as the implementation of microelectronics
has spread to the consumer industry. Fueled by the drive to less expensive,
but more complex and sophisticated, integrated systems, the growth of LSI
has in fact been phenomenol. The complexity of these circuits, in terms of
the number of individual devices on a chip, has approximately doubled each
year over this time span. This is shown in Fig. 1. There are, of course,
several factors which contribute to this increase in complexity, including
major effects arising from increased die size, increased circuit cleverness,
and reduced device size. This latter factor, reduction of the individual
feature size in a device, is of paramount importance and dimensions of laboratory systems are currently down to the sub-micrometer range. Indeed in Fig. 2,
the leukemia virus is overlaid over a modern integrated circuit in order to
emphasize the smallness of individual devices today. Progress in the microelectronics area is tied inevitably to the ability to continue to put ever
increasing numbers of smaller devices on a chip; i.e.--the continual move to
very-large-scale integration (VLSI) will be of paramount importance to this
continued progress. It is apparent that extrapolation of today's technology
will produce individual devices whose dimensions are of the order of 0.1-0.3
micrometers [3-7]. On the other hand, the advent of high-resolution electron,
X-ray, molecular, and ion beam lithography is leading us toward an era in
which individual feature sizes might well be fabricated on the molecular scale

*This work was supported in part by ONR and ARO.

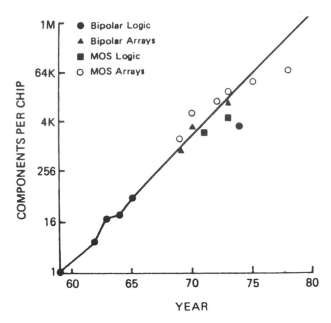

Figure 1. Growth of circuit complexity in large-scale integrated systems according to Moore [1].

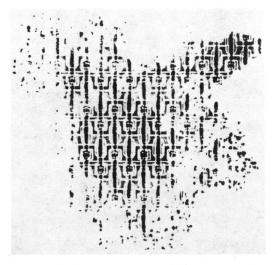

Figure 2. Projection of a leukemia virus cell onto a modern integrated circuit [2]. The outline of the devices is the size of the virus cell.

of 10-20 nanometers. In fact, individual metallization patterns already have
been fabricated on this scale by electron lithographic techniques using normal
processing [8]. It becomes feasible then to conceive of very small device
structures that are so small that the bulk properties of the host material may
be significantly less important than size and environmental related effects [9].

From the above discussion, it is obvious that one can ask just how far
can we expect device size to be reduced, and, more importantly, do we understand the physical principles that will govern device behavior in such small
structures. Indeed, extrapolation to the region of 0.1-0.3 micrometers is
made based upon today's understanding of device operation, but this understanding is often used to damp enthusiasm for new approaches to VLSI and particularly to very-high-speed VLSI. Rather, it should be remarked that the
push to effective gate (or channel) lengths at the 0.1 micrometer, or less,
level is bringing us to a point where our current Boltzmann equation approach
to transport processes is inadequate.

Transport in Small Structures

In the small semicondcutor device, where the active region length may
only be a small fraction of a micrometer, the average electron velocity cannot
easily be represented as an explicit function of the electric field through a
mobility. Rather, the important time processes such as transit-time, energy-
and momentum-relaxation times, and screening time are all comparable and the
carrier velocity must be calculated as a function of space and time [9-11],
and very complicated statistical processes due to the basic far-from-equili-
brium, nonlinear, and non-stationary characteristics of the transport become
important.

The dynamics of channel electrons may be obtained from moments of the
Boltzmann transport equation as [12]

$$\frac{\partial}{\partial t} (np) = neE - \frac{p}{\tau_m} \quad , \tag{1}$$

and

$$\frac{\partial}{\partial t} [\frac{1}{2} np^2 + \frac{3}{2} nk_B T_e] = nev_d E - \frac{nk_B T_e}{\tau_e} \quad , \tag{2}$$

where p (= $m^* v_d$) is the ensemble averaged carrier momentum, T_e is the ensemble
averaged carrier energy, and τ_m and τ_e are the momentum- and energy-relaxation
times, respectively. For multivalley semiconductors, such as GaAs, equations
of the type (1) and (2) must be written for each valley, and supplemented with
a particle continuity equation.

If a system of electrons is subjected to the combined influence of an
electric field and scattering centers, ignoring for the moment electron transfer as a scattering mechanism, then the drift velocity of the particles asymp-
totically approaches the steady state value

$$v_d = e\tau_m E/m^* \tag{3}$$

If we were just to consider the momentum balance equation, (1) we could be
satisfied that the particles would approach this value in a time approximately
equal to 3 τ_m seconds, as illustrated in Fig. 3. But considering the momentum
balance equation alone would give us an incomplete picture of events. Energy

balance tells us that the electron temperature increases with increasing electric field and departs significantly from room temeprature when the electric
field exceeds a threshold value. The effect of the increasing electron temperature is to decrease the average collision time and to decrease the steady-
state velocity, given by (3). If the momentum and energy scattering times are
similar in value, then both momentum and energy will follow changes in electric
field at approximately the same rate and the solid curve of Fig. 3 describes
the approach to steady-state. On the other hand, if the energy scattering
time is significantly longer than the momentum scattering time, the average
velocity of the carriers will find its value continually corrected until steady-
state in the energy distribution is reached. The velocity will then relax in
the manner shown by the dashed curve. A similar situation may be expected when
the electric field is decreased, for here it also takes a finite time for the
electric field to decrease and for the electron temperature to decrease.

       Most field-dependent velocities and values for the saturated velocity
assume that steady-state conditions are reached. Clearly, this is not the case
in very-small devices. In Fig. 4, we show the average velocity as a function
of distance for electrons in Si seeing an electric field of 50 kV/cm. Also
seen is the small change induced by retardation of the transport. It is clear
that the relaxation rates τ_m^{-1} and τ_e^{-1} are evolving on the same time scale
as the velocity response itself and that correlated motion needs to be considered.
Indeed, the correlation function for electrons in Si is shown in Fig. 5 and 6
The vertical scales are shifted to allow ease of plotting. What is clear here
is that $\phi(t)$ (the stationary quantity) lasts for a time fully comparable to the
transient portion of the velocity response. In fact, it can be shown that [13]

$$v_d(t) = \frac{eE}{mI} \int_0^t \phi(o,t') \, dt' \quad , \tag{4}$$

where $I = <v^2(o)>$ and $\phi(t'',t')$ is the general non-stationary two-time correlation function $[\phi(t'',t') \to \phi(t)$ for $t' \to t'' + t$ and $t'' \to \infty]$. The proper treatment of transport in the transient regime thus requires inclusion of memory
functionals which are beyond the channel Boltzmann equation approach [14]. This
leads to modifications of the relaxation terms in (1) and (2). The results for
Si are also shown in Fig. 4. It is evident however, that if the channel were
only 200 Å long, the velocity would never reach steady-state. While this is a
very short distance, the effect is pronounced in the III-V materials and results

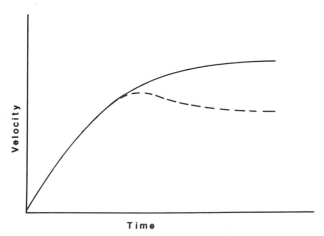

Figure 3. Approach to steady-state of the velocity response with and without
overshoot effects.

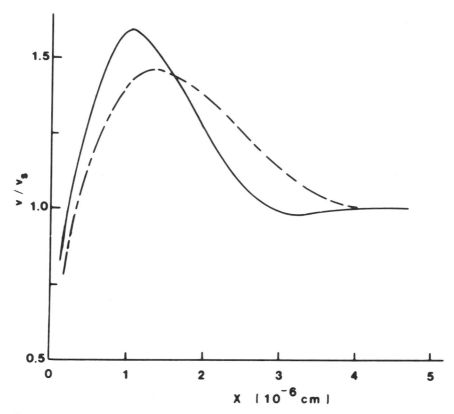

Figure 4. The velocity response of electrons in Si for an electric field of 50 kV/cm. The solid curve differs from the dashed curve by fully including retardation effects.

in far different apparent velocity-field curves. In fig. 7, we show a set of curves for GaAs. What is evident from here is the dramatic increase of the apparent saturated velocity in the short-channel devices. In Fig. 8, several semiconductors are compared to show how the effective saturated velocity increases in short channels. Here, the InP predictions were estimated from the Monte Carlo calculations of Maloney and Frey [15], and are probably over-optimistic. It becomes evident from this figure, that perhaps the most important aspect of short-channel overshoot effects is the indirect effect of increasing the effective saturated velocity and the concomitant increase in peak drive current I_{dm} that results.

Device-Device Interactions

In conventional descriptions of LSI circuits, each device is assumed to behave in the same manner within the total system as it does when it is isolated. The full function of the system is determined once the interconnection matrix is specified to join the individual devices together. A different function can only be assigned to the system by reconnecting the interconnecting pathways -- a practical impossibility for most systems. The conventional clean separation of device design from system design thus depends ultimately on being able to isolate each individual device from the environment of the other devices except for planned effects occurring through the interconnection matrix. In very-dense arrays of devices, line-to-line capacitance, a parasitic capacitance, is begin-

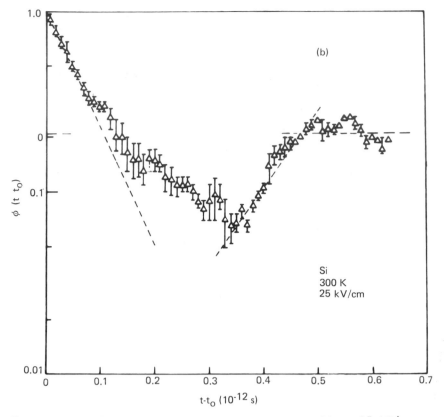

Figure 5. The correlation function for electrons in Si at 25 kV/cm.

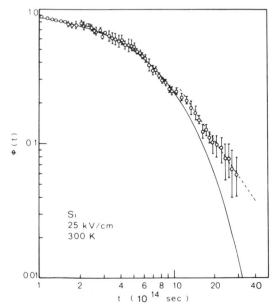

Figure 6. The correlation function of Figure 5 on a log-log plot to clearly
show the long-time $t^{-3/2}$ decay of the initial fall of $\phi(t)$.

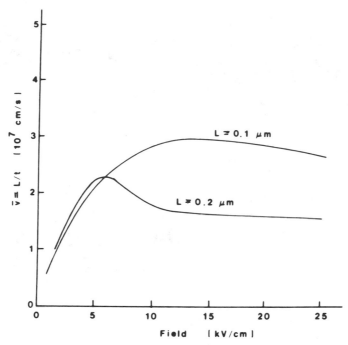

Figure 7. The effective, or time-of-flight, velocity observed for very-short transit lengths in GaAs. These curves assume a steady, homogeneous field with the carriers entering at x = 0 at t = 0 in thermal equilibrium with the lattice, and no contact effects. The dashed curve represents a purely ballistic response for L = 0.1 μm.

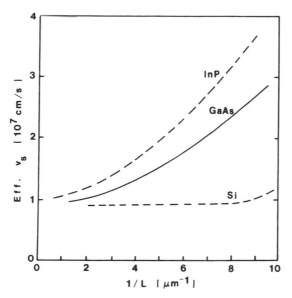

Figure 8. The effective, or time-of-flight, saturated velocity as a function of the inverse channel length. The InP curve is estimated from the data of [15].

ning to dominate the interconnection capacitance at a particular node. As a
result, the above simplification is likely to be seriously in error for submicron
configured VLSI systems, where the isolation of one device from another (and by
generalization, from the surrounding environment of insulating and conducting
regions) will be difficult to achieve.

The possible device-device coupling mechanisms are numerous and include
such effects as capacitance coupling, the line-to-line parasitic effect mentioned above, and wave-function penetration (tunneling and charge spill-over)
from one device to another. Formally, however, one may describe these effects
on system and individual device behavior by assuming the simplest form of inter-
device coupling -- nearest neighbor coupling -- and using the formally exact
Liouville-von Neumann density matrix equation for the full system to unravel
how the system behaves. This task has been described previously from various
different viewpoints [16,17], and the basic ideas are reviewed below in order
to provide a baseline to which the system approach can be compared.

In the present context, a VLSI system is defined as a net of N spatially
delineated structures, e.g. contacts, devices, interconnects, isolation/insulator
regions, etc. Control over the system is exercised via a set of applied fields
(or voltages) and input and output currents. These are labeled F_{ext}^i (i = 1,...,N)
where F_{ext}^i is the set of generalized applied forces acting on the i-th element.
The applied generalized forces give rise to local applied forces F^i which are the
self-consistent solutions of the appropriate macro-equations, e.g., Poisson's
equation and current continuity equation. The latter depend upon the dynamical
variables of the elements concerned, and these variables are completely specified
as quantum statistical expectation values of the individual device/element density matrix $\rho(i;t)$. If there is no coupling between devices, we have simply
the set of N Liouville-von Neumann equations of motion (using units such that
$\hbar = 1$)

$$i \frac{\partial}{\partial t} \rho(i;t) = \hat{H}(i)\rho(i;t) \quad ,$$

(5)

where $\hat{H} = [h.,,,]$ is the commutator generating Hamiltonian super-operator.
$H(i) = H(i,F^i(t))$ is the Hamiltonian for device i and is assumed to be time
dependent through the coupling to the generalized time dependent forces F^i.
If the device-environment coupling occurs on a time-scale fast compared to
processes within the device, (5) can be reduced to a single $\rho_d = \rho_j$ which satis-
fies [16]

$$ih \frac{\partial \rho_d}{\partial t} = \hat{H}_d \rho_d + \hat{H}_{ed} \rho_d + \hat{\Sigma}(o)\rho_d \quad ,$$

(6)

where $\hat{H}_d$ is the Hamiltonian for the single device, $\hat{H}_{ed}$ is the renormalization
term for the effective real part of the device-environment interaction, and
$\hat{\Sigma}(o)$ is a dissipative term for losses to the environment, such as surface-
roughness scattering in an MOS system. The term in $\hat{H}_{ed}$ is critical, in that
regularity in the replication of the devices, such as an array, can lead to
complete renormalization of the energy structure and super-lattice behavior.

Recently, Bate [18] has proposed a surface super-lattice structure that
formally is similar to a charge-coupled-device (CCD) array. The device dimensions required were $\sim$ 1000 Å spacings for the array, which is beyond the current
VLSI technology, but within the limits of research efforts in electron- and ion-
beam lithography. Although such lateral super-lattices are interesting in their
own right, since they easily allow full three-dimensional quantization within a
quantized inversion layer, they are especially interesting as they should also

exhibit charge instabilities (Peierl's instabilities) under population inversion, such as has been recently predicted in long-period one-dimensional super-lattices [19]. Such instabilities are characterized by a stationary charge-density wave commensurate with the super-lattice itself, but they also are clear examples of synergetic [20] switching of the super-lattice potential itself. Moreover, they are characteristic of possible instabilites in dense VLSI arrays.

The concept of a lateral super-lattice along a surface has considerable advantages, among which is the ability to control the magnitude of surface potential seen by an inversion layer. The basic structure proposed by Bate is a periodic gate array which, when viewed from the top, would appear as in Fig. 9, a structure that has been fabricated by normal electron lithography [21] (as will be seen below, this structure is already of the size required if the semiconductor material is suitably chosen). In actual practice, a blanket top gate structure would be added to provide gap potential control without requiring critical alignment of successive levels. If the periodic gates are biased positively the surface potential for electrons decreases under the gate electrodes, and to a lesser extent in the gaps. Minority carrier generation, or optical pumping, can be used to create the carriers necessary to form the inversion layer under the gates. Thus, in addition to the normal average surface potential, a periodic super-lattice potential is seen by the inversion layer electrons. The presence of the top electrode allows for critical control of the relative strengths of the average potential and the super-lattice potential.

In Fig. 10, we show a plot of the center-to-center spacing required to open a gap of $6k_BT$ in the electron energy spectrum [22]. The number of states in the lowest mini-band is closely related to the surface carrier density required in the inversion layer to fill the first mini-band, these densities correspond to a strong inversion layer existing at the surface. For these densities, at low temperatures, the Fermi level will be well into the conduction band.

In situations where the lowest mini-band is full (or the Fermi energy lies in the mini-gap), it can be expected that excitation of carriers across the mini-gap will produce potential contributions that lead to renormalization of

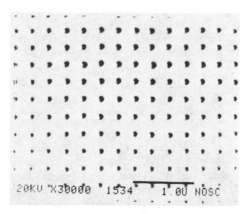

Figure 9. The Bate-super-lattice consists of an array of gates (two-dimensional) with a second, top gate to aid in control of surface potential. Source and drain structures, although not shown, could be added to make a multi-gate FET structure. The gate array could appear, from the tip, as above in which a dense metal array structure has been fabricated by electron-beam lithography L21L.

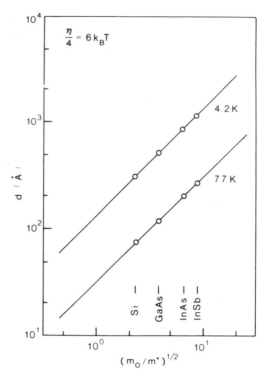

Figure 10. (a) Value of gate center-to-center spacing required for a super-lattice to form with n/4=6kBt, where n is the reduced energy L22L.

the mini-gap. These effects are well known in bulk semiconductor materials, leading, for example to correlation contributions [23] to band-gap narrowing [24]. Whereas a coulomb contribution to the potential of a few millivolts is small when compared to a band-gap of 1-2 volts, it can be a dramatic effect on a mini-gap whose total value is only 10 millivolts or so. This effect was carefully examined by Kroemer [19] for the case of a one-dimensional super-lattice, such as can occur in an organic chain molecule or polymer. The basic idea is of course that charge fluctuations across the mini-gap lead to a coulomb potential of $q \sim g \sim 2k_F$, so that the conditions for a Kohn anomaly [25] are already satisfied. While we have been concerned with optical pumping of the electrons, it should be pointed out that optical pumping of the phonons can lead to phase transitions as well [26].

If a population is induced by some technique, there exists the possibility of zeroes appearing in the dielectric response. In this case, a non-zero value of V_o can exist without the application of the external field V_a. This means that the super-lattice potential can be set up by a charge instability under the gates themselves. While it was initially pointed out that this charge affect on ε was similar to a Kohn anomaly, the instability itself is a classic example of a Peierl's instability. The charge instability spontaneous leads to a charge-density wave which creates the lattice potential. This behavior is illustrated in Fig. 11.

If suitable materials are selected, it appears that lateral super-lattices can be fabricated by today's technology, or indeed can be expected to arise in device VLSI arrays. The fact that these structures can show synergetic behavior under conditions of population inversion suggest that new functional performance

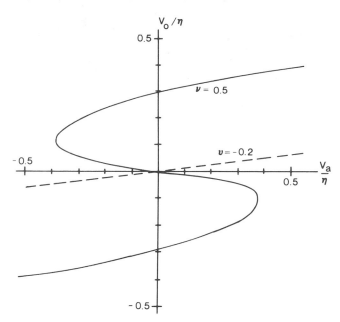

Figure 11. Relationship between applied potential V_a and total self-consistent potential V_o for just below inversion, $\nu = -0.2$, and well-above inversion, $\nu = 0.5$. The multi-valued structure leads to switching behavior in the arrays. ν is the fractional inversion ($\nu = 0$ is equal populations) [22].

characteristics may be important for their operation as devices. Here, new is used in the sense that normal device operation is hindered due to strong device-device interations [17] so that other modes of operation will arise.

References

1. G. E. Moore, in "Proc. Intern. Electron Dev. Conf.," 1976.
2. K. Hess has used this picture several times to illustrate the size of individual devices in modern integrated circuits.
3. M. T. Elliott, M. R. Splinter, A. B. Jones, and J. P. Reeskin, IEEE Trans. Electron Dev. ED-26, 469 (1979).
4. P. T. Greiling, in "Proc. 1979 Intern. Electron Dev. Mtg.," IEEE Press, New York, 1979, p. 670.
5. T. Mizutani, N. Kato, S. Ishida, K. Osafune, and M. Ohmani, Electron. Letters 16, 315 (1980).
6. W. Fichtner, E. N. Fuls, R. L. Johnston, T. T. Sheng, and R. K. Watts, in "Proc. 1980 Intern. Electron Dev. Mtg.," IEEE Press, New York, 1980, p. 24.
7. W. R. Hunter, T. C. Holloway, P. K. Chatterjee, and A. F. Tasch, Jr., IEEE Electron Dev. Letters EDL-2, 4 (1981).
8. A. N. Broers, J. M. E. Harper, and W. W. Molzen, Appl. Phys. Letters 33, 392 (1978).
9. J. R. Barker and D. K. Ferry, Sol.-State Electron. 23, 519 (1980).
10. D. K. Ferry and J. R. Barker, Sol.-State Electron. 23, 545 (1980).
11. H. L. Grubin, D. K. Ferry, and J. R. Barker, in "Proc. 1979 Intern. Electron Dev. Mtg.," IEEE Press, New York, 1979, p. 394.
12. D. K. Ferry, in Physics of Nonlinear Transport in Semiconductors, Ed. by D. K. Ferry, J. R. Barker, and C. Jacoboni, Plenum Press, New York, 1979.

13. J. Zimmermann, P. Lugli, and D. K. Ferry, to be published.
14. D. K. Ferry and J. R. Barker, J. Phys. Chem. Sol. 41, 1083 (1980).
15. T. J. Maloney and J. Frey, J. Appl. Phys. 48, 781 (1977).
16. J. R. Barker and D. K. Ferry, Sol.-State Electron. 23, 531 (1980).
17. J. R. Barker and D. K. Ferry, in "Proc. Intern. Conf. on Cybernetics and
     Society," IEEE Press, New York, 1979, p. 762.
18. R. T. Bate, Bull. Am. Phys. Soc. 22, 407 (1977).
19. H. Kroemer, Phys. Rev. B 15, 880 (1977).
20. H. Haken, Synergetics (Springer-Verlag, Berlin, 1978).
21. N. David and N. Flesher, Naval Ocean Systems Center, unpublished.
22. D. K. Ferry, to be published.
23. See, e.g., J. C. Inkson, J. Phys. C 9, 117 (1976); V. Heine and J. A. Van
     Vechten, Phys. Rev. B 13, 1622 (1976); and references therein.
24. H. Y. Fan, Phys. Rev. 82, 900 (1951); C. Haas, Phys. Rev. 125, 1965 (1962);
     H. C. Casey, Jr., D. D. Sell, and K. W. Wecht, J. Appl. Phys. 46, 250 (1975).
25. W. Kohn, Phys. Rev. Letters 2, 393 (1959).
26. S. A. Bulgadaev and I. B. Levinson, Sov. Phys.-JETP 44, 1043 (1976).

DISCUSSION

Dr. Sandman: GTE - I am trying to understand precisely what you meant by the term superlattice as you applied it apparently in the array of devices. There is a well-known class of semiconductor superlattices, gallium arsenide and aluminum arsenide, and I think you meant something different than that. Could you specify in some detail precisely what you meant by a superlattice in the context that you used it?

Prof. Ferry: You are referring to the extreme technique of laying down precise alternate monolayers of aluminum arsenide and gallium arsenide. This superlattice, of layered aluminum arsenide and gallium arsenide gives a narrow energy well and a classic one-dimensional Kronig-Penney model, and it works exceedingly well when you compare the results of that calculation to the experiments. Now the concepts of superlattices are, of course, much broader than that. What you should think of is that the reason you get superlattice effects is the fact you have a periodic array of energy wells.

Dr. Sandman: In an individual chip?

Prof. Ferry: Think of this in the following way: under the gate of a MOS FET, you have a potential well due to band bending. If you have a regular array of gates, you will have a periodic potential well induced along the surface in the context of a lateral superlattice. Now the spacing of those wells determines the potential and you have a two-dimensional Kronig-Penney model. This two-dimensional lattice is worked out in Brillouin's book on periodic structures, but you can have superlattice effects in the two-dimensional case. Now the challenge arises if you make this on top of a layered structure by MBE; because you can then have a three-dimensional superlattice effect.

Dr. Sandman: This is the context in which you were using it?

Prof. Ferry: This is the context, right.

Dr. Carter: NRL - Thank you for a very well presented and nicely balanced talk. I appreciate your effort. I have two questions. You have mentioned the quantum effects of an array of devices, and so my first question deals with the phase effect in Josephson's junctions which is a macroscopic quantum effect. Is that the sort of array that you are talking about? Have scientists seen such quantum effects in macroscopic arrays of Josephson junctions?

Prof. Ferry: I don't know if they have seen them in arrays, but there is a very nice driven instability in the Josephson junction field. If you take a thin wire, it shows an instability as a driven synergetic response or phase transition. When you start driving current through it, you get non-equilibrium superconductivity, and as you drive it harder and harder, you soon get a phase slip. That is, you spontaneously create a small Josephson junction where there were none before, and you get a potential drop across it. If you continue to drive even harder, a second one will appear and then a third. There are people studying this type of effect. Here, you are driving the system far from equilibrium and you should expect these things. This is a non-linear response and there are interesting non-linear functions that should appear out of these structures.

Dr. Carter: The second question deals with the interest that we are now seeing in a variety of areas in parallel processing. Is it conceivable that one could use the special effects among an array of devices to do parallel processing?

Prof. Ferry: In principle, yes, but the details have yet to be worked out. I challenge you to do that! That is an interesting area. A lot of work needs to be done. What I am saying is that we should quit thinking in the narrow view in which we have thought about arrays of devices and open our minds to a little more creative aspect as how to make devices work cooperatively together.

Dr. Flanders: MIT - The array of metal dots that you showed, I was confused. You were talking about using aluminum arsenide and gallium arsenide. What was that all about?

Prof. Ferry: The metal dots were laid on silicon. We are currently trying to lay them on something more appropriate like indium antimonide. We are doing some other things along that line in a slightly different context with MBE in connection with the Army.

Dr. Flanders: What's the idea? What are you trying to do?

Prof. Ferry: I am trying to make a two-dimensional superlattice, and I am going to look for those synergetic effects.

Dr. Flanders: That is a true artificial superlattice using a natural crystal sublattice?

Prof. Ferry: That's right, a true superlattice.

Dr. Beneking: AT Univ. - You showed the MOS system. I think one further effect might be the high velocity injection of hot carriers into the oxide layer.

Prof. Ferry: That is an area that has been investigated quite extensively by the group at IBM (who looked at oxide injection). A number of industries are also looking at that; as it is a well-recognized problem, I didn't address it.

Dr. Greene: NRL - I would like to point out that there is a quite different and non-local way of looking at information handling which is related to some of the things that Dave has been talking about that is familiar to people in the optical sciences and also that is using interference methods for storing the processing information. In Josephson's junctions, this has also been done in so-called SQUIDS where you do have well-known macroscopic interference effects, but what I think is the really interesting question is what happens to the theory of information in a non-local situation where you are not trying to transfer a single localized byte but the byte is spread over both an amplitude and phase over a large area, and I think there are people in the brain business who have some strong ideas that this is already taking place inside our head--some of us.

Prof. Ferry: Last week in Phoenix, I learned there is a group at Cal. Tech. which is trying to apply the microscopic concept of spin glasses to the way in which the brain handles information. I mention that only in passing because I also learned at the same time that there is a group at IBM which is trying to apply the theory of spin glasses to the way in which systems operate. If you tie the two together, it might be interesting.

Dr. Buot: Cornell Univ. - I was wondering if you have thought of using BiSb alloys as a matrix on which to lay the small metal dots? (Added in editing - Two things conspire to increase the change of practically observing quantum cooperative behavior in an array of normal metal dots or islands, namely: 1) small effective electron mass in each metal dot, and 2) a small potential barrier between metal dots).

Prof. Ferry: I have enough trouble handling the III-V's. I have tried to forget about bismuth antimonide. That is from the days when I was doing instability experiments.

Dr. Buot: I was wondering if anybody has successfully grown bismuth antimonide semiconducting crystal films.

Prof. Ferry: The last person I remember working on bismuch antimonide was at Bell; it was some years ago.

Dr. Cooper: There was somebody at Illinois, I think Joe Green.

Prof. Ferry: I don't know if he was doing bismuth antimonide There is a classic rule of thumb which has been put forward by Cyril Hilsum at RSRE, which is that to bring any new material to the level at which you can begin thinking about making devices requires something like a man century of effort. I don't know that there is the intense effort on bismuth antimonide yet which would bring it to the level that people could think about using it. Silicon has at least a kiloman century work of effort on it just since the war.

CHAPTER XX

RECENT ADVANCES IN THE CHEMISTRY AND PHYSICS OF POLYACETYLENE: SOLITONS AS A MEANS OF STABILIZING CARBONIUM IONS AND CARBANIONS IN DOPED $(CH)_x$

A. G. MacDiarmid
Laboratory for Research on the Structure of Matter
Department of Chemistry
University of Pennsylvania
Philadelphia, PA 19104

A. J. Heeger
Laboratory for Research on the Structure of Matter
Department of Physics
University of Pennsylvania
Philadelphia, PA 19104

INTRODUCTION

There exists a new class of electronic materials formed as quasi-one-dimensional organic polymers, which have the properties of semiconductors or metals when suitably doped with donor or acceptor species. The prototype example of these conducting polymers is polyacetylene, the simplest conjugated polymer, which consists of parallel chains of CH groups as shown in Figure 1.[1]

Both the cis- and trans-forms (see Figure 1) can be prepared as silvery, flexible films, which can be made either free-standing or on a variety of substrates, such as glass or metal, with thicknesses varying from 10^{-3} to 0.5 cm. The trans-isomer is the thermodynamically stable form; complete isomerization from cis- to trans-$(CH)_x$ can be accomplished after synthesis by heating the film to temperatures above 150°C for a few minutes. Electron-microscopy

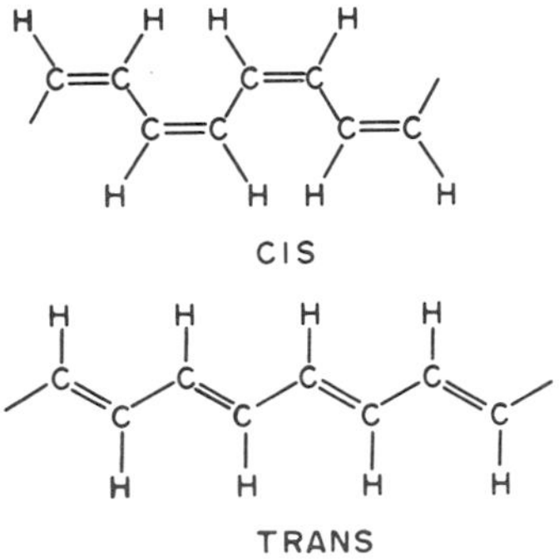

CIS

TRANS

Figure 1. Cis and trans isomers of $(CH)_x$.

259

studies show that the as-formed $(CH)_x$ films consist of randomly oriented
fibrils (typical fibril diameter ~200Å). The films can be stretch-oriented in
excess of three times their original length with concomitant partial alignment
of the fibrils. The bulk density is 0.4 g/cm^3, compared with 1.2 g/cm^3 as obtained by flotation techniques. Therefore, the polymer fibrils fill only
about one third of the total volume and the effective surface area is quite
high (~60 m^2/g). X-ray studies show that the $(CH)_x$ films are highly crystalline.

Recent studies have demonstrated that, after synthesis, $(CH)_x$ films can
be chemically doped at room temperature with a variety of donors or acceptors
to form n- or p-type semiconductors.[1] (See Table I) Doping to high levels
(above ~1%) results in a semiconductor-metal transition giving a whole new
class of metals with a wide range of electronegativity. Moreover, the existing experimental data already show that these materials have potential for use
in a number of areas of future technology. Experimental studies at the University of Pennsylvania have demonstrated that doped polyacetylene might be useful
in such diverse applications as: (1) the replacement of increasingly scarce
conventional conductors by synthetic metals; (2) the development of lightweight,
high-energy-density batteries; and (3) low-cost solar photovoltaic materials.

The electrical conductivity of polyacetylene can be varied in a controlled
manner over thirteen orders of magnitude through chemical or electrochemical
doping; results for three typical dopants are shown in Figure 2.[1] Values greater
than $3 \times 10^3 \ \Omega^{-1}cm^{-1}$ have already been achieved with only partially aligned
samples, and analysis of the transport (electrical conductivity and related
properties) and optical data implies that a further increase of at least one
order of magnitude should be possible.

In simple terms, one may regard the bonding in $(CH)_x$ as being derived from
the linking together of sp^2 hybridized (CH) units, the fourth carbon valence
electron being in a p_π orbital perpendicular to the plane of the $(CH)_x$ molecule.
A diagrammatic representation of the energy levels (band diagram) associated

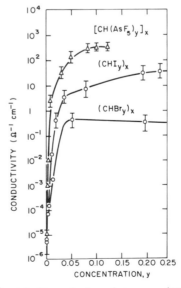

Figure 2. Electrical conductivity of doped <u>trans</u>-$(CH)_x$ film as a function
of dopant concentration.

TABLE I

Examples of p- and n-Type Doping of $(CH)_x$

Selected Dopants for $(CH)_x$

p-Type Dopants	(ohm^{-1}cm^{-1} at 25°C)
cis-$(CH)_x$	1.7×10^{-9}
trans-$(CH)_x$	4.4×10^{-5}
cis-$(CHI_{0.30})_x$	5.5×10^{2}
trans-$(CHI_{0.20})_x$	1.6×10^{2}
cis-$[CH(IBr)_{0.15}]_x$	4.0×10^{2}
cis-$[CH(AsF_5)_{0.10}]_x$	1.2×10^{3}
cis-$[CH(PF_6)_{0.033}]_x$	2.5×10^{1}
cis-$[CH(H^{+}AsF_6^{-})_{0.1}]_x$	$7 \quad \times 10^{2}$
cis-$[CH(H_3O^{+}ClO_4^{-})_{0.127}]_x$	1.2×10^{3}
cis-$[CH(ClO_4)_{0.065}]_x$	9.7×10^{2}
cis-$[CH(H_3O^{+}HSO_4^{-})_{0.106}]_x$	1.2×10^{3}
n-Type Dopants	
cis-$[Li_{0.30}(CH)]_x$	2.0×10^{2}
cis-$[Na_{0.21}(CH)]_x$	2.5×10^{1}
cis-$[K_{0.16}(CH)]_x$	5.0×10^{1}
trans-$[Na_{0.28}(CH)]_x$	8.0×10^{1}
cis-$[(^{n}Bu_4N)_{0.03}(CH)]_x$	1.0

Cis or trans refers to the principal isomeric species before doping.

with the overlapping molecular orbitals of pi symmetry formed by joining (CH) units together is given in Figure 3. The species depicted range from $(CH)_2$, i.e., $H_2C=CH_2$, to $(CH)_x$. The filled π molecular orbitals correspond to the valence band, the empty π^* orbitals to the conduction band, and the $\pi \rightarrow \pi^*$ transition energy to the band gap in a semiconductor or insulator. If all the C-C bonds were of equal length, having a bond order of 1.5 (one σ bond and half-filled π bond), $(CH)_x$ would be a metal with zero band gap; if the band gap were large, the resulting material would be an insulator. In the case of trans-$(CH)_x$, where the C-C bond length alternation is small, a band gap of approximately 1.5 eV results; the pure material is therefore a semiconductor.[1]

The carriers (electrons and/or [positive] holes) generated by the doping of $(CH)_x$ result from charge transfer. Charge transfer occurs from polymer to acceptor (A) with the polymer chain acting as a poly(cation) in the presence of an A^- species. For a donor (M), the polymer chain acts as a poly(anion) in the presence of M^+ species. The A^- or M^+ ions reside between polymer chains. Reversible doping can be carried out electrochemically,[2] and chemical compensation has been demonstrated. For example, after doping and subsequent chemical compensation, the optical absorption spectrum converts back to that of the undoped polymer.[3] Therefore, since the anisotropic optical properties of the undoped polymers are characteristic of the quasi-one-dimensional $(CH)_x$ chains, the reversibility implies that the $(CH)_x$ chains remain intact in the doped polymer.

In trans-$(CH)_x$, three main electronic regimes are observed: (1) the semiconducting regime where the dopant concentration is small (<0.1%) and the properties are similar to those of a doped semiconductor; (2) the metallic regime where the dopant concentration is $>\sim 6\%$ and the electronic properties (i.e., conductivity, thermoelectric power, absorption and reflectance spectra, specific heat, magnetic susceptibility, etc.) are characteristic of a metal;[1] and (3) the transitional region where the properties are intermediate between those of the semiconducting and metallic limits.[4] This intermediate regime is in many ways the most interesting; for example, although the electrical conductivity is high,

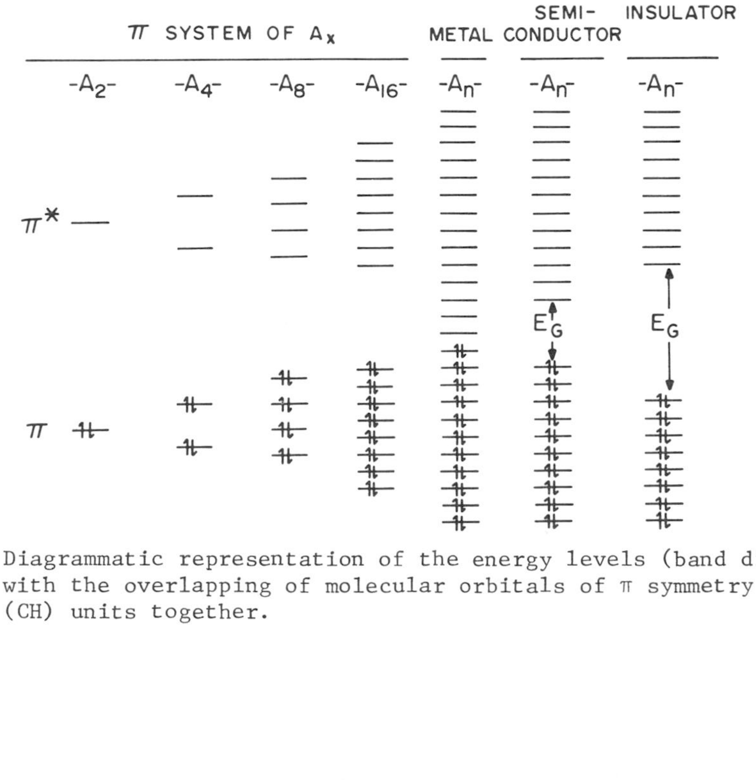

Figure 3. Diagrammatic representation of the energy levels (band diagram) associated with the overlapping of molecular orbitals of π symmetry formed by joining (CH) units together.

there appears to be no Pauli susceptibility suggesting the possibility of a non-traditional transport mechanism.[4] However, since this transitional regime is not well understood, the present discussion will be limited primarily to the semiconducting regime and to the soliton concepts which are relevant to dilute doping.

SEMICONDUCTING REGIME: SOLITONS IN POLYACETYLENE

If the bond lengths in pure trans-$(CH)_x$ were uniform, the polymer would be a quasi-one-dimensional metal with a half-filled band. Such a system is unstable with respect to a dimerization distortion (the Peierls instability) in which adjacent CH groups move towards each other, forming alternately short (or double) bonds and long (or single) bonds, thereby lowering the energy of the system and opening the semiconductor band gap. Clearly, by symmetry, one could interchange the double and single bonds without changing the energy. Thus, there are two lowest-energy states, A and B, having two distinct bonding structures as shown in Figure 4. This twofold degeneracy leads to the existence of nonlinear topological excitations, bond-alternation domain walls or solitons, which appear to be responsible for many of the remarkable properties of $(CH)_x$.

When a single chain of cis-$(CH)_x$ begins to isomerize, the isomerization process can, in principal, commence at different parts of the chain, one having configuration (A), the other, configuration (B). When these two different configurations meet, a free radical is produced as shown schematically in Figure 4. This has been confirmed experimentally - when pure cis-$(CH)_x$, possessing no free spins, undergoes isomerization, approximately one in 3000 of the (CH) units in the resulting trans-$(CH)_x$ is in the form shown in Figure 4 with an unpaired spin and a Curie law magnetic susceptibility. This species is actually a valid excited state of trans-$(CH)_x$, which could be formed in principal, for example, if trans-$(CH)_x$ could be heated to a sufficiently high temperature without thermal decomposition. It would be expected that this free spin could be readily ionized leaving behind a positive charge. This has indeed been observed. Thus if $(CH)_x$ is carefully and slowly oxidized by, for example, AsF_5, a stabilized carbonium ion is formed; the Curie spins originally present decrease almost to zero, and the conductivity of the material increases greatly.

If, for simplicity, it is first assumed that the unpaired spin resides completely on one (CH) unit, it may be regarded as being located in a non-bonding π molecular orbital, since it is not formally involved in π bonding to either of the adjacent (CH) units. Since a non-bonding π molecular orbital will lie

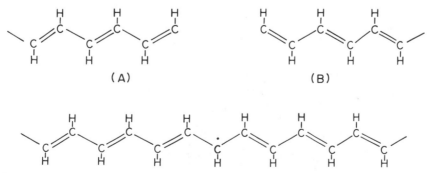

Figure 4. Formation of a neutral soliton by joining together the two lowest energy states, (A) and (B) of trans-$(CH)_x$.

midway between the π and π^* molecular orbitals, it is apparent that the energy level giving rise to this free spin will fall in the center of the band gap as shown in Figure 5. This localized non-bonding state formed at the boundary between the two degenerate phases (A and B) has been termed a "neutral soliton." Analogously, when this electron is removed, as described earlier, to give a carbonium ion, a mid-gap "positive soliton" is produced, as shown in Figure 6. Alternatively, if an electron is added to a neutral soliton as, for example, in the n-doping of $(CH)_x$ by sodium to produce a stabilized carbanion, the mid-gap state is doubly occupied and a "negative soliton" is generated as depicted in Figure 7.

The presence of neutral solitons induced as defects during isomerization is a fortunate accident, for the number of thermally induced neutral soliton excitations in undoped $(CH)_x$ would be far too small to be observable. In this context, however, it must be stressed that it is not necessary to first have neutral solitons in order to obtain positive (or negative) solitons. For example, it has been shown experimentally[4] that on careful p-doping of $(CH)_x$ with AsF_5 that: (i) the original free Curie spins in $(CH)_x$ decrease as indicated above and (ii) even though the amount of dopant species is far in excess of that necessary to remove the original free spins, no additional Curie spins appear. This is consistent with the generation of charged solitons according to the doping model shown in Figure 8.

In the previous discussion, it has been assumed that a soliton has been localized on a single (CH) unit. Detailed calculations have shown that minimization of the total energy spreads the soliton over a region of about 15 (CH) units.[5] Thus, for example, in the case of a positive soliton, although the maximum charge density is adjacent to the counter anion, A^-, ~85% of the charge is spread out symmetrically on either side over ~15 (CH) units. This is qualitatively understandable, since it is recognized from symmetry considerations that the positive soliton formally located on a single (CH) unit will actually have some interaction with the p_π orbitals on the adjacent (CH) units. This delocalizes the non-bonding mid-gap state over many bond-lengths as shown schematically in Figure 9(b). It is apparent that considerable bond length distortion will be involved near the center of the soliton, since these bonds alone are responsible for adjusting the bond lengths of segment (A) with those of segment (B) (Figure 9(a)) in which the relative positions of the formally single

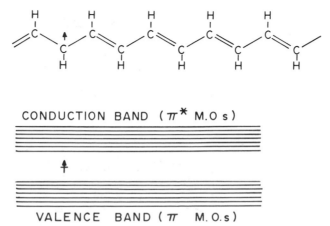

Figure 5. Diagrammatic representation of a neutral soliton (free radical located on a non-bonding π molecular orbital) in trans-$(CH)_x$.

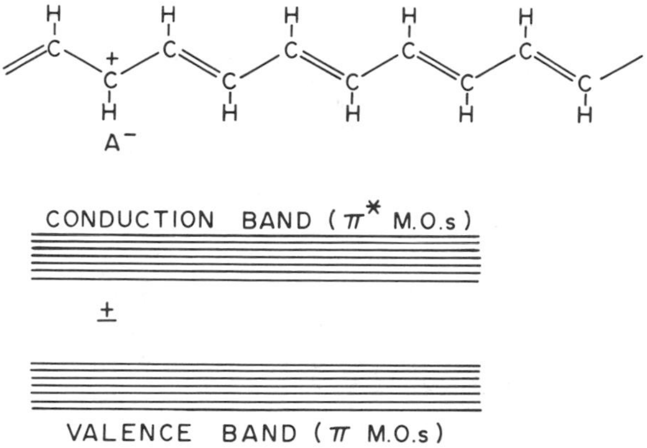

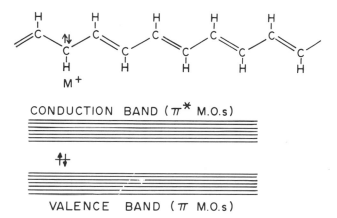

Figure 6. Diagrammatic representation of a positive soliton (carbonium ion located on a non-bonding π molecular orbital) in <u>trans</u>-$(CH)_x$.

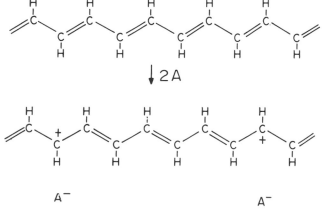

Figure 7. Diagrammatic representation of a negative soliton (carbanion located on a non-bonding π molecular orbital) in <u>trans</u>-$(CH)_x$.

Figure 8. Diagrammatic representation of p-type doping of <u>trans</u>-$(CH)_x$ with no production of Curie or Pauli spins.

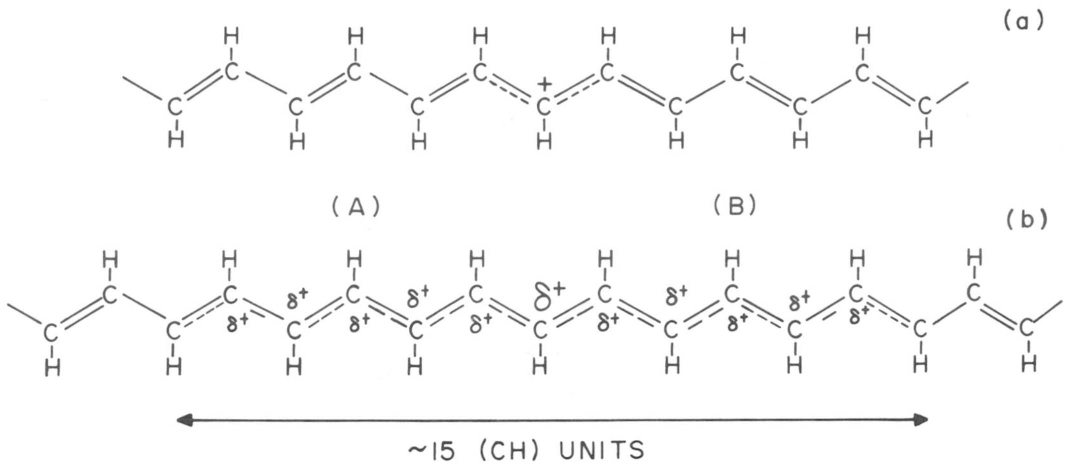

(a)

(A)   (B)   (b)

~15 (CH) UNITS

Figure 9. Diagrammatic representation of the delocalization of a positive soliton in <u>trans</u>-(CH)$_x$: (a) charge localized on one (CH) unit; (b) charge localized over ~15 (CH) units.

and double bonds are reversed. Since the energy to distort a bond is proportional to the square of the distortion, it is apparent that if the distortion were spread out over several bonds, the distortional energy required would be less. Hence, the system is stabilized if the bond distortion is taken up by several bonds as shown diagrammatically in Figure 9(b) to produce a positive soliton or domain wall, which separates (A) type domains from (B) type domains. We note that within these domain walls (particularly near the center), the C-C bond lengths tend to become very nearly equal. It might at first be thought that the greatest stabilization would result if the distortion were spread out over the whole chain. This, however, is not the case because of the Peierls distortion stabilizing energy, which, for a hypothetical 1-dimensional molecule, predicts that a single-double bond alternating structure has a lower total energy and thus, is more stable than one consisting totally of equal (bond order 1.5) linkages. These two opposing distortional effects involving bond lengths result in the soliton domain walls in (CH)$_x$ being extended to approximately 15 (CH) units.

Conductivity-temperature studies show that the conduction process in (CH)$_x$ in the semiconducting regime proceeds by a hopping mechanism.[6] Although this may involve movement of a positive or negative soliton along a chain, recent calculations predict that an interchain hopping mechanism involving the "capture" of a mobile electron from a neutral soliton in one chain by a relatively non-mobile positive (or negative) soliton in an adjacent chain may be the dominant mechanism. The experimental results for undoped <u>trans</u>-(CH)$_x$ are in excellent agreement with this inter-soliton hopping theory.

Implicit to the whole concept of soliton doping in (CH)$_x$ in the semiconducting regime is that as doping proceeds, there is no increase in the number of free spins (neutral solitons). This is consistent with measurements on carefully doped (CH)$_x$.[4] In this respect, the behavior of (CH)$_x$ is exactly the opposite of that found during the doping of a classical semiconductor such as silicon, in which the number of unpaired spins increases as doping proceeds. This phenomenon in (CH)$_x$ is due to the unique symmetry of the material in the <u>trans</u> form

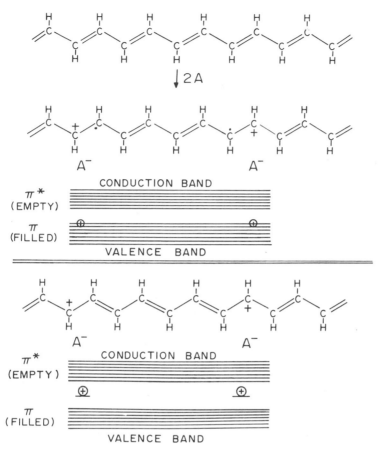

Figure 10. Diagrammatic representation of the formation of a positive soliton on p-doping trans-(CH)$_x$.

as shown in Figure 10. Thus if a perfect (diamagnetic) trans-(CH)$_x$ sequence were treated with two p-type dopant species, A, and two electrons were removed from two different filled π orbitals, then two unpaired electrons would be found (associated with two positive holes in the valence band), provided no change in the direction of bond alternation had occurred. However, as noted above, the production of unpaired electrons is not observed experimentally. If, however, a rearrangement of electrons occurs as shown in Figure 10 with a con-comitant rearrangement of formally single and double C-C bonds, the positive holes will rise out of the valence band as shown. Since (A) and (B) segments of (CH)$_x$ are energetically identical and since the "rising" of positive holes results in stabilization of a system,* the formation of mid-gap positive soli-tons is favored energetically as compared to positive holes in the valence band. As noted previously, the positive charge is not localized on just one (CH) unit as shown in Figures 9 and 10 but is actually spread over approximately 15 (CH) units, the magnitude of the charge on each (CH) unit diminishing with increas-

*Electrons may be regarded as analogous to billiard balls - a system is stabil-ized by their rolling downhill! Positive holes may be regarded as analogous to balloons - a system is stabilized by their floating upwards!

ing distance from the counter anion, A^-, adjacent to the chain. Thus, the observation that the Curie susceptibility of trans-(CH)$_x$ decreases on careful p-doping due to the conversion of neutral solitons to positive solitons and that additional positive solitons are formed with no production of Curie spins is consistent with the soliton concept of doping.

Spectroscopic evidence for the mid-gap soliton state is obtained from the change in the absorption spectrum of trans-(CH)$_x$ as a result of doping. The intensity of the band gap transition at approximately 1.5 eV decreases as a new transition, turning on at approximately 0.75 eV, appears and increases in intensity during doping.[7] Further strong evidence for the formation of solitons during p-doping is obtained from the infrared spectra of both trans-(CH)$_x$ and trans-(CD)$_x$ doped to the semiconducting regime.[8] The soliton infrared active vibrational modes in (CH)$_x$ appear at 1385 cm^{-1} and 900 cm^{-1}; the corresponding modes in the deuterated material occur at 800 cm^{-1} and 1100 cm^{-1}, respectively. These modes are predicted both for (CH)$_x$ and (CD)$_x$ within a few percent accuracy by calculations based on the soliton theory.

CONCLUSION

In conclusion, experimental and theoretical evidence obtained to date is consistent with the soliton concept of bonding in parent (CH)$_x$ and (CH)$_x$ doped within the semiconducting regime. The solitons in trans-(CH)$_x$ are proving to be fascinating to both chemists and physicists. To the physicists, they represent non-linear topological excitations resulting from the fundamental broken symmetry of the trans-(CH)$_x$ chain. As a result, the study of polyacetylene is leading to a deeper understanding of such esoteric concepts as fractional charge and particle confinement. To the chemists, solitons represents a fundamental mechanism for stabilization of the carbonium ion and the carbanion. In effect, the switch in bond alternation and the associated distortions provide a kind of "solvation" energy which acts to stabilize and delocalize the added charge on the chain. In this sense, the existence of solitons is fundamentally responsible for the ease with which polyacetylene can be doped, n-type or p-type, through charge transfer.

Although results of detailed calculations have been presented to describe the transition from isolated solitons at low dopant concentrations to the metallic state at high dopant concentration, much remains to be done. Heavily doped (CH)$_x$ exhibits the electronic properties of a true metal. Above ~6% doping, (CH)$_x$ displays high conductivity,[6] a Pauli temperature independent paramagnetic susceptibility,[4] a linear dependence on temperature of the thermopower[9] and low temperature heat capacity,[10] the infrared properties of a metal,[1] etc. There is strong evidence leading to the conclusion that in this metallic regime, the C-C bond lengths have become equal since (for both p- and n-doped (CH)$_x$) the band gap (π-π^*) transition disappears.[3] At this degree of doping, the solitons may be regarded as having overlapped with each other to form a conduction band which fills in the semiconductor band gap. On heavy doping, (CH)$_x$ becomes a metal, not a degenerate semiconductor, as does a classical semiconductor such as Si, in which the band gap remains even after it is heavily doped to concentrations well above the semiconductor-metal transition. In a general sense, the implied change from bond-alternating to nearly uniform bond structure is consistent with the soliton doping mechanism. However, a detailed understanding of the transition to metallic behavior is lacking. The intermediate transition regime remains as the least well understood aspect of the problem and presents an exciting challenge for continued study.

ACKNOWLEDGMENT

This work was supported jointly by the Office of Naval Research and the Defense Advanced Research Projects Agency (through a grant monitored by the Office of Naval Research) and the National Science Foundation Materials Research Program (Grant No. DMR 7923647).

REFERENCES

1. A. G. MacDiarmid and A. J. Heeger, "Organic Metals and Semiconductors: The Chemistry of Polyacetylene, $(CH)_x$, and its Derivatives," Synthetic Metals, 1, 101-118 (1979/80).

2. D. F. MacInnes, Jr., M. A. Druy, P. J. Nigrey, D. P. Nairns, A. G. MacDiarmid, and A. J. Heeger, "Organic Batteries: Reversible n- and p-Type Electrochemical Doping of Polyacetylene, $(CH)_x$," J.C.S. Chem. Comm. 317 (1981).

3. T. C. Clarke and G. B. Street, "The Chemical Nature of Polyacetylene Doping," Synthetic Metals 1, 119-131 (1979/80); T.-C. Chung, A. Feldblum, A. J. Heeger, and A. G. MacDiarmid, "Experimental Studies of Sodium-Doped Polyacetylene: Optical and ESR Results for Metallic $[CHNa_y]_x$," J. Chem. Phys., in press, (1981).

4. S. Ikehata, J. Kaufer, T. Woerner, A. Pron, M. A. Druy, A. Sivak, A. J. Heeger, and A. G. MacDiarmid, "Solitons in Polyacetylene: Magnetic Susceptibility," Phys. Rev. Lett. 45, 1123 (1980).

5. W. P. Su, J. R. Schrieffer, and A. J. Heeger, "Soliton Excitations in Polyacetylene," Phys. Rev. B 22, 2099 (1980).

6. Y.-W. Park, A. J. Heeger, M. A. Druy, and A. G. MacDiarmid, "Electrical Transport in Doped Polyacetylene," J. Chem. Phys. 73, 946 (1980).

7. N. Suzuki, M. Ozaki, S. Etemad, A. J. Heeger, and A. G. MacDiarmid, "Solitons in Polyacetylene: Effects of Dilute Doping on Optical Absorption Spectra," Phys. Rev. Lett. 45, 1209 (1980).

8. S. Etemad, A. Pron, A. J. Heeger, and A. G. MacDiarmid, "Infrared Active Vibrational Modes of Charged Solitons in $(CH)_x$ and $(CD)_x$," J. Chem. Phys., in press (1981).

9. Y.-W. Park, A. Denenstein, C. K. Chiang, A. J. Heeger, and A. G. MacDiarmid, "Semiconductor-Metal Transition in Doped $(CH)_x$: Thermoelectric Power," Sol. State Comm. 29, 747 (1979).

10. D. Moses, A. Denenstein, A. Pron, A. J. Heeger, and A. G. MacDiarmid, "Specific Heats of Pure and Doped Polyacetylene," Sol. State Comm. 36, 219 (1980).

DISCUSSION

Dr. Cukor: GTE - Does this theory explain the higher conductivity in undoped trans-polyacetylene as compared to undoped cis-polyacetylene?

Prof. MacDiarmid: The conductivity of parent trans-$(CH)_x$ is approximately 10^{-5} ohm^{-1}cm^{-1}; whereas in parent cis-$(CH)_x$ it is approximately 10^{-9}

$ohm^{-1}cm^{-1}$. Because of the symmetry of the trans-$(CH)_x$ chain, an unpaired
electron, that is a neutral soliton can move freely along a trans-$(CH)_x$
chain whereas in the cis isomer, because of different site symmetries on
adjacent carbon atoms, neutral (or charged) solitons cannot exist. Both
parents cis and trans-$(CH)_x$ are already slightly doped p-type, i.e., they
have some positive solitons which can act as carriers. These have, however,
we believe, a relatively small mobility because they are bound electrostatically
to their corresponding negative dopant ion. Recent theoretical studies by
Kivelson suggest that, as the neutral soliton moves down a chain and comes
close to a positive soliton in an adjacent chain, it can hop to a positive
soliton site. The neutral and positive soliton sites are therefore inter-
converted. The positive soliton therefore moves from chain to chain and
through the material, by virtue, in effect, of the mobility of the neutral
soliton. The existence of solitons in the trans isomer as compared to none in
the cis isomer therefore leads to a greater conductivity in the trans-isomer.
This concept is consistent with the known transport phenomena in $(CH)_x$.

Prof. Code: Xerox, Univ. of Toronto - I would like to ask a question
of nomenclature because I am a laser physicist. Is the motivation for the
name 'soliton' the same as in optics, i.e. meaning an undamped wave propagating
in a non-linear medium, or is it simply used here in a looser sense to describe
a solitary bond defect which is slightly delocalized?

Prof. MacDiarmid: I believe the word soliton as applied to $(CH)_x$
was introduced by Alan Heeger and Bob Schrieffer. You have a soliton (or
domain wall) which can move down the chain. It is a topological soliton
in that the direction of the bond alternation, i.e., the slope of the double
bond changes as the soliton moves down the chain.

Prof. Code: It seems a poor choice because it always causes
confusion between physicists and chemists.

Dr. MacDiarmid: I agree.

Prof. Honig: Univ. of Ill. - It is possible to synthesize polymers
of perhaps cyanine dyes with odd numbers of atoms where you have complete
delocalization from the start? Do they conduct?

Prof. MacDiarmid: It is interesting to consider the possibility
of making a conducting polymer which is highly conducting right from the
start, without having to dope it. This has not yet been attained, but in
principle, it seems that such a polymer could exist.

Prof. Lamb: Univ. of Glass. - Due to the interdisciplinary nature
of your team, you have developed semiconductors and metals. Have you made
p/n junctions or diodes?

Prof. MacDiarmid: Yes. We have made p/n junctions by taking p-doped
and n-doped $(CH)_x$ film and pushing them together. Because the film is so
soft, we can get p/n junctions in this way. We have not looked at these in
detail. We are concerned that the p and n dopants will migrate and compensate
each other. p-n heterojunctions (e.g., p-$(CH)_x$:n-CdS) have been studied in
more detail. They make good rectifying diodes. One can make a Schottky
barrier using $(CH)_x$ in two different ways. Firstly, you can coat a crystal of,
for example, n-ZnS or n-CdS or n-Si with $(CH)_x$ and then dope the $(CH)_x$ to the
metallic regime with AsF_5. The doped $(CH)_x$ then acts as a high work function
metal. Secondly, recent work at Chronar Corp. has shown you can evaporate
a thin film of Al onto the surface of parent p-type $(CH)_x$. This gives a photo-

voltaic cell with interesting large open circuit voltages and short circuit currents when illuminated.

Dr. Greyber: NSF - I think you and Krumhansl and Heeger wrote a paper on DNA, analyzed the equations, and showed that a soliton is really a mathematical entity. It comes up in the non-linear solutions of certain differential equations. Thus, it is quite a specific entity.

Prof. MacDiarmid: Right. That is a very good point. I was not involved with this, but Heeger, Krumhansl, Kallenbach and Englander have considered the possibility of soliton excitations in DNA. They have shown that solitons may be important chemical rate-limiting excitations of the duplex. As you say, that is a very good point, because it comes from the soliton concept.

Dr. Greyber: NSF - Soliton-like solutions have been found in a number of differential equations, and therefore it seems to be a widely-accepted concept.

Dr. Pomerantz: IBM - I had a question on the one-dimensional character of this material. How do the electrons move in this material? Do they go down the fibril and then hop to another fibril? How does this material change from metallic to semiconducting?

Prof. MacDiarmid: One firstly needs to consider the conductivity in the semiconducting regime and secondly in the metallic regime. In the semiconducting regime, it is believed that the conductivity is by an electron hopping process down and between chains as described in response to a previous question. In the transition and metallic regime, things are less clear. In the metallic regime, we know the band gap disappears. In the transition regime in $\underline{p}$-doped material, it is possible that mid-gap, non-magnetic bands are formed by the overlap of positive solitons giving metallic-like conductivity with zero Pauli susceptibility. By the time the metallic regime is reached (above 6% doping), it is possible that these positive mid-gap bands have widened and overlapped the valence and conduction bands to give a finite (non-zero) Pauli susceptibility.

Dr. Carter: NRL - First, on the question of the nomenclature of solitons, I would hate to have it left with the audience that a carbonium ion was identical to a soliton. A soliton is a moving distortion, a pseudo-particle with definite energy, velocity, and momentum. Its application to chemistry would be very interesting to pursue. For example can one predict reaction rates from the motion of a soliton move down a small molecule with soliton reflection from the ends. That is can one develop a reaction rate theory from the soliton distribution and hence know where the next reactions are going to occur.

Prof. MacDiarmid: All I am saying in effect is that a positive soliton has many resemblances to a stabilized non-classical carbonium ion.

CHAPTER XXI

RELIABILITY PROBLEMS CAUSED BY

NUCLEAR PARTICLES IN MICROELECTRONICS

Charles S. Guenzer
Naval Research Laboratory
Washington, DC 20375

Modern integrated circuits have enjoyed such commercial success because their evolution has resulted in ever increasing capacity while costs have decreased substantially for a given capacity. Semiconductor memories constitute an important yet easily understood part of this evolution. The dominant technology of today, MOS (metal-oxide-semiconductor) was barely used in integrated circuits (ICs) in 1965. By the early 1970's the first dynamic MOS memory was introduced. This was a 1K device, i.e., 1024 individual storage element. At that time circuit geometries were typically around 20 microns (1). In 1981, 16K dynamic memories are in widespread use, 64K memories are being introduced and development is rapidly progressing on 256K memories. To accomplish this progress, the IC designers have shrunk the geometries of production devices to 3-4 microns, and 1-2 micron widths are expected on newly designed ICs. The Very High Speed Integrated Circuit program of the Defense Department was based on an expectation of 0.5 micron geometries being eventually produced (2).

The discovery of a new device reliability problem has called into question such optimistic projections. Semiconductor vendors in the period preceding 1978 were developing the 16K dynamic memory but were experiencing unexplained, seemingly random bit flips, i.e., one bit out of the 16,384 would spontaneously change state thereby losing the stored information. However, the bit cell was undamaged and would subsequently operate in a manner indistinguishable from other cells. This effect was then labelled as a soft error.

May and Woods in 1978 (3) published their discovery of the cause of soft errors, radioactive contaminants. A silicon chip is surrounded by substantial amounts of heavy metal, such as ceramic packages or sealing glass. These materials contain measurable quantities of uranium and thorium, typically less than parts per million, which are difficult to remove by the normal purification processes and which up to then were considered unimportant. These two atomic species are naturally radioactive with half-lives of some ten billion years. The two reactions are

$$U^{238} \; \text{-----} > \; Pb^{206} + 8 \; alpha \; (average \; E = 5.4 \; MeV)$$

and

$$Th^{232} \; \text{-----} > \; Pb^{208} + 6 \; alpha \; (average \; E = 6.6 \; MeV)$$

in which many alpha particles, i.e., ionized helium atoms, of significant energy are given off. The range of a 4.5 MeV alpha particle is about 20 microns which was the size of the storage capacitor in the 16K dynamic memories. An alpha particle of this energy loses most of its energy in creating electron-hole pairs, i.e., in ionizing its path. The presence of additional minority charge carriers in a semiconductor can, in the case of dynamic memories, cause a loss of stored information. In silicon, 3.6 eV of ionization energy is required for each electron hole pair. Thus the 4.5 MeV alpha particle can deliver 1.3 million electrons or 0.2 pC of charge. It was only with some 4K and most 16K dynamic memories that 0.2 pC, delivered at the right time and place, was sufficient to switch the memory device.

Soft errors or, as radiation physicists prefer to call them, single event upsets, were first discovered in dynamic memories. However it is now recognized that all semiconductor devices are subject to them at some point of miniaturization. Static memories are upset prone although usually at a lower rate (4). Charge coupled devices (CCDs), a memory technology with very low power consumption, i.e., switching energy, are so upset prone that single particles can upset ten or more adjacent memory cells (5). Semiconductor logic devices have generally a larger switching energy and only recently have upsets been observed.

The alpha particle emission from radioactive contaminants have dominated the efforts of commercial vendors. However, the problem is more widespread. Cosmic rays, the galactic environment of extremely high energy particles, can penetrate the earth's atmosphere to produce a low but measurable noise environment (6). These cosmic rays have been observed, albeit infrequently, to cause upsets in CCDs. Satellites, being above the earth's protective atmosphere, are subject to the unattenuated cosmic ray flux. These cosmic rays have significant intensities out to atomic number of Z = 26, i.e., iron and their energies average near 1 Gev per nucleon (7). The ionization density of a particle track is roughly proportional to the square of the atomic number, Z^2 so that the heavier cosmic rays are more effective at deposition charge and thus upsetting devices. The track ionization density peaks near 1 MeV per nucleon, the so-called Bragg peak (8) so that the very high energy particles have no direct effect. However, there is sufficient mass, even in a satellite to degrade the more plentiful higher energy cosmic rays down to the Bragg peak energies. Satellites are also subject to a relatively high flux of protons, whether they be galactic cosmic rays, solar flare protons or protons trapped in the van Allen belts, if the satellite passes through the belts. The protons may be able to directly deposit sufficient charge but may also induce a nuclear reaction. The high energy products of these reactions, being of higher atomic number, may possess sufficient ionization density to upset the device (9). There is also the radioactive contaminant problem which was the cause of the 16K memory problem (10). The natural radiation environment has been reported in some detail by a number of researchers (11). Thus, we see that there are particles available in many supposedly benign environments to cause deposition of enough ionization energy to cause upset in electronic devices.

Single event research has been concentrated up till now on devices of semiconducting silicon technology but there is no reason to restrict such effects to a narrow technology. Simple electronic upset relies on extra electronic energy being densely deposited in the active volume. The band gap for silicon is 1.12 eV which is the minimum energy to move a carrier from the valence to conduction band. The average energy for ionizing a silicon atom and creating an electron-hole pair is somewhat larger, 3.6 eV. Severe degradation in insulator dependent technologies, such as metal-oxide-semiconductor, require somewhat higher energies, about 18 eV to create extra holes which are trapped at the oxide semiconductor interfaces. Any technology which relies on electronic states which can be populated or depopulated with electron volts of energy is subject to ionization effects from background radiation.

Single event radiation phenomena are not restricted to soft failures. It is anticipated that single nuclear particles can cause sufficient damage in an electronic device to permanently degrade or disable one cell in that device. Several mechanisms have been proposed although none has been reported for semiconductor devices. Nuclear particles at lower energy, well below 1 MeV of energy, lose a significant amount of that energy by atomic collisions such that a dense displacement volume is formed. If this occurs in the active volume of a device, any crystalline ordering will have been lost (12). A second mechanism is based on the high ionization density of particle track as it passes through an insulator. The average dose in the small volume may be sufficiently high that electron-hole effects in the insulator will introduce voltage shifts (13). A third mechanism involves a high field across a thin insulator. One particle track may provide an initial conduction path which thereafter is raised to such a high temperature that the insulator properties are lost (14). A fourth type, rather difficult to generalize, equates ionization charge to electrical noise or transients. Some circuits are sensitive to such voltage spikes and may be permanently switched into a stable but unwanted and possibly injurious state. Some CMOS memories have burnt out after being irradiated with krypton ions (15) because they "latched-up" in a high current state. All but the last hard failure have not been observed in present semiconductor devices of 1 to 3 micron size but are expected to become a problem if sizes are reduced by a factor of ten.

Solutions to single event failures of various types usually involve a substantial trade-off. One remedy to the memory upset problem uses error correction code (ECC) so that any single error can be corrected. Its most popular form is the 21-bit Hamming code (16) which is a coded version of a 16-bit data word. The extra five bits, a type of exhaustive parity check, allow correction of any 1-bit error in the 21 bits, and detection of 2-bit errors. More complete schemes exist (17). Any ECC requires both additional memory and additional time to perform the coding, decoding and possible correcting. Extensions of error correction code to logic is possible in some limited circumstances (18) but is much more difficult and costly. Logic circuitry lacks the repetitiveness and predictable types of upset which enable error correction in memory.

Developers of silicon technology have found various design methods to minimize the single event problem (19). Some are clever (20), some are of

limited applicability (21), while others simply admit the limitation that
switching energies below that which can be delivered by a random nuclear
particle require a larger than desired switching energy. Thus the single
event upset phenomena has forced the semiconductor designers to limit, at
least for awhile, further miniaturization. Efforts to reduce switching
energies still further will inevitably increase the susceptibility to nuclear
particles. Further reductions are possible but they must be made consistent
with the single event failure phenomena.

REFERENCES

1. Electronics, 17 April 1980, p. 388.

2. Electronic Warfare/Defense Electronics, January 1979, p. 39.

3. T.C. May and M.H. Woods, IEEE Trans. Elect. Dev. ED-26, 2 (1979).

4. P.J. McNutty, et al. IEEE Trans. Nucl. Sci. NS-27, 1516 (1980).

5. J.F. Ziegler and W.A. Lanford, Science 206, 776 (16 November 1979).

6. D.J. Redman, et. al., Military Electronics/Countermeasures, April 1980,
    p. 40.

7. J.L. Osborne and A.W. Wollendale, "Origin of Cosmic Rays", Reidel Publ.
    (1975).

8. L.C. Northcliffe and R.F. Schilling, Nuclear Data Tables A, 7, 233 (1970).

9. C.S. Guenzer, et. al., IEEE Trans. Nucl. Sci. NS-27, 1485 (1980).

10. T.C. May, presented at 1979 Electronic Components Conference, Cherry Hill,
    NJ, 14-16 May 1979.

11. "Natural Radiation Environments III" symposium held at Houston, TX, 23-28
    April 1978, CONF-780422, Technical Information Center, U.S. Dept. of
    Energy.

12. G.P. Mueller and C.S. Guenzer, IEEE Trans. Nucl. Sci., NS-27, 1474 (1980).

13. T.R. Oldham and J.M. McGarrity, to be published IEEE Trans. Nucl. Sci.
    (Dec. 1981).

14. P. Vail, presented at Digital Avionics Conf., 6-8 November 1979, Fort
    Worth, TX.

15. W.A. Kolasinski, et. al., IEEE Trans. Nucl. Sci. NS-26, 5087 (1979).

16. E.L. Wall, Electronics, 22 November 1979, p. 103.

17. W.W. Peterson and E.J. Weldon, "Error-Correcting Codes", MIT Press,
    2nd Ed. (1972).

18. J.L. Rainard and Y.J. Vernay, IEEE Journal of Solid State Circuits, SC-16,
    174 (1981).

19. M. Brodsky, Electronics, 24 April 1980, p. 117.

20. R.P. Cafece, Electronics, 15 February 1979, p. 123.

21. W.R. Iverson, Electronics, 11 September 1980, p. 41.

DISCUSSION

Due to an unavoidable schedule conflict, Dr. Guenzer was unable to give his paper. Dr. Arthur B. Campbell (NRL) was able to make an excellent presentation of Dr. Guenzer's paper on short notice.

Prof. Ratner: NW Univ. - I hate to be completely trivial. Why don't you put the memory chip in a lead box? These things are pretty small?

Dr. Campbell: Because of the range of these GEV particles; the point is, with modern dynamic memories what they have done to "solve" the problem of soft upsets due to contamination in packaging is simply to put a coating on the top of the chip itself; but when you are talking about GEV protons, you should be informed that they have ranges in terms of meters. In fact, one of the calculations that was done as part of this project by people at IBM, Siegler et al., showed that under concrete the problem becomes worse because of the extra secondary particles that are produced. So shielding isn't the answer. There are several solutions. You find in devices that there is a tremendous difference in sensitivity. Some people that concern themselves with it can change the circuitry, adding a few resistances here and there and make a big difference.

Dr. Greyber: NSF - I guess the same problems come with nuclear weapons explosions affecting satellites in space.

Dr. Campbell: Yes. In fact, concerning one slide I showed you with the proton flux, the real problem is not necessarily what is produced, but that proton flux is trapped in the Van Allen Belt; so there are long-term effects. If your satellite goes through these belts, it is continuously exposed. It is not just the blast. It is what is held in the Van Allen Belt.

Dr. Aller: NSF - As you get smaller and smaller, though, doesn't the probability go the other way?

Dr. Campbell: What you have to consider is that it not only becomes smaller, but it becomes denser as a rule. When they went from the 16K to the 64K, the cells were smaller, but of course, you are putting more in approximately the same volume; but remember the track of one of these particles is very small. They are Angstroms wide by microns deep, so as long as one of them can hit one of your cell elements, you still have the problem of upset. You are saying if you make them smaller, there is less chance of an interaction which is true, but usually when you go smaller you also try to become denser.

Dr. Greyber: Is it true that with sufficient error correction and repetitiveness, you can get arbitrary reliability?

Dr. Campbell: I guess the point was made in the paper about the tradeoffs. The Hemming code that I described is fairly simple. It doesn't cost you very much, but you have to make your data words longer, and it takes longer to do a computation because you have got the extra bytes and that only detects double errors, and it depends on the size of your memory, but yes, error correcting codes can go a step in trying to solve the problem, but then you have always have to balance off how big is your memory system

going to be and how fast do you want to operate? Nowadays people want to
operate very fast and that is a possible solution, but error detection becomes
extremely complicated beyond the single byte detection, as in a double byte
detection and correction system.

CHAPTER XXII

MONOMOLECULAR THICKNESS, ORDERED MAGNETS OF MANGANESE STEARATE

Melvin Pomerantz
IBM Thomas J. Watson Research Center
Yorktown Heights, NY 10598

INTRODUCTION

In this paper I will describe briefly the preparation and properties of magnetic materials that are one magnetic atom in thickness. As such, they are an approach to the kinds of materials envisaged by this Workshop: device materials on a molecular scale. These magnets are of molecular dimension only in their thickness, however. A more complete description of the work has been published elsewhere (1). It should be remarked in passing that, although magnetic switching is not currently used in the high speed storage of the fastest computers as it once was, at present magnetic materials are used for the storage of large amounts of data, and bubble memories are under development. I will not emphasize the practical aspects since that is premature, but in a general way one can appreciate the advantages in density, speed and power-dissipation per device that might be attained by reducing the size of the storage element to a molecular scale. Another question that might concern this Workshop is whether there will be some limitations on phenomena as one approaches molecular sizes (2). For example, there is a theoretical argument that ferromagnetism (and antiferromagnetism) are impossible in two dimensions, for particular interactions between the magnetic entities (3). Does that mean that magnetic ordering in a monolayer magnet is impossible? There has been much interest lately in the electrical conductivity in two and one dimensions. There are predictions that low dimensional conductors cannot be metals (4). Since some of the materials discussed at this Workshop will approximate low dimensional conductors, one wonders about the relevance of the theoretical predictions to practical devices. I believe this work, which is the first measurement on a macroscopic system that is literally two dimensional, illustrates that the theory may not prohibit useful devices. I will discuss this point after first describing the fabrication of two-dimensional (2D) magnets by the Langmuir-Blodgett technique, and then presenting results of magnetic measurements on the films.

PREPARATION AND CHARACTERIZATION OF 2D MAGNETS

The objective of the experiment was to study the properties of a magnetic material that is precisely one magnetic atom in thickness. It is doubtful if this kind of sample can be produced by conventional techniques, such as evaporation of magnetic metals. One could not be sure, a priori, that one had a uniform monolayer rather than a collection of islands. Doing the evaporation while keeping the substrate at a very ˙low temperature and then overcoating to avoid migration of the film might work, but how could one prove it?

Around 1975 two different and less conventional techniques were turned to the problem of magnetic monolayers. One method was the adsorption of gases on the surfaces of grafoil. This approach has the advantage that grafoil, exfoliated or "puff-pastry" graphite, provides an area of about 100 cm^2 per gram of substrate. Because of this large area, a sizable fraction of a gram of gas can be adsorbed at monolayer coverage on a gram of substrate. This quantity makes many conventional measurements feasible. From adsorption isotherms one can be confident of the coverage. The disadvantages are that the individual surfaces are only about 100 nm in diameter, which limits the coherence of the films on them. Also, the surfaces are not uniformly oriented; a spread of about 15° in orientation is found. The magnetic gas studied was the O_2 molecule. The initial observation (5) of antiferromagnetism, using neutron diffraction, has lead to measurements of magnetic susceptibility (6), specific heat (7), and more refined scattering experiments (8). Clearly the device applicability of this material is limited because the gas will desorb if the sample is raised to room temperature.

The second method for constructing monolayer magnets is an application of the Langmuir-Blodgett (L-B) technique (9). This is based on combining the water-repelling quality of oils with the water-seeking propensity of acids into a single molecule. The material we have used is stearic acid ($C_{18}H_{35}OOH$). As illustrated in the inset of Fig. 1, the carbons form a long chain terminated at one end by a COOH group, a carboxylic acid. The H of this group will dissociate in water under appropriate conditions. When this molecule is spread on water the oily, hydrophobic CH_2 chain will try to emerge whereas the acid group will try to dissolve. The result is that the molecule is suspended approximately vertically at the water surface, forming a natural monolayer. The L-B technique consists of trapping the monolayer with a movable surface-barrier, or piston. Pressure is applied which compacts the film into a "solid", i.e., increasing the surface pressure elicits relatively small changes in the surface area. The film is then removed from the water surface by dipping a suitable substrate through the surface. A hydrophobic substrate (e.g., carbon) picks up film on each insertion and withdrawal; with a hydrophilic substrate (e.g., glass) as illustrated in Fig. 1, film is deposited on every pass except the first insertion, if all goes well. An advantage of the L-B method is that it yields large area films, with a single orientation. They are stable under normal room conditions. However, the quantity of sample is about a microgram per cm^2 of substrate.

To produce a magnetic monolayer, one wishes to attach a magnetic entity to the molecule so that it is deposited with the film. We chose to do this by reacting Mn^{2+} ions with the acid end of the molecule. This has the advantages, compared to attaching to the hydrocarbon, of leaving the chains intact so that they can be packed nicely. The choice of Mn^{2+} was made because it has a half-filled 3d shell, and thus an S state. Its high symmetry minimizes the coupling to the lattice, and its magnetic properties are particularly simple. One consequence is that the electron spin resonance (ESR) of Mn^{2+} can be observed at room temperature because spin relaxation to the lattice is slow. Also, and importantly, Mn^{2+} should be the best example among transition metals of the kind of magnetic entity which should be governed by the theory that says that magnetic ordering in 2D is impossible (3). Thus, a L-B film with Mn^{2+} ions would seem to represent a physical realization of a 2D arrangement of highly symmetrical magnetic entities. If the prohibition of magnetic order can be

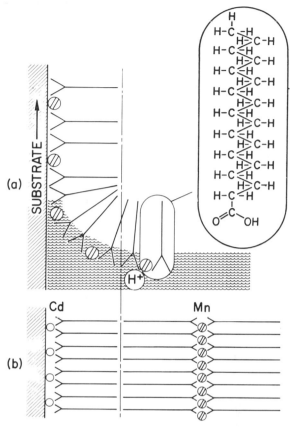

Fig. 1.   The Langmuir-Blodgett technique for the deposition of magnetic monolayer films.   (a) Molecules of stearic acid (whose structure is shown in the
inset) were spread on the water. Mn^{2+} in the water was caused to bind to the
ionized acid to form manganese stearate.   The monolayer was compacted and then
lifted off the surface by the (hydrophilic) substrate.   (b) A literally 2D
magnet formed by first depositing a non-magnetic layer of Cd stearate and then
two layers of Mn stearate.

overcome, it is possible that the material might have interesting magnetic
properties on a molecular scale.

      We studied the bonding of Mn^{+2} to a layer of stearic acid on a water
surface which lead to the formation of Mn stearate ($Mn(C_{18}H_{35}O_2)_2$, abbr. $MnSt_2$).
We found that with a concentration of 10^{-3} molar Mn^{+2} in the water, at pH = 7
the reaction was complete within the accuracy of our measurements.   A quick
way of monitoring the reaction was by skimming films off the surface and
examining them by infrared absorption.   The COOH group has a characteristic
absorption at 6 µm.   When the H is removed and a divalent ion is bound, the
absorption shifts to about 6.5 µm.   (Fig. 2)   By this means we are assured
that Mn is bound to the COO^- group.   Having established these conditions for
the bonding of Mn, films were pulled and checked.   Further tests of the total
quantity of Mn on the substrate showed that there was no observable excess Mn.
(One must guard against the inclusion of precipitates from the water.)
Techniques that proved useful in chemical analysis of films were electron
microprobe and nuclear backscattering.   These have useful sensitivities down
to about 5 and 50 monolayers, respectively.

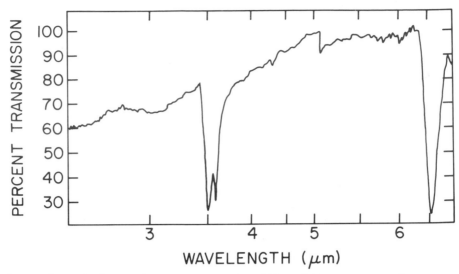

Fig. 2. Infrared absorption spectrum of a film of Mn stearate that was
skimmed off the surface of the water bath. The peak at about 6.5 μm is due to
the COO$^-$ group bound to Mn^{2+}. Absorption that would appear at 6.0μm, arising
from unreacted COOH, is absent. (pH=7, Mn concentration = 10^{-3} molar).

Another valuable technique is ESCA which we (10) used to verify that the
spin state of Mn in the films was indeed S=5/2. This was done to insure that
the chemical environment had not altered the valence from the original +2.
(The source of Mn was $MnCl_2$ dissolved in the water.)

In the case of magnetic films it may be possible to use the electron spin
resonance (ESR) in the high temperature paramagnetic phase to check whether the
magnetic ions are in a 2D array. A 2D paramagnet will have characteristic
magnetic anisotropies due to dipolar interactions. It has been shown by
Richards and Salamon (11) that the shift of the ESR field, δH_o, due to dipolar
interaction in 2D will be of the form $\delta H_o \propto H_o (3 \cos^2\theta - 1)$, where θ=angle
between the applied field, H_o, and the film normal. By contrast, a 3D array
would tend to have smaller anisotropy because of the more uniform distribution
of magnets in space resulting in a dipolar interaction which will be more
independent of direction. We have observed the predicted anisotropy of H_o in
a multilayer sample, measured in a field $H_o \approx 12$ KOe. (A high field is
desirable because, as indicated above, the magnitude of the anisotropy scales
with the applied field.) The observation of this dipolar anisotropy is
predicated on the absence of some other larger anisotropy that might conceal
it. Mn is a favorable case because its high symmetry leads to weak
magnetocrystalline anisotropy.

Another characteristic feature of 2D magnetism is the anisotropy of the
ESR line width. A theory has been given (11) which explains the observation
that the line width varies as $\Delta H = A + B (3 \cos^2\theta - 1)^2$. The angle-dependent
term depends crucially on the 2D character of the magnetic structure. It
arises because the dipolar broadening is affected by the correlations among
the spins. If the spins lose correlation rapidly there is a reduction in the
time average dipolar field. This gives rise to "motional narrowing" and
exchange narrowing. Conversely, if the correlations persist for long times
there is an enhancement of the time-independent dipolar term, which is of the
form $(3 \cos^2\theta - 1)^2$. It is believed that the important spin correlations are

determined by spin diffusion, which, like other diffusive processes, depends
on the dimensionality of the space. For 2D magnets the spin diffusion of
long wavelength fluctuations is sufficiently slow that enhancement of the
$(3 \cos^2\theta - 1)^2$ term is expected. This is superimposed on the isotropic background due to short wavelength, fast decaying correlations. We have observed
(1,12) this anisotropy of the line width; it is another indication that the
2D character is dominant in the $MnSt_2$ films.

   In addition to the chemical and magnetic tests, it was important to check
the structure of the films. There are two important properties: (a) the
packing of the molecules within the planes. One wishes to know whether the
molecules are packed in a regular crystalline array, whether it is polycrystalline, or whether it is amorphous. (b) The second question is whether the
layers are flat and uniform, or if there was rearrangement ("balling up") of
the layers, so that they no longer are two dimensional. To study the in-
plane packing, electron diffraction has been used to study L-B films since the
days of Davisson and Germer (13). With $MnSt_2$ we observed a slightly diffuse
but crystalline diffraction pattern even with the smallest number of layers.
(In our case that was two monolayers because the support was a carbon film on
an electron microscope grid. Carbon is hydrophobic and thus normally a bilayer
is pulled on the first cycle.) A difficulty with this measurement, as has been
noted by others (14) is that the diffraction pattern rapidly deteriorates upon
exposure to the electron beam. Nevertheless, photographs of the diffraction
patterns have been made. These reveal a pattern of broad spots, indicative of
a somewhat disordered structure. The pattern was similar to that observed (14)
from films of lead stearate, for which it was concluded that the space group
was either $P112_1/b$ (monoclinic) or $P2_12_12$ (orthorhombic). The lattice
constants of $MnSt_2$ were found to be $a_o = 4.85$Å, $b_o = 7.73$Å. The resulting nearest
neighbor Mn-Mn separation is 4.56Å. We derived some information about the
range of structural order by moving the sample across the beam. The diffraction pattern wandered slightly in orientation, but from the absence of abrupt
reorientations within a given grid opening, we concluded that there was
crystallinity at least over about 80 μm. We obtained a demonstration of film
continuity, if not crystallinity, from the observation of electron tunneling
between evaporated metal electrodes separated by a monolayer. Although the
area of the electrodes was about 1 cm^2, the tunneling dominated the
conductivity, rather than electrical shorting through holes in the film. (An
extremely small area of metallic punch-through would have shorted out the
tunneling.) The continuity must have been nearly perfect over macroscopic
distances.

   To study the layer structure we used x-ray (12,15) and neutron diffraction
(16). Although the amounts of material are small, about 1 μgram/cm^2 per
monolayer, it proved possible to observe diffraction effects down to one
monolayer with x-rays and three monolayers with neutrons, from samples with
areas of about 4 cm^2. Some results are shown in Figs. 3 and 4. The remarkably
intense diffraction arises from the combination of two properties. Firstly,
the unit cell size in the direction normal to the films: these are $d \approx 25$ Å
for a monolayer, and, because the molecules attach ionic to ionic ends, $d \approx 50$
Å for the bilayers. This rather large unit cell spacing gives rise to Bragg
diffraction peaks at grazing angles of about 1°. The second property is that
x-rays are totally reflected from solids at a grazing angle of about 0.1°,
depending on the electron density of the solid. At grazing angles greater
than this critical angle the reflectivity decreases. It is sufficiently great
at the low angles at which constructive interference occurs, the Bragg angles,
that the total intensity is much higher than it would be at larger grazing
angles. The strong reflections enabled us to observe not only the Bragg peak

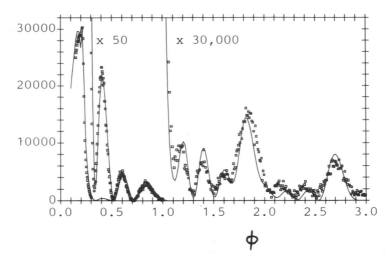

Figure 3. X-Ray diffraction from seven layers of MnSt$_2$ on a glass slide.
X-Ray wavelength = 1.54 Å, and ϕ = grazing angle.

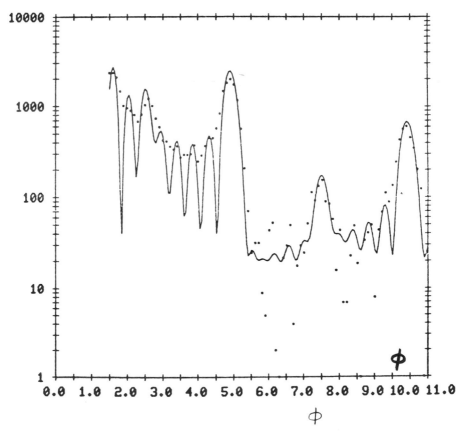

Fig. 4. Neutron diffraction from eleven layers of MnSt$_2$ on a polished silicon
wafer. Neutron wavelength = 4.15 Å and the abscissa is the grazing angle.

but additional interference effects in the x-ray diffraction. These arise from the fact that there are a finite, indeed small, number of layers. Each unit cell is analogous to a slit in an optical diffraction grating. It is well known in the optical case (17) that the diffraction from N slits gives rise to N-2 subsidiary maxima between the principal diffraction orders (analogous to the Bragg peaks). Thus by simply counting the number of subsidiary peaks one can determine the number of unit cells. The mere observation of a set of clean subsidiary peaks suggests that there is only a single set of layers; if it were doubled-over the pattern would be entirely different. One can do better. Segmüller has calculated the expected diffraction from a system comprising planar lamina modeled after the $MnSt_2$ layers. There are lamina representing the chemical composition of the molecule, i.e., Mn, COO, $(CH_2)_{16}$, CH_3. The thicknesses of the layers are fairly well known from the covalent and atomic radii, and the density of molecules was found from the chemical analysis of the films. Using these parameters in the calculation of the interference patterns Segmüller obtained a semiquantitative fit to the data. Rather slight variations, corresponding to slight tipping of the molecules and different densities resulted in an excellent fit to the data over an intensity range of 10^5 (18). The solid lines in Figs. 3 and 4 were calculated. Similar diffraction effects were observed with neutrons, and calculations reproduced the experimental data. The neutron data does not display the subsidiary structure because the resolution was not sufficiently high, or said another way, the flux of neutrons is much lower than the x-ray flux, so that resolution and signal/noise are not as high as for x-rays. (It should be remarked that the x-ray data were taken on a diffractometer in which the beam was highly collimated and monochromatized. This permitted the taking of data below a grazing angle of 0.1° without the divergence of the beam swamping the detector.) An attractive potentiality of neutron diffraction, on the other hand, is for the determination of magnetic structures.

The conclusion we draw from these diffraction studies is that the molecules form layers with the number and structure expected from the L-B process. There is a high degree of crystallinity in the packing of the molecules which extends at least to the limit of our ability to measure it, which is about 80 μm.

SEARCH FOR MAGNETIC ORDER

Having prepared L-B monolayer films containing Mn, the next goal was to search for magnetic ordering by lowering the temperature and looking for abrupt changes in magnetic behavior. There are only 2×10^{14} Mn ions/cm^2 of film. Thus, if one wishes to study monolayer behavior it is necessary to use highly sensitive techniques. We used ESR, which has high sensitivity, but because of the large line widths at low temperatures the signal was not easy to observe. In order to get some idea of the properties to be expected in the monolayers we did a number of preliminary experiments on bulk powders and multilayers of $MnSt_2$. I shall summarize these results before returning to the monolayer experiments.

The $MnSt_2$ powders were synthesized by Dr. A. Aviram (19). There was a variability in the composition of the samples, but some twelve early batches had generally similar magnetic properties. The static susceptibility, measured with a force balance, showed Curie-Weiss behavior at high temperatures, and extrapolated to a negative Weiss temperature, indicating anti-ferromagnetic (A-F) interactions among the spins (Fig. 5). (This is the most common inter-action in Mn salts.) At a temperature $T \leq 20$ K the susceptibility is larger than that extrapolated from the Curie-Weiss Law. (The inverse decreases more rapidly as seen in Fig. 5). This direction of deviation usually indicates

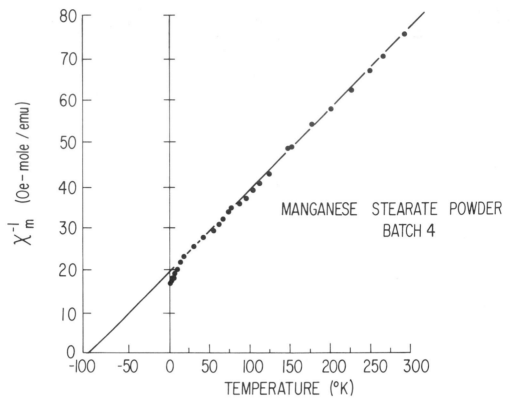

Fig. 5. Curie-Weiss plot of inverse molar susceptibility vs absolute temperature for a powder of $MnSt_2$.

the onset of magnetic ordering of the ferromagnetic type, however. This behavior led us to suggest (19) that at $T \lesssim 5$ K $MnSt_2$ powders are "weak-ferromagnets", i.e., the interaction is dominantly antiferromagnetic but the opposing magnetic sublattices do not cancel exactly, as in a pure A-F. This kind of interaction is known in other Mn and Fe salts which have sufficiently low crystal symmetry (20). The hypothesis of weak ferromagnetism was supported by the observation that at $T \lesssim 5$ K the magnetization (M) vs. applied field (H) curves at high fields did not extrapolate to M=0 at H=0. This suggested that there is a spontaneous magnetization below a transition temperature, as expected for a weak-ferromagnet. More support for weak-ferromagnetism came from ESR measurements. We observed a shift of the field for resonance, H_0, below about T=6 K. The direction of the shift, to lower fields, and its magnitude were compatible with weak-ferromagnetism. These results were important because the bulk powders of $MnSt_2$ seemed to undergo ordering. I say "seemed" because the most definitive test of long-ranged magnetic order, neutron diffraction, has not been accomplished. Such experiments were performed on $MnSt_2$ but they were not able to detect the A-F structure (21). Calculations showed that it will be very difficult to observe an in-plane A-F structure in $MnSt_2$ by neutron diffraction because the Mn density is low (21).

We also prepared multilayer samples of $MnSt_2$ by the Langmuir-Blodgett technique. The largest number of layers we made were 501, deposited on both faces of two quartz plates. This gave a comfortably large ESR signal. It was not sufficient for static susceptibility measurements, however. The limit on

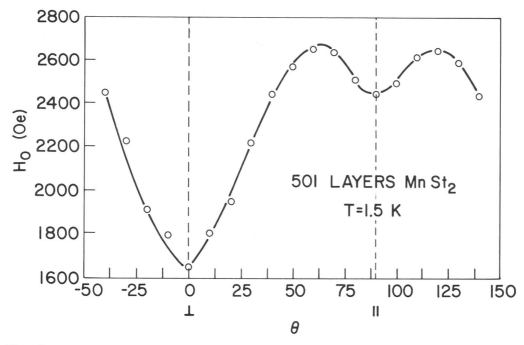

Fig. 6. ESR resonance field vs. the angle between the normal to the film and the field, for a film of 501 layers. Frequency = 9.3 GHz, T = 1.5 K.

the number of layers arises when defects occur, and the film starts to peel. We obtained considerable information from the ESR of multilayers. For the first time in MnSt$_2$ we were able to observe the anisotropies of the resonance line-width and position at room temperature (described in the previous section) which had the angular dependences characteristic of 2D paramagnets. This was not possible to observe in powders, of course. Although static susceptibility could not be measured, from the ESR one can measure the susceptibility because it is proportional to the area under the absorption curve. In this way we observed the Curie-Weiss behavior in multilayers to be rather similar to that of powders: there was a negative Weiss temperature, and at low temperatures, the susceptibility increased above the extrapolated value from the Curie-Weiss formula. It was found that below about 4 K the resonance field shifted downwards, and the shift was anisotropic, as shown in Fig. 6. With multilayer samples it was also feasible to measure the ESR at two difference frequencies in the ordered (low temperature) phase. Such measurements are shown in Fig. 7. The lower set of points corresponds to 9.3 GHz and the upper points to 35.0 GHz; this is implied by the values of ω/γ on the y-axis. The fields for resonance, H_O, at three angles $\theta=0$ ( ), 60°, and 90° ($\parallel$) are shown at these paramagnetic phase (i.e., H_O fall to the left of the dotted line). Moreover, unlike the paramagnetic case, they do not extrapolate to $H_O=0$ at $\omega=0$. This shows that the shifts of H_O are not caused merely by shifts in g values. The temperature dependence of the shift, as shown by the squares in Fig. 8, was not particularly rapid. All of these observations were compatible with weak-ferromagnetic ordering. Thus, the ESR on multilayers confirmed the observations on powders. Added information on the anisotropies of the resonances was possible because the films were uniformly oriented.

The materials thus far had not reached our ultimate goal of having only a single magnetic layer. Such samples were prepared in two ways. The first was

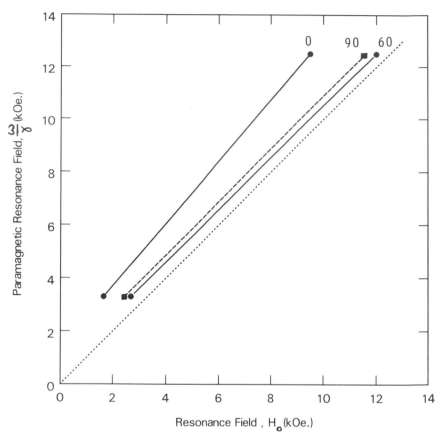

Fig. 7. Resonance diagram for MnSt$_2$ multilayers at T = 1.5 K. For a paramagnet all the points would lie on the dotted line. For the three angles indicated the actual resonance fields are lower than the paramagnetic field, and do not extrapolate to H=0 when ω=0.

to deposit, on both faces of a thin quartz plate, one layer of MnSt$_2$. This kind of sample has the disadvantage of placing the Mn in an unsymmetrical environment, being sandwiched between the stearate and the quartz. Also, the density of Mn is not as high as it might be. Both of these deficiencies can be ameliorated by first depositing a nonmagnetic stearate, we used CdSt$_2$, and then depositing two layers of MnSt$_2$. This is illustrated in Fig. 1b. The Mn ends of both layers attached to each other, which gave a concentration of Mn twice that of a single layer. Moreover, the Mn was now sandwiched between stearate layers only. Samples of both types were prepared, and measured with ESR. In order to have sufficient signal/noise we prepared the films on separate plates and then stacked the plates with 0.003 cm thick bits of mylar separating the plates. This prevented them from being damaged by rubbing on each other, and also separating them so that no significant magnetic interaction occurred between the plates. They remained 2D magnets. With approximately 50 plates (1 cm x 3 cm in area), good ESR was observed. The sample made of a single MnSt$_2$ layer did not show the characteristics of an ordered state above 1.4 K, and I will not discuss it further here.

The major experimental results at low temperatures are shown in Figs. 8 and 9 for the sample composed of MnSt$_2$ bilayers. It was found (22) that there was a significant shift of H$_o$ which was most rapid at about T=2 K, as shown by the circles in Fig. 8. The magnitude of the resonance field at low temperature

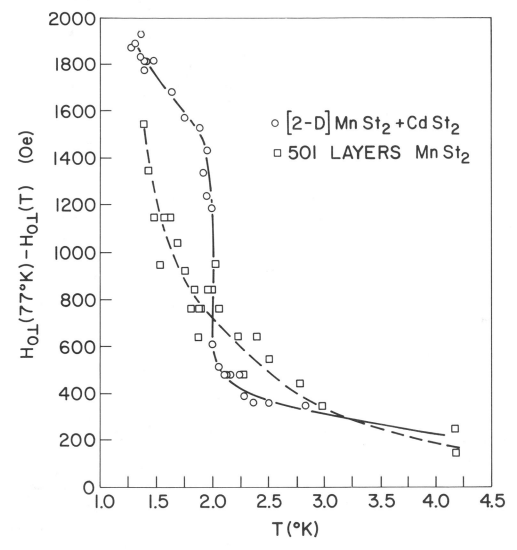

Fig. 8. Temperature dependences of the downward shift in the resonance field, for the field normal to the film. The squares are for the 501 multilayer sample, and the circles are for the literally 2D sample of the type shown in Fig. 1(b). ESR frequency = 9.3 GHz.

depended on the direction of the magnetic field, as shown in Fig. 9. These results are generally similar to those found for the multilayer sample, Figs. 6 and 8. Comparing the temperature dependences shown in Fig. 8 it appears that the shift of the resonance is more abrupt in the 2D sample than in the multilayer sample. This is surprising if one believes that a 2D magnet should not order at all, because in this case it gives a better defined transition than a more 3D sample.

    This evidence thus indicates that a phase transition has occurred in the 2D magnet at $T \leq 2$ K. One may question whether the observed magnetic changes are a consequence of a structural change and are not directly a magnetic transition. This is unlikely for the reasons that Mn spins should be insensitive to structural changes because Mn couples weakly to the lattice. There was also direct observation of the structure of $MnSt_2$ powders in the

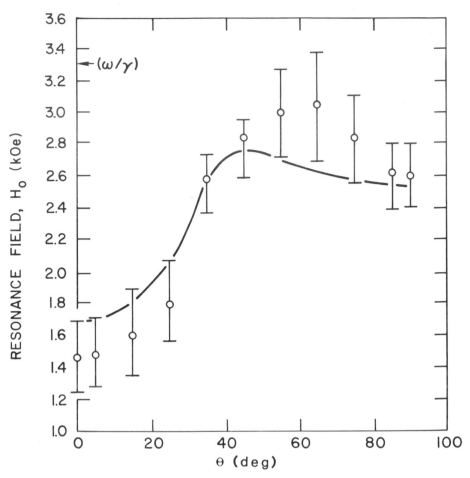

Fig. 9. ESR resonance field vs. angle for the literally 2D magnet. Experimental
data are the circles. The solid line is a fit to the data using a theory of
resonance in weak ferromagnets (23). T = 1.5 K, frequency = 9.3 GHz.

neutron diffraction experiments described above. To within the resolution of
those measurements there was no change in the structure between 77 K and 1.9 K.
That sample was a powder but it is a reasonable assumption that films would
behave similarly and not have a structural change.

The question remains: what kind of magnetic order does 2D $MnSt_2$ take below
2 K? The data on the 2D layers is qualitatively similar to the comparable
measurements on multilayers and powders, which were compatible with weak-
ferromagnetism. A more quantitative test of this hypothesis is possible
because there is a theoretical calculation (23) of the angular dependence of
ESR of a certain class of weak-ferromagnets. As I have shown elsewhere (1),
the crystal structure and ESR data of $MnSt_2$ permit it to belong to that class.
Therefore, we have fitted the observed angular dependence of H_O, the data
points of Fig. 9, to the theory. Parameters that gave the best fit were found
to be reasonable insofar as we knew. The resulting theoretical curve, shown
by the solid line in Fig. 9, reproduces the qualitative features including the
peculiar nonmonotonic variation of $H_O(\theta)$.

Some recent developments cast some doubt on this model for the magnetic structure. Ferrieu has compared (24) the ESR line width at room temperature in $MnSt_2$ multilayers to the theory (11) as reformulated by him. A value for the exchange constant was thereby deduced which is difficult to reconcile with parameters found by fitting the data in the ordered state. Another observation (25) by Aviram and myself is that $MnSt_2$ powders can be prepared that behave like pure anti-ferromagnets, with a surprisingly high ordering temperature of about 10 K. This has caused us to wonder whether the earlier samples, powders and L-B films, were perhaps not of sufficiently perfect stoichiometry. This might cause a decrease in their ordering temperature, and also produce some ferromagnetic moment because of the incomplete occupation of the opposing magnetic sublattices, an early idea (26) by Neel. There may also be an effect due to different crystal structures in the recent samples. Thus, there is still uncertainty about precisely what kind of ordering the 2D magnets undergo, but the evidence seems very strong that an ordered state does exist below 2 K.

CONCLUSIONS

One aspect of the relevance of this work to the subject of "molecular" electronics is whether there are special fundamental laws which will intervene at the microscopic level of truly low dimensional structures. I mentioned in the Introduction the well-known and oft-quoted Mermin-Wagner theorem (3), which denies the possibility of ferromagnetic and anti-ferromagnetic order in a 2D symmetrically interacting (Heisenberg) magnet. We have now produced a magnet material that was designed to be Heisenberg-like because of the high symmetry of the Mn^{+2} ions, and it is two-dimensional by construction. And yet it orders!

The resolution of the seeming contradiction between this experiment and well-established theory may lie in the extent to which one must achieve the assumptions of the theory. For example, the theory postulates highly symmetrical interactions. One must then inquire how much and what kinds of dis-symmetry will produce ordering. The theory also assumes that the magnet extends to infinity in two-dimensions. What are the effects of finite sizes?

The influence of anisotropy has been studied by several theoreticians. Nelson and Pelcovits have found (27) an approximate relation of the ordering temperature, T_N, to the anisotropy A, of the form $T_N \propto |1/\log A|$. As A vanishes, T_N goes to zero as required by the Mermin-Wagner theorem. But since the variation of T_N with A is logarithmic, even for small values that might be found in real materials T_N will be not grossly smaller than for a highly anisotropic material. This was evident in earlier calculations (28) by Lines, made by other theoretical methods.

The importance of finite sizes was emphasized long ago (29). More recently attempts are being made to calculate (30) the influence of finite sizes in order to interpret experiments. The theory gives the result that the spin deviations vary as log N, where N is the number of particles in two dimensions. As shown, e.g., by monte-carlo simulations (31), the spin fluctuations are not very large even for macroscopic arrays. Complete disorder would require astronomical sizes.

Thus, the theoretical prohibition on magnetic ordering in two dimensions may be vitiated by the presence of even small amounts of anisotropy. This seems very likely to be present becasue a 2D object is inherently anisotropic and some of the structural anisotropy may be mirrored in the magnetic interaction. If an easy-axis anisotropy results there will be magnetic ordering. The factor that seems to be inevitable is the finite size of the sample. Its effects are still being clarified, but for many purposes the sample will appear to undergo an ordering transition.

The general conclusion I have drawn is that one must examine in detail the assumptions and limitations of a theory rather closely when 2D objects are involved. The approach to the limiting case of infinite size and zero anisotropy is so slow that real materials may appear to be rather different from the predicted state of disorder. There appears to be effectively no theoretical prohibition of useful ordered states in two dimensions.

It is pertinent to this Workshop that this work shows that potentially useful materials can indeed be prepared on a molecular scale. The Langmuir-Blodgett technique can be applied to a variety of materials and is relatively simple and inexpensive. In this paper I have endeavored to show how one can proceed from the examination of the properties of bulk materials, where a large range of techniques is available, to smaller samples, eventually culminating on the monolayer scale. The monolayer magnetic material is perhaps a paradigm in preparation for future developments. These could include materials with higher ordering temperatures and ordering to ferro- or ferrimagnetic states, which would be more useful.

ACKNOWLEDGMENT

This work has benefitted from discussions with many colleagues including A. Aviram, P. Brosious, T. McGuire, F. Mehran, R. Pelcovits, T.D. Schultz, B. Scott, B.D. Silverman, J. Slonczewski and K.W.H. Stevens. The experimental work was done in collaboration with A. Aviram, J. Axe, F. Dacol, R. Evans, F. Ferrieu, W. Hammer, S. Herd, J. Kirtley, H. Lillienthal, R. Linn, R. Nicklow, R. Pollak, A. Segmüller, E. Simonyi and A. Taranko. I am grateful to them and to N. Shiren for early support.

REFERENCES

1. M. Pomerantz, Studies of Literally Two-Dimensional Magnets of Manganese Stearate, in "Phase Transitions in Surface Films" (Ed. by J.G. Dash and J. Ruvalds) p. 317, Plenum Pub. Corp., 1980.

2. An issue of Proc. I.E.E.E. (Feb. 1981) is devoted to fundamental limits in electrical engineering. Dimensionality is not mentioned.

3. F. Bloch, "Zur Theorie des Ferromagnetismus", Z.f. Physik 61, 206 (1930).

    N.D. Mermin and H. Wagner, "Absence of Ferromagnetism or Antiferromagnetism in One- or Two-Dimensional Isotropic Heisenberg Models", Phys. Rev. Lett. 17 1133 (1966).

4. E. Abrahams, P.W. Anderson, D.C. Licciardello, T.V. Ramakrishman, "Scaling Theory of Localization: Absence of Quantum Diffusion in Two Dimensions", ibid. 42, 673 (1979).

5. J.P. McTague and M. Nielson, "Magnetic and Structural Phases of Monolayer O_2 on Graphite", ibid. 37, 596 (1976).

6. S. Gregory, "Magnetic Susceptibility of Oxygen Adsorbed on Graphite", ibid. 40, 723 (1978).

7. J. Stoltenberg and O.E. Vilches, "Heat Capacity of O_2 Films Adsorbed on Grafoil", Phys. Rev. B. 22, 2920 (1980).

8. P.W. Stephens, et al, "X-Ray and Heat-Capacity Study of Molecular Oxygen Adsorbed on Graphite", Phys. Rev. Lett. 45, 1959 (1980).

9. Reviewed by G.L. Gaines, "Insoluble Monolayers at Liquid-Gas Interfaces", Interscience, N.Y. (1966).

10. M. Pomerantz and R.A. Pollak, "Spin State of Manganese in Monolayer Films of Mn Arachidate", Chem. Phys. Lett. 31, 602 (1975).

11. P.M. Richards and M.B. Salamon, "Exchange Narrowing of Electron Spin Resonance in a Two-Dimensional System", Phys. Rev. B9, 32 (1974).

12. M. Pomerantz, F.H. Dacol, and A. Segmüller, "Preparation of Literally Two-Dimensional Magnets", Phys. Rev. Lett. 40, 246 (1978).

13. L.H. Germer and K.H. Storks, "Arrangement of Molecules in a Single Layer and in Multiple Layers", J. of Chem. Phys. 6, 280 (1938).

14. J.F. Stephens adn C. Tuck-Lee, "The Structure of a Multilayer of Lead Stearate", J. Appl. Cryst. 2, 1 (1969).

15. M. Pomerantz and A. Segmüller, "High Resolution X-Ray Diffraction from Small Numbers of Langmuir-Blodgett Layers of Manganese Stearate", Thin Solid Films 68, 38 (1980).

16. R.M. Nicklow, M. Pomerantz, and A. Segmüller, "Neutron Diffraction from Small Numbers of Langmuir-Blodgett Monolayers of Manganese Stearate", Phys. Rev. B23, 1081 (1981).

17. See your favorite optics text.

18. A. Segmüller, "Small-Angle Interferences of X-Rays Reflected from Periodic and Near-Periodic Multilayers", in A.I.P. Conf. Proc. No. 53, p. 78 (1979).

19. M. Pomerantz and A. Aviram, "Weak-Ferromagnetism of Quasi Two-Dimensional Manganese Stearate", Solid State Comm. 20, 9 (1976).

20. Reviewed by T. Moriya, Weak Ferromagnetism, in "Magnetism" (Ed., Rado and Suhl), Vol. 1, p. 85, Academic, 1958.

21. J. Axe (private communications).

22. M. Pomerantz, "Experimental Evidence for Magnetic Ordering in a Literally Two-dimensional Magnet", Solid State Comm. 27, 1413 (1978).

23. H. Yoshioka and K. Saiki, "Resonance Frequencies of Antiferromagnets Having Antisymmetric Exchange Interactions", J. Phys. Soc. Jap. 33, 1566 (1972).

24. F. Ferrieu and M. Pomerantz (to be published).

25. A. Aviram and M. Pomerantz, Bull. A.P.S., 26, 348 (1981), and to be published.

26. L. Neel, "Essai D'Interpretation des Proprietes Magnetique du Sesquioxyde de Fer Rhomboedrique", Ann. Phys. Ser. 12 4, 249 (1949).

27. R.A. Pelcovits and D.R. Nelson, "Bicritical Points in 2+ε Dimensions", Phy. Lett. 57A, 23 (1976).

28. M.E. Lines, "The Quadratic Layer Antiferromagnet", J. Phys. Chem. Solids 31, 101 (1970).

29. H.N.V. Temperley, Changes of State, p. 184, Interscience Pub, 1956, critically discusses the spin-wave theory.

30. Reviewed by Y. Imry, "Long Range Order in Two Dimensions", in Critical Reviews in Solid State - Mat'l Science 8, 157 (1979).

31. J. Tobochnik and G.V. Chester, "Monte Carlo Study of the Planar Spin Model" Phys. Rev. B20, 3761 (1979).

DISCUSSION

Prof. DeArmond: NC St. Univ. - You whizzed the ESR spectras too fast and I would like to see them. They have an unusual lineshape.

Dr. Pomerantz: The first figure is the paramagnetic case, at T = 17°K. This is a disordered magnetic material. The ESR absorption has a g = 2 and Lorentzian lineshape. It is a few hundred Gauss wide, typical of concentrated Mn salts.

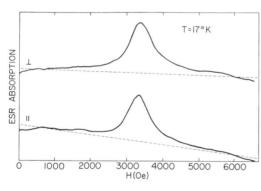

Fig. 10

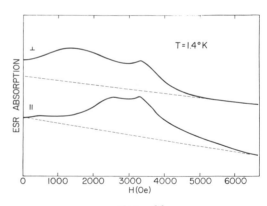

Fig. 11

Then when you lower the temperature, what happens is that if you put the field perpendicular to the plane, the main body of the line has a peak at about 1400 Gauss. There remains a small peak where the original line was, which I think is due to some kind of poorly ordered material. This residue line is useful in that it tells you where the line started, and one can see clearly to where it shifted. What is interesting is that the line has shifted about 1900 Gauss downfield, and it is anisotropic. If you put the field parallel to the plate, the line shifts down from where it started, but not nearly as much. There is a very anisotropic shifting of the line. For those not familiar with this kind of thing, the resonance will occur when the spins in the film see a certain magnetic field. They want to see 3,300 Gauss for an applied frequency of about

9 GHz. Now at low temperatures even though I apply only about 1400 Gauss, they are still absorbing energy which means the spins are still seeing 3,400 Gauss. That tells me that the film itself is providing 1900 Gauss. I interpret this to mean that there is an ordered magnetic state in the film which is providing an additional field to produce resonance.

Prof. DeArmond: The g factor is dependent upon the number of mono-layers?

Dr. Pomerantz: This data refers to one monolayer of magnetic atoms. The shifts are due to the fact that I had an ordered magnetic state which is anisotropic. The effect is not due to a simple change in the g factor, at least in a multilayer sample, as is shown by Fig. 7. If I make samples with different numbers of layers, as far as I have measured, the shift behavior is generally similar. So I infer that for a monolayer sample, the shift is not due to g shifts.

Dr. Tsai: Std. Oil - Can you observe the magnetic domain?

Dr. Pomerantz: No. I haven't seen that. That would require a very sophisticated experiment which I am not in a position to do. The difficulty of such an experiment is increased because we are forced now to work at low temperature (less than 2°K) to get the ordered magnetic state.

Dr. Greyber: NSF - Two points--precisely what was wrong with the Bloch derivation, and No. 2, could you instead of an antiferromagnetic state obtain a ferromagnetic state, perhaps by using iron 3 which would have 5 d electrons?

Dr. Pomerantz: Really I didn't tell you the whole story of Bloch's paper. He actually uses a more complicated magnetic energy, including both the highly symmetrical Heisenberg exchange and also anisotropy. The spin wave energy with a pure Heisenberg interaction is DK^2. It turns out if you have anisotropy, there is an additional constant term. Bloch concluded that in the limit of vanishing anisotropy, the magnetic order would also vanish. However, aniso-tropy occurs as a common feature in real magnets. The problem is when you had only DK^2 for the energy, when you made the integration, that DK^2 went to zero and things blew up. If you have a DK^2 plus a constant anisotropy, the integral doesn't blow up because you are left with a constant, so anisotropy opposes the disorder. It can organize the spins so even for the shortest wavelength, the magnet can still be ordered. The other catch in the theory is that it assumes one can have an infinite wavelength fluctuation. We have a finite film, sorry to say. It is about a centimeter across which is macroscopic, but it isn't infinite. That is a limitation in making comparison of experiment to a theory which assumes an infinite size. I think that is very important for our purposes because if you try to apply these statistical theories to a real material you should be wary of the effects of the assumption of an infinite size. As for your question about Fe^{+3}, we have tried that, as a matter of fact. It turns out iron is more difficult to incorporate in films. In the bulk powders, the way Dr. Aviram makes them, it does have interesting magnetic properties. It seems to be antiferromagnetic still, but the ordering occurs at a higher temperature, and that's a big help. It seems to order at about 50 or 60 K. We have tried to make films containing Fe^{+3} but we have not been satisfied with the results.

        Prof. Ferry: Col. St. Univ. - If there is a size dependence, you
should see a size dependence in the shift. Have you looked for that?

        Dr. Pomerantz: No, I haven't. That would also be a good experiment.
What it means is cutting the samples. I hate to do that, but the other problem
is that the predicted dependence on size is logarithmic. If I change the size
by a factor of ten, say from 10^7 atoms on an edge to 10^6, the logarithm of the
size changes only from 7 to 6. It would be tough to produce really big effects.
I have a feeling that ordering is probably mostly due to anisotropy. As I
suggest in the paper, a two-dimensional object is intrinsically anisotropic in
its structure. It would be surprising to me if some of this structural
anisotropy were not reflected in the magnetic interaction. So a pure Heisenberg
interaction seems very unlikely. Then one gets into other cases, such as planar
symmetry or uniaxial symmetry, where various kinds of ordered states are
predicted.

CHAPTER XXIII

INELASTIC SCATTERING OF LIGHT BY THE TRANSPORT OF LOCALIZED CHARGE STATES
IN AMORPHOUS POLYMERS

David B. Cotts
Polymer Science Department
SRI International
Menlo Park, CA 94025

INTRODUCTION

The observation of conduction in amorphous materials has aroused considerable interest in both academic and industrial circles. The importance of this process is amply demonstrated by the award of a Nobel Prize to Sir Nevil Mott for his fundamental studies of conduction in chalcogenide glasses[1] and the enormous commercial success of the xerographic process using poly(N-vinylcarbazole) (PVK).[2] Our understanding of this process is however nowhere near complete. The very existence of this workshop on Molecular Electronic Devices is witness to the continuing development of amorphous conducting materials.[3] There are many reasons for this interest. They include the fact that amorphous materials, and in particular amorphous organic materials, are intrinsically less expensive to manufacture and process than single crystalline silicon. In addition, while the minimum dimension of active elements in conventional semiconductor devices is limited to the resolution of the lithographic process, devices operating on a molecular level in amorphous media are limited only by molecular dimensions themselves.

Along with the application of amorphous conductors to devices of increasing sophistication must come a refinement in our understanding of the conduction process itself. As the dimensions of active elements are reduced to the molecular scale, so must our understanding of electron transport include processes occurring at this level.

This paper is concerned with the application of an inelastic light scattering technique to the characterization of charge transport in amorphous materials. It will summarize the current understanding of electronic transport based on so called time of flight techniques and present an analogy between the diffusion of a particle and the transport of localized charge states. The mathematical formalism of the analysis will be presented as well as experimental results derived from various conduction mechanisms.

BACKGROUND

Much of what we know about conduction in amorphous materials has been learned through time of flight techniques.[4] These experiments are schematically illustrated in Figure 1. A thin layer of the material under investigation is sandwiched between electrodes. A DC potential is applied across the sandwich and a thin sheet of charge carriers created on one side. Photo generation and charge injection mechanisms can each be used. The number of carriers reaching the opposite electrode per unit time or current is recorded as a function of time after carrier formation. The shape of the current versus time curve is then related to specific conduction mechanisms.

The results of these investigations may be summarized by equation 1.

$$\mu \propto \rho^2 \exp(-\gamma\rho) \exp(-\Delta(E)/KT) \tag{1}$$

The overall mobility μ is given by the product of two exponential terms. One contains a field dependent thermal activation energy $\Delta(E)$; the other a product of the average distance between charge acceptors (or donors) ρ and an empirical measure of the orbital overlap between molecules γ. The average distance between acceptor/donor molecules ρ is approximately proportional to the one-third root of their concentration. This concentration dependence requires that charge transport occur through a hopping mechanism. That is, a charge is

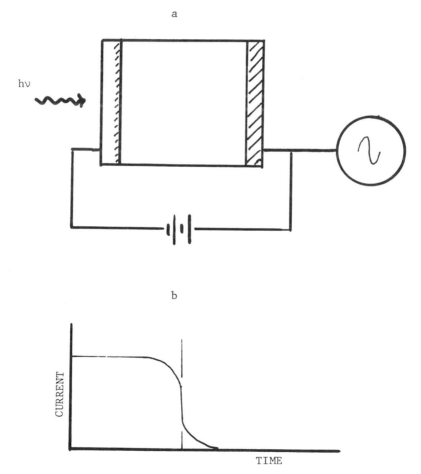

Figure 1. Schematic illustration of (a) the time of flight experiment and (b) the experimental data from which mobilities are calculated.

localized at a molecular anion (cation) for a period of time and that it hops instantaneously to an adjacent charge acceptor. The residence time at a given site is dependent on the bias field, temperature and intermolecular orbital overlap. Although the distance between charge acceptors must remain relatively constant in rigid media their respective orientations, and hence electron overlap, will vary in time as they vibrate and reorient.

This model is relatively successful in describing the conductive properties of intrinsically semiconducting poly(N-vinylcarbazole) and doped systems like triphenylamine in polycarbonate and trinitrofluorenone poly(N-vinylcarbazole). It fails however in accounting for the field dependence of the mobility and must invoke an effective temperature T_{eff} for the Arrhenius term $\exp \Delta(E)/KT$. While this empirical parameter is successful in reducing experimental data it however has little rational basis. This discrepancy is a prime example of the need for a better understanding of the fundamental physical processes responsible for conduction in amorphous materials.

CONCEPTUAL APPROACH

A new perspective on the problem of charge transport in amorphous materials may be gained by considering an analogy to the diffusion of particles in solution. The experimental technique through which we will describe this process is known as photon correlation spectroscopy or quasi-elastic light scattering. Consider a particle diffusing through a homogeneous media of constant refractive index. The scattering intensity from a given microscopic volume will, on a time scale much larger than that for individual molecular rotation, remain constant. The refractive index and hence the scattering intensity of such a microscopic volume will however increase as a particle difuses into it. The magnitude of this increase depends on the difference in refractive index between solvent and solute and the number of solute particles. The length of time during which the scattering intensity is increased for a given scattering volume is therefore related to the length of time it takes the particle to diffuse through the scattering volume, and hence the particle mobility. Application of this procedure to the analysis of molecular diffusion in solution is well developed.[5]

The analogy we propose is that the transport of molecular charge states through amorphous media may be treated in a manner similar to the diffusion of particles in solution. The solid polymer matrix is of a constant refractive index. The molecular anion (or cation) created when an electron is localized at (or withdrawn from) a molecular residue is, in this example, analogous to the particle in solution. Its refractive index is considerably different than that of uncharged molecules around it. It will enhance the scattering from regions into which electrons are injected, and the temporal properties of the enhanced scattering may be interpreted to yield information about the mobility of charge and hence the environment of localized molecular anions (cations).

MATHEMATICAL FORMALISM

A quantitative description of the temporal and angular dependence of the light scattered by localized charge states requires the introduction of a molecular correlation function $C(\tau)$.[6] This function describes the joint probability that if a particle (localized molecular anion) is in a given volume at time t it will still be there at time t + τ, or

$$C(\tau) = \langle n(t)n(t + \tau) \rangle \qquad (2)$$

One can readily see that such a correlation function would be useful in describing the way in which localized charge states diffuse through amorphous media. We will in fact develop some model correlation functions which include variable such as a distribution of activation energies and illustrate how this information would be represented in the experimental data.

The electric field scattered from an amorphous medium of an average dielectric constant ϵ_0 at a distance R and time t is given by equation 3

$$E_s(R,t) = \frac{-K_f^2}{4\Pi R \epsilon_0} \exp i(K_f R - \omega_i t) \, \delta\epsilon(q,t) \qquad (3)$$

where E_0 and ω_i are the incident amplitude and angular frequency respectively.[5] The momentum vector K_f is approximately equal to $2\Pi n/\lambda$. The second term in the exponential, $\delta\epsilon(q,t)$ specifies how the local dielectric constant fluctuates in time and with the scattering vector $q = (4\Pi \tilde{n}/\lambda) \sin \theta/2$. This local fluctuation in dielectric is due to the presence, or absence, of charged states.

The temporal autocorrelation of the scattered field and equivalently the spectrum of scattered light are given in equations 4 and 5, respectively.

$$\langle E_s^*(R,0)E_s(R,t)\rangle = \frac{K_f^4 |E_0|^2}{16\Pi^2 R^2 \epsilon_0^2} \langle \delta\epsilon(q,0) \; \delta\epsilon(q,t)\rangle \exp - i\omega_i t \qquad (4)$$

$$I(q, \omega_f) = \left[\frac{|E_0|^2 K_f^4}{16\Pi^2 R^2 \epsilon_0^2}\right] \frac{1}{2\Pi} \int_{-\infty}^{+\infty} \langle \delta\epsilon(q,0) \; \delta\epsilon(q,t)\rangle \exp i(\omega - \omega_i)t \; dt \qquad (5)$$

This equivalence is based on the Wener-Kinchem theorem which states that intensity spectra and temporal correlation functions are Fourier transform pairs. The connection to scattering by charge transport is made by pointing out that the integral quantity in equation 5 has been shown to be the space-time Fourier transform of the molecular correlation function $C(R,t)$.[7] When this fundamental identity was first demonstrated, in the context of neutron scattering, it may have appeared to be of small utility. The development of intense, coherent laser sources however has made this an extremely useful tool in analyzing the structure and dynamics of condensed media on a molecular scale.

EXPERIMENTAL

The apparatus necessary to measure the spectrum (or temporal correlation) of light scattered by this transport process is outlined in Figure 2. An etalon stabilized gas laser is focused on to the sample. Optical components for varying the beam size, intensity, or plane of polarization may be provided. The sample configuration is similar to that used in time of flight experiments. It may be oriented with the applied field normal to the incident light or, using transparent electrodes, at an angle to reduce the path length and hence multiple scattering phenomena. A photon counting detector monitoring an extremely small scattering volume converts the scattered light into TTL pulses. These pulses or photocounts are autocorrelated to form a quantity similar to $\langle E_s(o)E_s(t)\rangle$ and may be Fourier transformed to obtain the scattered spectrum.

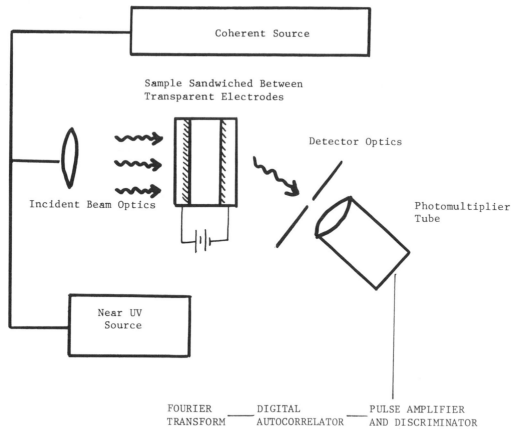

Figure 2. Experimental design for the observation of scattering by localized charge transport in amorphous materials.

TRANSPORT MECHANISM ANALYSIS

In order to interpret dynamic scattering data with equations (4) or (5) a molecular correlation function must be specified. This function should be relatively simple and dependent on relevant experimental parameters, including as a minimum the applied field and drift mobility. The molecular correlation functions and corresponding scattering spectrum for several model systems are illustrated in Figure 3.

The first example is that of particles (molecular anions) moving or hopping at a constant hop rate ν and in a fixed direction and field E. C(t) is therefore of the form

$$C(t) = \exp(iq \cdot t\mu E) \tag{6}$$

The scattering vector q has previously been defined, the mobility is in units of cm^2/Vsec and the field strength in volts/cm. The velocity μE is equal to the hop frequency in reciprocal seconds times the hop length. The scattered spectrum $I(\omega)$ then becomes

$$I(\omega) = N|E_o|^2 \, \delta(\omega - \omega_o + q \cdot \mu E) \tag{7}$$

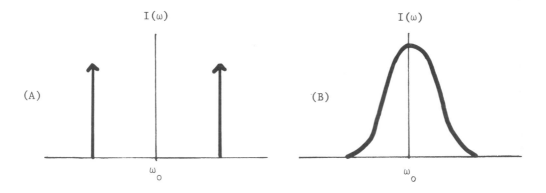

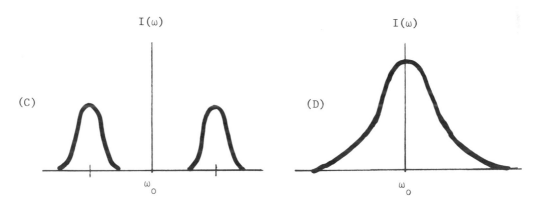

Figure 3.   Spectra of scattered light calculated for four models of charge
transport.   (A) One mobility along the applied field (e.g., Figure 4B).
(B) Diffusive transport.   (C) Dispersive transport biased by an electric
field (e.g., Figure 4A).   (D) The effect of two or more mobilities (e.g.,
deep trapping).

The scattering spectrum is therefore a delta function shifted $\omega = q \cdot \mu E$ from the
incident frequency ω_0.   Note that the direction of the shift, to higher or
lower frequencies, is governed by the sign of the mobility in a given field.
Negative and positive charges shift the scattered intensity maximum in opposite
directions and hence may be resolved in a single experiment.

     The requirement that all particles or localized charge states transport
parallel to, and only parallel to the applied field is certainly too restrictive
for real systems.   The probability that charge acceptor sites are (1) in close
proximity, (2) of a favorable intermolecular orientation, and (3) oriented
along lines of the applied field is certainly low.   The path that localized
charge states trace throughout the media must include a non-zero component
oriented normal to the field lines.   The probability distribution about the
field lines is symetric and can be treated as a random or brownian diffusion
process.

This situation is illustrated in Figure 4. The electrodes are located in the x-y plane and the field lines along the z axis. Benzene rings are used to simulate aromatic charge acceptor molecules distributed through space, in an inert matrix. Their center of gravity is fixed, however each is able to reorient. The extent of the reorientation depends on the local environment. Transport solely along the field lines as in the bottom of figure 4 requires a high degree of local molecular overlap which is extremely unlikely.

In the top of figure 4 is a more reasonable microscopic piture. The actual path of transport depends on short-lived conditions of favorable molecular overlap. Transport is strongly biased in the direction of the applied field but not limited to it.

The molecular correlation function for brownian diffusion is given by equation 8. Here we are separating the mobility μ, measured across the

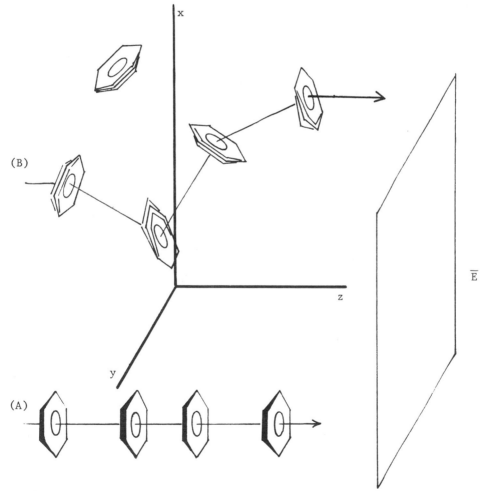

Figure 4. Molecular picture of charge transport through amorphous media. (A) Transport solely along the applied field. (B) Biased transport with a dispersive component.

electrode sandwich (z-axis transport) from the diffusive component D, parallel
to the electrode surface (x, y plane).

$$C(t) = \exp(-Dq^2 t) \tag{8}$$

The scattered spectrum then becomes

$$I(\omega) = N|E_o|^2 \left[\frac{Dq^2/\Pi}{(\omega - \omega_o)^2 + (Dq^2)^2} \right] \tag{9}$$

Analysis of real systems must include both of these effects, represented
by equations (7) and (9); linear transport in an applied field as well as
diffusion off of this axis. The molecular correlation function and spectrum
of scattered intensity take the form of equations (10) and (11).

$$C(t) = \exp(iq \cdot uEt) \exp(-q^2 D) \tag{10}$$

$$I(\omega) = N|E_o|^2 \left[\frac{q^2 D}{(\omega \pm q \cdot V)^2 + (q^2 D)^2} \right] \tag{11}$$

Transport in an electrostatic field leads to a shift in the frequency of
maximum intensity, which is in turn broadened by off-axis diffusion.

The maximum in $I(\omega)$ occurs at frequency ω given by equation 12

$$\omega = 2q\mu E \cos\phi \sin\theta/2 \tag{12}$$

where ϕ is the angle between the field and the scattered light.

The demonstration of this scattering phenomena would provide invaluable
information for comparison with that obtained by time of flight techniques.
Analysis of the later assumes that charge transport proceed, along a straight
line parallel to the applied field. The scattering technique however can
resolve between the transport component that is field dependent and that which
is random in direction, controlled instead by favorable molecular overlap
between acceptor sites.

These experimental results would also help explain the insensitivity of
the field dependent activation energy $\Delta(E)$ in equation (1). This apparent
anomaly is currently rationalized by invoking an effective temperature T_{eff}
equal to the difference between the actual and a higher reference temperature
T_o. This empirically derived reference temperature is, for doped polycarbonate
and poly(N-vinylcarbazole), very close to their glass transitions temperatures.
Many polymer properties related to local segmental motion may also be analyzed
in terms of an effective temperature which is often the temperature difference
between the actual and the glass transition temperature. A possible explanation for the lack of a strong temperature dependence of the field dependent
activation energy would acknowledge the contributions of molecular motion.
In such a model diffusional, unbiased transport would occur with a very low
activation energy between sites, whose static, intermolecular overlap was high.
Transport mitigated by an applied field however requires good overlap between
acceptors along the field lines. Static overlap is enhanced by transient overlap due to the motion (rotation and vibration) of charge acceptors. The relative molecular freedom is of course sensitive to the so called free volume in
the polymer, increasing with increasing temperature. This model can be verified
by the observation of a scattering spectrum similar to that in Figure 3, and by
measuring the temperature and pressure dependence of the spectrum.

The observation of dynamic scattering in amorphous semiconducting polymers will contribute to the picture of charge transport drawn by time of flight experiments in another important way. It can resolve the contributions of species with different mobilities and the presence of charge traps of varying depth. For two mobilities, or sites with different residence times the molecular correlation function is proportional to equation (13) and the spectrum of scattered light to (14). In the same way the spectrum of light scattered by a distribution of mobilities may be calculated and compared to experimental spectra.

$$C(t) = \exp(iq \cdot \mu_1 Et) + \exp(iq \cdot \mu_2 Et) \tag{13}$$

$$I(\omega) \alpha \ |E_o|^2 [N_1 \delta(\omega - \omega_o + q\mu_1 E) + N_2 \delta(\omega - \omega_o + q\mu_2 E)] \tag{14}$$

CONCLUSION

The spectrum of light scattered by the transport of charge through amorphous polymers has been calculated in analogy to the diffusion of particles in solution. The spectra are directly related to the molecular correlation functions, and experimental results may be readily compared to calculations based on a variety of models. Several models have been presented, the scattered spectrum calculated for each, and the parameters which would be obtained from such an experiment compared to those obtained from time of flight experiments. The results of dynamic scattering experiments may contribute towards the refinement of current models for charge transport.

REFERENCES

1.   Sir Nevil Mott, "Electrons in Glass," Reviews in Modern Physics. 50, 203 (1978).

2.   R. C. Pennel et. al., "Poly(N-Vinylcarbazole): A Selective Review of its Polymerization, Structure, Properties, and Electrical Characteristics," Macromolecular Reviews. 13, 63 (1978).

3.   R. B. Fox, ed. "The NRL Program on Electroactive Polymers - Second Annual Report," NRL Memorandum Report 4335, Naval Research Laboratory, Washington, DC 1980.

4.   J. Mort and G. Pfister, "Photoelectronic Properties of Disordered Organic Solids: Molecularly-Doped Polymers," Polymer-Plastics Technology and Engineering. 12, 89 (1979).

5.   B. Berne and R. Pecora, "Dynamic Light Scattering," Wiley Interscience, NY 1976.

6.   R. Zwanzig, "Time Correlation Functions and Transport Coefficients in Statistical Mechanics," Annual Reviews of Physical Chemistry. 16, 67 (1965).

7.   L. Van Howe, "Correlations in Space and Time and Born Approximation Scattering in Systems of Interacting Particles," Physical Review. 95, 249 (1954).

DISCUSSION

Prof. Ferry: Col. St. Univ. - I have a couple of comments. First, the concept of mobility is not a single particle concept. It is always an ensemble average, and that would give you a spread even if you are talking about average velocity in one direction along the field.

Dr. Cotts: I understand, I use the single particle as an over-simplified limit from which the scattering relations may be developed. Increasing refinement of models for conduction may then easily be incorporated into the light scattering analysis.

Prof. Ferry: The other comment has to do with the fact that a lot of the time of flight measurements always assume that the pulse you create when you start is a Gaussian pulse which propagates non-dispersively, which will in general not be true. One of the most interesting problems goes back to the Alder-Waynewright calculations. It said you have these diffusion tails and the importance is that in calculations of propagation along one-dimensional chains, these tails also crop up but in particular, there is work by Montroll and coworkers which say if you have trap-dominated hopping in an amorphous material, you quite often will have dispersive transport that doesn't show a normal type of mobility. In fact the current doesn't smoothly drop off.

Dr. Cotts: With the experimental technique I talked about, one can see dispersive components in the mobility. Time of flight won't do that for us.

Dr. Sandman: GTE - Could you tell us precisely on which experimental systems you did the light scattering experiments?

Dr. Cotts: I haven't done the experiment yet. This is purely an analogy between the transport in time of flight experiments and the transport of particles in solution.

Dr. Sandman: Okay. Precisely the comment that Dr. Ferry made is correct. The transport in systems like polyvinyl carbazole has been extensively analyzed by Scher and Montroll in terms of dispersive transport.

Dr. Pomerantz: IBM - In your last viewgraph of the cylindrical columns, how long are they or how long can they be made?

Dr. Cotts: This morphological structure is a consequence of the phase equilibrium of the system. In principle there is no limit to the length of the cylindrical domains. Their continuity depends on how carefully they are cast from solution. Micron long structures can be made without too much difficulty.

Dr. Greene: NRL - How do you read out that last polycarbazole thing?

Dr. Cotts: Electrical contacts must be fabricated on one side of the device. The procedures for metalizing 100 $\overset{\circ}{A}{}^2$ which were presented yesterday could be used.

Dr. Greene: But you read it out?

Dr. Cotts: Yes.

Prof. Ledwith: Univ. of LP - To have such well-defined morphological separation in polymer mixtures or block copolymers you would need very careful control of polymer molecular weights and poly(N-vinyl carbazole) is particularly difficult to obtain with a narrow dispersion form. How do you deal with this problem?

Dr. Cotts: To make these polymers, you have to use anionic polymerization techniques. Polyvinyl carbazole has been very difficult to prepare anionically. There is however a catalyst system that will do it.

Prof. Ratner: NW Univ. - Did you mean to imply that the mechanism of diffusion is the same or that the measurements could be made in the same way?

Dr. Cotts: The experimental techniques and the formalism for interpreting the results are analogous.

SECTION FIVE
Biological Processes

CHAPTER XXIV

PRIMARY EVENTS OF PHOTOSYNTHESIS

Lester L. Shipman
Chemistry Division
Argonne National Loboratory
Argonne, IL 60439

INTRODUCTION

The primary events of photosynthesis are those photophysical and photo-chemical events that occur immediately after absorption of a photon by the photosynthetic pigments. The primary events include the migration of singlet excitons among the antenna pigments, exciton trapping by the reaction center, and a sequence of several electron transfer steps that leads to the formation of a stable electron-hole separation. All of the primary events occur within protein complexes which include chlorophylls, carotenoids, quinones, and various other electron transfer components. These complexes are called photosystems. Photosystems reside in a special photosynthetic membrane in organisms such as algae, higher plants, purple photosynthetic bacteria, and green photosynthetic bacteria.

In this manuscript the primary events of photosynthesis are summarized with particular attention to the principles that they might hold for the design of "molecular" electronic devices. In a companion paper (1) the two-electron gates in photosynthesis are discussed along with their implications for the design of "molecular" electronic devices.

EXCITONS AND ANTENNAS

A singlet exciton is created when a photon is absorbed by the photosynthetic pigments in the photosystem. The antenna pigments, whose primary function is the harvesting of photons, greatly outnumber the pigments that directly participate in the light-induced electron transfers. Each photosystem has one reaction center (trap) in which primary photochemistry takes place and many antenna pigments feeding singlet excitons into the trap. For example, a fully developed green plant photosystem II has approximately 300 antenna chlorophylls and one trap, called P680 (2).

There is an important design reason for the high antenna/trap ratio and that is the matching of the rate at which photons are harvested to the overall electron transfer rate. Because of this, shade plants have a significantly higher number of antenna chlorophylls per trap (3). Many antenna chlorophyll molecules act cooperatively to harvest photons and deliver the resultant singlet exciton to the trap.

Electronic excitation energy moves through the bed of antenna pigments in the form of a migrating singlet exciton (2,4). The pigments are packed closely together at high concentration (0.1-0.3 Molar) (2) to facilitate the rapid migration of singlet excitons. This concentration of pigments can be compared to the concentration of pure chlorophyll (approximately 1 Molar). Migration of singlet excitons to the trap must be subnanosecond to avoid significant losses from fluorescence and intersystem crossing. The concentration dependence of the singlet exciton migration rate lies in the R^{-6} dependence (Förster transfer) of the pigment to pigment transfer rate (5,6) on the distance (R) between the pigments.

Triplet excitons are also formed in the photosystems by intersystem crossing on individual pigment molecules or by electron-hole recombination in the trap (7). It is very important for there to be a design provision for the rapid dumping of triplet excitons from molecules whose triplet state is sensitive to molecular oxygen. Triplet chlorophyll, in particular, is quite sensitive to molecular oxygen through the following two reactions.

$$^{T}Chl + {^{T}O_2} \rightarrow {^{S}Chl} + {^{S}O_2} + \Delta \tag{1}$$

$$^{S}Chl + {^{S}O_2} \rightarrow \text{oxidized chlorophyll derivatives} \tag{2}$$

The photosystems provide a rapid in vivo decay channel for triplet excitation on chlorophylls by placing carotenoid molecules in close proximity (perhaps even in contact) with chlorophyll molecules. The carotenoid molecules protect the chlorophylls from photodestruction by molecular oxygen. The way the carotenoids protect is by accepting the triplet excitation from the chlorophylls. The carotenoid triplet state lies lower in energy than the chlorophyll triplet so the triplet excitons tend to stay on the carotenoids once there. Triplet carotenoids are much less susceptible to attack by molecular oxygen, in part because their triplet lifetime is much shorter than the triplet lifetime of a chlorophyll (microseconds compared to milliseconds). The protection mechanism is shown in equation 3.

$$^{T}Chl + {^{S}Car} \rightarrow {^{S}Chl} + {^{T}Car} + \Delta \tag{3}$$

Optical studies on the disappearance of triplet states on chlorophyll in vivo (8) have shown that the reaction 3 takes approximately 35 nsec on the average. Thus, the chlorophyll triplet lifetime is reduced by over four orders of magnitude in vivo compared to in vitro. If this were not the case, the chlorophylls in the photosynthetic membrane would be bleached away by the action of light and molecular oxygen. The protection mechanism indicated in equation 3 has an even more severe concentration requirement than the singlet exciton migration rate because the triplet exciton migration rate falls off exponentially (e^{-R}) with the distance (R) between the pigments.

The overall function of the antenna is to harvest photons and to deliver them rapidly to the trap without getting destroyed in the process. Once the singlet exciton has reached the trap, electron-hole separation occurs via a sequence of electron transfer steps which are discussed in the next section.

PRIMARY CHARGE SEPARATION

After a singlet exciton reaches the trap from the antenna pigments (equation 4) an electron is transferred rapidly (approximately 1 picosecond) from the excited primary electron donor, D*, to a nearby electron acceptor, A1 (equation 5). From A1 the electron hops to another nearby electron acceptor,

$$Chl^*_{ant} + D \rightarrow Chl_{ant} + D* \qquad (4)$$

$$D*A_1 \rightarrow D^+A_1^- \qquad (5)$$

A2, in a few picoseconds (equation 6) (9). In all of the photosystems studied to date, D and A1 are chlorophyll species (monomeric or dimeric). A2 is a

$$D^+A_1^-A_2 \rightarrow D^+A_1^-A_2^- \qquad (6)$$

pheophytin a (10-13) and bacteriopheophytin a (9,14-16) for green plants and purple photosynthetic bacteria, respectively. From A2 the electron hops to a protein-bound quinone in green plant photosystem II and purple photosynthetic bacteria (see the companion paper, ref. 1).

The quantum yield for charge separation in photosynthesis is nearly unity in purple photosynthetic bacteria (17). This high quantum yield for the forward electron transfers and corresponding low quantum yield for reverse electron transfers is achieved by precise positioning of a sequence of electron acceptors A1, A2, quinones such that the acceptors farther away from the cation hole, D^+, are easier to reduce. In addition, the neighboring acceptors must be sufficiently close together so that the exchange integrals responsible for electron migration are large enough for rapid electron transfer.

CHEMICAL AND ELECTRONIC STRUCTURE OF CHLOROPHYLL

Chlorophylls have important functions in both the photon harvesting and electron transfer processes in photosynthesis. The most abundant chlorophyll in green plants is chlorophyll a (Figure 1A) and the most abundant chlorophyll in purple photosynthetic bacteria is bacteriochlorophyll a (Figure 1B). The corresponding pheophytins, pheophytin a and bacteriopheophytin a, are derived from the parent chlorophylls by replacement of the central magnesium by two hydrogens.

Several electronic states of chlorophylls and pheophytins are important in photosynthesis. In particular, excitation by light from the ground singlet state, S_0, populates the first excited singlet, S_1. The S_1 state of chlorophyll is especially important for the description of chlorophyll antennas; basically it is the singlet exciton composed of local S_1 states on individual molecules that dominates the description of both light absorption and the flow of singlet excitation in the antenna. Occasionally chlorophyll triplet states, T_n, are populated by intersystem crossing on individual molecules or by electron-hole recombination in the trap (7). If an excited triplet state is initially populated, there is a rapid relaxation to the lowest triplet state, T_1. The first couple of electron transfers induced by light populate charge transfer states; these states can be described using the lowest chlorophyll cation doublet, the lowest chlorophyll anion doublet, and the lowest pheophytin anion doublet states.

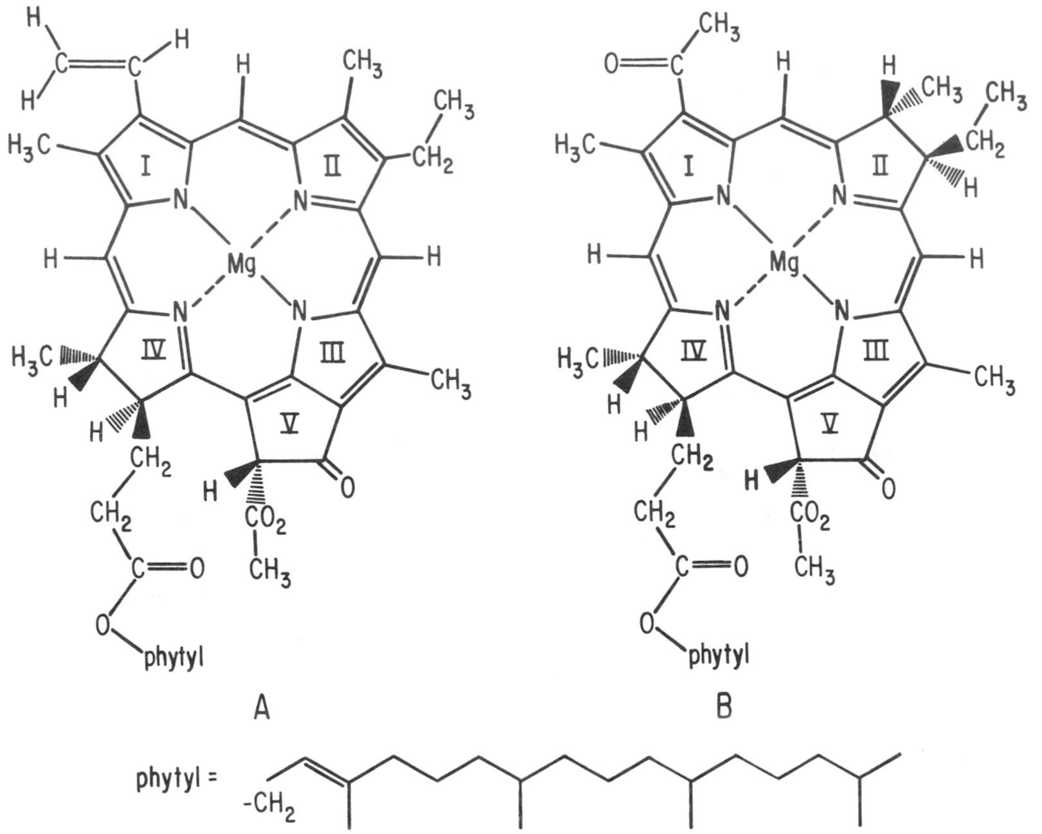

Figure 1.   Chemical structures for (A) chlorophyll a and (B) bacteriochlorophyll a.

Recently ab initio configuration interaction (CI) calculations have been carried out for the singlet (18,19), triplet (18,19), cation doublet (20), and anion doublet (21-22) states of chlorophylls and pheophytins.   The energy levels in the singlet and triplet manifolds are shown in Figure 2.   Four molecular orbitals (MOs) from the ground state SCF wavefunction (19,23) contribute significantly to the configurations that dominate the description of these states; in particular, the highest occupied MO, 1, the next to highest occupied MO, 2, the lowest unoccupied MO, 1*, and the next to lowest unoccupied MO, 2*. These MOs are shown for chlorophyll a and bacteriochlorophyll a in Figures 3 and 4, respectively.   The corresponding MOs for the pheophytins are quite similar and are not shown.   The dominant configurations, expressed in terms of MOs, for chlorophyll and pheophytin electron states, are given in Table 1.

IMPLICATIONS FOR "MOLECULAR" ELECTRONIC DEVICES

The primary events of photosynthesis demonstrate several principles for the design of "molecular" electronic devices using light to induce electron-hole separation.   Photochemical fatigue is to be expected in the operation of an optical "molecular" electronic device.   Therefore, it is important to understand how fatigue can be minimized; photosynthesis provides a model for fatigue resistance.   A potentially major source of fatigue is the attack on the photo-generated triplet states of molecules by molecular oxygen.   One way to eliminate this type of fatigue would be to rigorously eliminate molecular oxygen from the device.   Another way would be to provide a rapid decay channel through which to dump triplet excitation.   In photosynthesis the chlorophylls are pro-

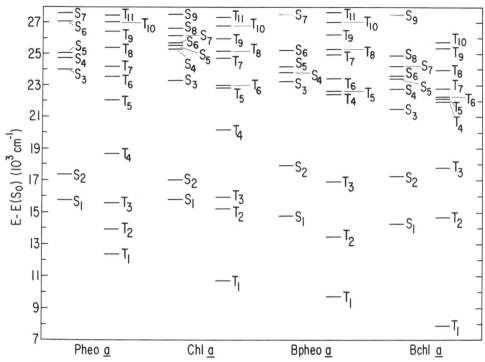

Figure 2. Calculated singlet and triplet state energy levels for pheophytin a (pheo a), chlorophyll a (chl a), bacteriopheophytin a (bpheo a), and bacteriochlorophyll a (bchl a).

Table 1. Dominant Configurations in the Configuration Interaction Wavefunction for Various Chlorophyll and Pheophytin States[†]

State	Configurations
S_1	$1 \rightarrow 1^*$, $2 \rightarrow 2^*$
T_1	$1 \rightarrow 1^*$
D_0(cation)	1
D_0(anion)	1^*

[†]$1 \rightarrow 1^*$ and $2 \rightarrow 2^*$ indicate one-electron excitations from MO 1 to MO 1* and from MO 2 to MO 2*, respectively. 1 and 1* indicate an unpaired electron in MO 1 and 1*, respectively.

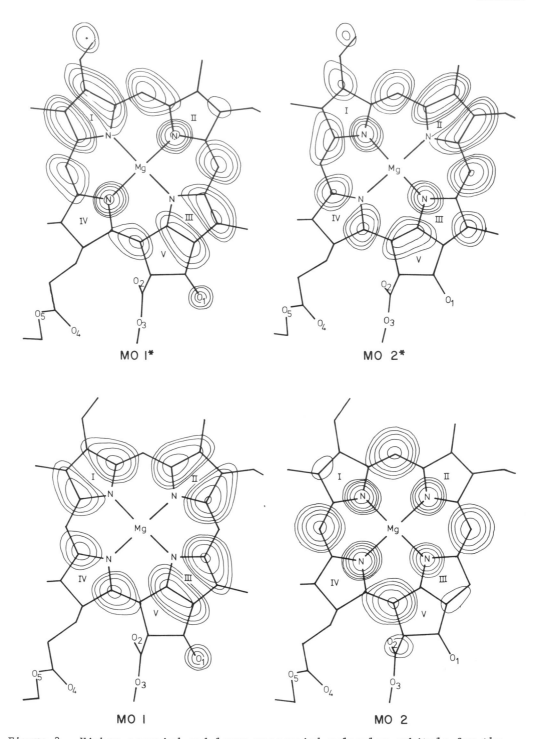

Figure 3. Higher occupied and lower unoccupied molecular orbitals for the ground electronic state of chlorophyll a.

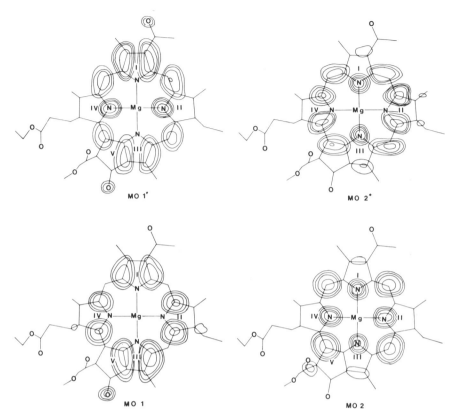

Figure 4. Higher occupied and lower unoccupied molecular orbitals for the ground electronic state of bacteriochlorophyll a.

tected from photodestruction through the rapid transfer of triplet excitation from chlorophylls to nearby carotenoids. Occasionally, the carotenoids are oxidized and must be replaced.

How can a very high quantum yield for charge separation be obtained? In photosynthesis forward electron transfer reactions are favored over cation hole-electron recombination by moving the transferred electron through a sequence of electron acceptors, each more easily reduced than the acceptor that came before it in the electron transfer chain. This arrangement of acceptors leads to a very small electron tunnelling rate for the return of the electron to the cation hole after the first couple of electron transfers are complete. In addition, cation hole-electron recombination is slowed down by the unfavorable Franck-Condon factors for the mixing of a vibrationally relaxed charge transfer state with the highly vibrationally excited ground singlet electronic state.

ACKNOWLEDGMENT

My work in photosynthesis is supported by the Division of Chemical Sciences, Office of Basic Energy Sciences, U.S. Department of Energy, under Contract W-31-109-Eng-38.

REFERENCES

1. L.L. Shipman, "Two-Electron Gates in Photosynthesis", in this volume.

2. L.L. Shipman, Photochem. Photobiol. 31, 157 (1980).

3. S. Malkin and D.C. Fork, Plant Physiol. 67, 580 (1981).

4. R.S. Knox, Excitation Energy Transfer and Migration: Theoretical Considerations, in "Primary Processes of Photosynthesis", J. Barber, ed., Elsevier, New York, 1977, pp. 183-221.

5. Th. Förster, Ann. Physik 2, 55 (1948).

6. L.L. Shipman and D.L. Housman, Photochem. Photobiol. 29, 1163 (1979).

7. M.K. Bowman, D.E. Budil, G.L. Closs, A.G. Kostka, C.A. Wraight, and J.R. Norris, "Magnetic Resonance Spectroscopy of the Primary State, pF, of Bacterial Photosynthesis", Proc. Natl. Acad. Sci. U.S.A., in press.

8. P. Mathis, Fast Absorption Spectroscopy for Studying the Primary Photoreactions, in "Primary Processes of Photosynthesis," J. Barber, ed., Elsevier, New York, 1977, pp. 269-302.

9. W.W. Parson, C.C. Schenck, R.E. Blankenship, D. Holten, M.W. Windsor, and C.V. Shank, Kinetics of Photochemical Electron Transfer Reactions In Vivo and In Vitro, in "Frontiers of Biological Energetics, Vol. 1, Academic Press, New York, 1978, pp. 37-44.

10. V.V. Klinov, E. Dolan, and B. Ke, FEBS Lett. 112, 97 (1980).

11. V.V. KJinov, E. Dolan, E.R. Shaw, and B. Ke, Proc. Natl. Acad. Sci. U.S.A. 77, 7227 (1980).

12. V.A. Shuvalov, V.V. Klimov, E. Dolan, W.W. Parson, and B. Ke, FEBS Lett. 118 279 (1980).

13. J. Fajer, M.S. Davis, A. Forman, V.V. Klimov, E. Dolan, and B. Ke, J. Am. Chem. Soc. 102, 7143 (1980).

14. K.J. Kaufmann, P.L. Dutton, T.L. Netzel, J.S. Leigh, P.M. Rentzepis, Science 188, 1301 (1975).

15. P.L. Dutton, R.C. Prince, and D.M. Tiede, Photochem. Photobiol. 28, 939 (1978).

16. M.Y. Okamura, R.A. Isaacson, and G. Feher, Biochim. Biophys. Acta 546, 394 (1979).

17. C.A. Wraight and R.K. Clayton, Biochim. Biophys. Acta 333, 246 (1974).

18. J.D. Petke, G.M. Maggiora, L.L. Shipman, and R.E. Christoffersen, Photochem. Photobiol. 30, 203 (1979).

19. J.D. Petke, G.M. Maggiora, L.L. Shipman, and R.E. Christoffersen, Photochem. Photobiol. 32, 399 (1980).

20. J.D. Petke, G.M. Maggiora, L.L. Shipman, and R.E. Christoffersen, Photochem. Photobiol. 31, 243 (1980).

21. J.D. Petke, G.M. Maggiora, L.L. Shipman, and R.E. Christoffersen, Photochem. Photobiol. 32, 661 (1980).

22. J.D. Petke, G.M. Maggiora, L.L. Shipman, and R.E. Christoffersen, "Stereoelectronic Properties of Photosynthetic and Related Systems. IX. Ab Initio Quantum Mechanical Characterization of the Electronic Structure and Spectrum of the Bacteriochlorophyllide a Anion Radical", Photochem. Photobiol., in press.

23. D. Spangler, G.M. Maggiora, L.L. Shipman, and R.E. Christoffersen, J. Am. Chem. Soc. 99, 7478 (1977).

DISCUSSION

Dr. Carter: NRL - Is it possible to study these systems, especially those of the excited states, with XAFS?

Dr. Shipman: Several investigators have looked at the iron ion in the reaction centers from purple photosynthetic bacteria. They were interested in determining whether its coordination environment changed when the quinones are removed. They found that the XAFS spectrum was unchanged by quinone removal. This strongly implies that the quinones are not coordinated to the iron atom.

Dr. Carter: What about looking at the magnesium?

Dr. Shipman: To the best of my knowledge, nobody has looked at the XAFS spectrum of Mg in the photosynthetic pigments. Is that fairly easy to do?

Dr. Carter: I would think it is possible.

Dr. Shipman: We already know the structure of the pigment and the environment of the Mg atom in the center of the chlorophylls. From XAFS you might get some new information about the nature of the fifth ligand. Is that what you are thinking of, to see what the difference in Mg environment is in excited states? Of course, remember that in the full photosystem we are looking at 300 chlorophylls, so there is a lot of magnesium present. In the case of iron in the reaction centers there is just one present. In the same reaction center there are four Mg ions present. By the way, iron isn't absolutely required; in low iron media, the purple photosynthetic bacteria will put manganese ions in their reaction centers and the reaction center still works.

Dr. Sandman: GTE - You keep alluding to the necessity of having the five molecular entities and maintaining the charge separation. In a photosynthetic membrane is an electric field developed or have people done experiments where the system is placed in an external field to facilitate charge separation?

Dr. Shipman: The physical measurement made to detect the presence of an electric field across the membrane is the carotenoid bandshift. Carotenoids normally have only a small dipole moment difference between their ground and excited singlet state. The observed bandshift in vivo is linear in the electric field, implying that there is a large static electric field across the membrane before excitation by light. Otherwise the bandshift should be quadratic in the applied field. The electric field generated by light collapses in time. The kinetics of the collapse are appropriate for the redistribution of ions on the surface of the membrane in response to local charge separation induced by light. Undoubtedly there is some relaxation of the proteins within the membrane as well. I should say that the surface of the photosynthetic membrane is normally negatively charged. There is an excess of aspartate and glutamate residues on the exposed parts of the protein. This negatively charged surface is shielded by another layer of positively charged ions. The positively charged ions can redistribute in response to local electron field changes such as the light-induced electric field.

Dr. Cukor: GTE - I would like to comment on your last statement. Even if you emulated nature's reactions you have trouble with the dark reaction. Isn't it true that for device applications it would be most cumbersome to use an enzymatic reaction?

Dr. Shipman: You are talking about the dark reaction that re-reduces the donor?

Dr. Cukor: There is one possibility--the dark reaction, or backward, reaction is catalyzed by enzymes. However that would probably be a cumbersome reaction to build into a device. On the other hand, we have some other tricks that nature doesn't have, like different wavelengths of radiation; so it may be worthwhile to study some kind of induction mechanism which induces the fast backwards reaction, taking the place of nature's dark reaction.

Dr. Shipman: We have tried exciting the chlorophyll donor, the chlorophyll antenna, and the ubiquinones and the rate of the back reaction did not seem to increase. After excitation of these species, there is a local relaxation, heating up the immediate environment. This relaxation is much faster than the reverse electron transfer. You can add lipid soluble electron carriers to facilitate the back reaction. They act by carrying the electron back to the oxidized donor. The major problem associated with using added electron carriers is the question of how you get the carrier out of the membrane once it has done its job. If you don't get it out, it will continue to collapse charge separation in other photosystems as well. I did a rough calculation to estimate the density of the photosystems in the photosynthetic membrane. They are packed at an area density of about 10 to the 14th per square centimeter. I am not sure how that compares with the densities on chips that are presently in use today. For the case of the photosystems from purple photosynthetic bacteria and photosystem I from green plants, the photosystems tend to act independently of each other. Photosystem II in green plants does not function independently of the other photosystem; singlet excitons are transferred from one photosystem II to another and from photosystem II to photosystem I.

Dr. Haddon: Bell - What is the difference in the redox potential between photosystems I and II. What happens to the extra energy?

Dr. Shipman: In purple photosynthetic bacteria the electron hops first from an excited donor to a bacteriochlorophyll and then onward to a bacteriopheophytin molecule. In vitro, the difference between the reduction potentials of these two species is approximately 0.3 volt with the bacteriochlorophyll being the species that is harder to reduce. We don't know the actual redox potential for these two species in their in vivo environment where they are buried in a protein which is in turn buried in a membrane.

Dr. Haddon: What do you think happens to that energy?

Dr. Shipman: The excess energy comes off as heat. For the case of green plants they have to give off water to keep from heating up; they have their own air conditioning system of sorts. When the pores on the leaves open up to let carbon dioxide in, they also let water vapor out.

Dr. Carter: What is the form and the role of the iron? Is that as a sulphite and is it functioning as temporary storage for electrons?

Dr. Shipman: Nobody has yet found conditions under which the iron atom in the reaction centers changes redox state upon illumination of the bacteria or reaction center. The iron has been difficult to study via EPR because its very rapid magnetic relaxation leads to very broad lines. The ESR signal of the quinone sitting near and influenced by the iron has been studied. Under normal redox conditions, it has been shown that the iron is normally in the high spin ferrous state. Also, it has been shown that the iron has a catalytic role in the transfer of an electron from the first to the second quinone. Feher and Okamura, Univ. of California at San Diego, have suggested that the iron may function as a kind of wire between the quinones, but this suggestion remains to be proven. Another possibility is that the ferrous ion is easier to oxidize to ferric when the first quinone is reduced to its anion form. Under these conditions, the iron may transfer an electron to the second quinone and have the ferric form transiently before being reduced to ferrous by the electron on the first quinone. This transient ferrous to ferric to ferrous conversion would not show up in any of the measurements conducted to date.

Dr. Carter: Maybe the sulfurs around it are picking up the charge?

Dr. Shipman: As I recall from the XAFS measurements, there is probably no more than one sulfur ligand on the iron. Thus, it isn't a true iron sulfur protein like rubridoxin which has four sulfur ligands surrounding an iron.

Dr. Greyber: NSF - Assuming a similar thing happens in vision, is the system in primitive organisms essentially the same as this?

Dr. Shipman: No. In photosynthesis electrons are being pumped directly by light and protons are being pumped as a result of the electron pumping. In vision, light energy is used to bring about a conformation change in a protein and the pigment is not a chlorophyll. In the bacterium, halobacterium halobrium, light is used to pump protons, but electrons are not pumped. The pigment is the same as in vision.

Dr. Greyber: My notion was in primitive species, whether or not we are talking about plants, where there is very little evidence of vision, are the systems essentially the same?

Dr. Shipman: You mean like the bacteria compared to a higher plant?

Dr. Greyber: Yes. Is there an evolutionary process?

Dr. Shipman: Interestingly, the bacteriochlorophyll pigment which is found in the so-called primitive organisms that carry out photosynthesis is made by going through a stage of biosynthesis in which the chlorophyll from higher plants, chlorophyll a, is temporarily made. Certainly this doesn't look like an evolutionary process from the point of view of the pigment. However, in terms of the structure and functions of the photosynthetic membranes from the primitive organisms and higher plants, there does seem to be an evolutionary process at work.

Dr. Nagel: NRL - I am struck by the similarity between photosynthesis and another photochemical system, namely, film. The build up of a development center in photographic film leads to the same kind of thing as in photosynthesis, namely, increasing stability with an increasing number of trapped or transferred electrons. The similarity is probably superficial because of the very different materials involved in photography and in photosynthesis, but it is nevertheless curious.

Dr. Shipman: There is an analogy between photosynthesis and an imaging process in which a thin film rests on a metal. In the case of green plant photosynthesis the hole is being filled by electrons from water and in the case of the imaging process the holes are being filled by electrons from the metal. The charge separation in thin films is maintained by filling the hole.

CHAPTER XXV

PARAMAGNETIC RESONANCE PRODUCED SWITCHING IN HEMOGLOBIN
WITH VISIBLE LIGHT

T. W. Barrett
Department of Physiology and Biophysics
University of Tennessee Center for the Health Sciences
Memphis, TN 38163

FOREWORD

A general account of paramagnetism in all paramagnetic salts and compounds measured by any one of the several methods used in measuring susceptibility and paramagnetic rotation, relaxation, and resonance would amount to a considerable volume. In this present communication, only one aspect of paramagnetism, the resonance phenomenon, is dealt with, and also in a limited way: mainly with respect to that most important of biomolecules, hemoglobin, and with respect to resonance with visible rather than radio-frequency radiation.

The property of paramagnetic resonance with visible light is of interest not only for its own sake, but because of the insight that study of this property offers into the molecular dynamics of oxygen binding, release, and storage possessed by metalloproteins. The property of switching from the diamagnetic to the paramagnetic state is the result of a particular design adequately described by ligand field theory (1), in which the metal electrons are in interaction with the crystal field potential of the surrounding proteins. Thus, the situation resulting in the property of functioning as a paramagnetic switch also results in the property of paramagnetic resonance in the visible spectrum.

In the case of hemoglobin, there is a complex four-chain molecule, one chain of which has Fe^{2+} surrounded by a porphyrin ring with either an α or β protein attached, and, if in the oxy form, an oxygen molecule in the sixth position of the metal ion (Figure 1). Thus, hemoglobin is one of a class of molecules consisting of a central ion surrounded by a cluster of ions or molecules. This class includes the electronic structures involving the transition series of elements, i.e., those elements having unfilled d or f electronic shells. These are the first transition series, where the 3d shell is being filled up; the second transition series, where the 4d shell is being filled up; the third transition series, involving 5d electrons; and the rare earths and the actinides, where the 4f and 5f shells, respectively, are being filled up.

In the present review, hemoglobin will be compared and contrasted only
with metal compounds of the first transition series, as these have much of the
angular momentum "quenched", and thus their paramagnetism corresponds more to
a "spin-only" value (2,3).

INTRODUCTION

Basic to the creation of the situation resulting in the paramagnetic
switch property of hemoglobin are three influences on the metal electrons: 1)
a Jahn-Teller instability; 2) a large crystal field potential; and, because of
1) and 2), 3) a zero-field splitting. These three influences result in the
magnetic pliability characteristic of hemoglobin (4).

In order for the possibility of paramagnetism to exist in a compound,
there must exist the possibility of a permanent magnetic dipole, which occurs
whenever an atom or ion contains a partly filled electron shell. This requirement restricts the occurrence of paramagnetism to compounds in the transition groups of the periodic table; and, in the case of biological compounds,
this would be the iron group (5,6).

Quantum theory provided a quantitative theory for paramagnetism (2),
which was related to the electronic angular momentum and the electron spin.
The recognition of the strong interaction between iron electrons and neighboring
diamagnetic charged electrons accounted for the fact that the measured susceptibility of the iron electrons is closer to that of the electron spins alone
than it is to both spins and angular momenta. This is because whereas the
angular orbital motion of the outermost iron 3d electrons is exposed to the
electrostatic field of the neighboring diamagnetic electrons and hence constrained, the electron spin, on the other hand, has no direct interaction with
the electrostatic field. Thus, the angular orbital motion of the metal electrons does not make a contribution to the complex of metal and surrounding
compound, whereas the spins of those same electrons may. In such a situation,
the orbital angular motion is said to be "quenched", and this quenching may be
total or partial (7). If a molecule has "spin only" magnetism, then susceptibility measurements will show little magnetic anisotropy; i.e., the spin
moments are oriented readily by an external magnetic field. On the other
hand, if the orbital angular momentum is not completely quenched, there is a
spin-orbit coupling resulting from the magnetic field of the orbits interacting
with the spin moments. An external magnetic field will orient both spins and
orbits. However, as the crystal field of the surrounding diamagnetic electrons
distorts the orbital motion of the metal electrons, the resultant magnetic
field will have directional properties determined by those crystal field
influences. As the spin moment will orient itself according to the resultant
of the distorted magnetic field due to the orbital angular momentum and the
external magnetic field, magnetic anisotropy will result (2,8,9).

The existence of a state of resonance in a compound presupposes that
ground and excited states exist separated by an energy equivalent to that provided by the resonating radiation. The situation which results in the possibility of visible radiation being in resonance comes about in hemoglobin because of a degeneracy in the $(3d)^6$ metal electrons removed by a Jahn-Teller
instability in the porphyrin-protein complex in conjunction with the crystal
field potential of the complex; i.e., there is a zero-field split. Darwin
(10) first demonstrated that a weak magnetic field could induce optical activity
in a system with multiplet lines; and Atkins & Miller (11) demonstrated the
possibility of an inverse Faraday effect. Darwin & Watson (12) also demon-

strated a "paramagnetic" B term influencing rotational strength, which is of direct relevance here.

The Jahn-Teller instability alone would appear too weak for a degeneracy to be lifted. Together with a crystal field of C_{4v} symmetry in the deoxy state, the dynamic Jahn-Teller coupling produces an out-of-plane bending of the square-pyramidal chromophore FeN_5 (13). For purposes of exposition when considering paramagnetic resonance, therefore, one may consider a "ground state" to be the state of the 3d electrons of the metal in oxyhemoglobin when the crystal field potential and the Jahn-Teller instability are insufficient to result in bending of the chromophore FeN_5; and the "excited state" to be the state of the 3d electrons when the crystal field potential and the Jahn-Teller instability are sufficient to result in bending of the chromophore. The difference in the crystal field in the two states is due, of course, to oxygen binding.

Oxygen binding in metal containing systems is a much discussed problem. Drago & Corden (14) have proposed a spin-pairing model of dioxygen binding in transition metal systems, the key feature of which is that the metals have one or more unpaired electrons in d orbitals with high enough energy to spin-pair with the electron in the oxygen binding orbitals. In support of this proposition, Cerdonio et al (15,16) have demonstrated, using the SQUID (superconducting quantum intensity differential) technique that HbO_2 deviates from the Curie law and shows temperature dependence. HbO_2, unlike HbCO, is not diamagnetic above about 50°K, and the iron-oxygen complex contains a coupled $S=\frac{1}{2}$ spin pair. The authors conclude that the characteristic nonlinear behavior of the atomic susceptibility is due to a triplet state that becomes thermally populated from a singlet state.

JAHN-TELLER INSTABILITY

Kamimura and Mizuhashi (17) and Mizuhashi (18) investigated the Jahn-Teller effect contribution to the reduction in symmetry of low spin ferrihemoglobin. As the calculation revealed that the reduction in energy due to the Jahn-Teller effect was of the same magnitude as the zero-point energy of the associated vibrational mode, only a dynamic effect exists. That is, there is a coupling of the motions of the nuclei with the low frequency electronic motions (dynamic effect), rather than a stable molecular configuration, being obtained by minimizing the electronic energy with respect to the parameters specifying the nuclear framework (static effect). For anisotropy in the heme plane of low spin ferrihemoglobin azide to occur, a combined action of the dynamical Jahn-Teller effect and, possibly, as mentioned above, the rhombic crystal field of the azide and the imidazole must take place. It should be noted, however, that the electronic states of ferric hemoglobin are quite different from those in ferrous hemoglobin, so this work remains suggestive but not definitive for the ferrous case.

Weissbluth (19), on the other hand, has proposed that Jahn-Teller distortion in ferrohemoglobin leads to the simultaneous removal of the oxygen molecule and the displacement of the Fe^{2+} from the heme plane by 0.8 Å. This proposal was criticized on the grounds that the symmetry of the chromophore is not octahedral, but C_{4v} at most, which for $Fe-O_2$ is not active (20). However, the Jahn-Teller effect may provide a local distortion which would function in a way similar to that suggested by Weissbluth. For example, Bacci (13,21,22) attempted a calculation of the Jahn-Teller coupling constant using the angular overlap model (AOM), which is a simplification of the LCAO-MO theory in the Wolfsberg-Helmholz approximation. Bacci found two extreme values of the bond angle, 112.5° and 157.5°, as a function of the coupling constant with the bonding angle β_1. The largest value was discarded as unlikely; but the value of 112.5° favorably compares with the experimentally obtained one of about 107° for deoxyhemoglobin (23).

If, then, the Jahn-Teller instability influences the metal electrons in conjunction with rhombic crystal field effects, one may then ask for evidence for the existence of the rhombic field. Eicher, Bade, and Parak (24) calculated the electric field gradient tensor by means of a Hamiltonian involving: 1) the Coulomb repulsion of the 3d electrons; 2) their interaction with the tetragonally arranged ligands; 3) a small rhombic perturbation of the C_{4v} point symmetry; and 4) spin-orbit coupling. The temperature dependence of the quadrupole splitting in both hemoglobin and myoglobin was investigated using the Mössbauer effect. It was found that the five lowest singlets in Mb and Hb essentially result from the rhombic-split ^5E high-spin level. These investigators conclude that although the rhombic perturbation is much smaller than the tetragonal crystal field effects, the charge distribution of the 3d electrons in Mb and Hb have essentially rhombic character (24,25,26).

Hoffman and Ratner (27) have described the unique aspects of the Jahn-Teller problem for four-fold symmetric systems. In a study of the dynamic effect in four-fold systems utilizing both perturbation theory and a numerical solution to the Schrödinger equation, these authors discovered a dependence of Jahn-Teller distortion on small off-diagonal strain and second-mode coupling. It appears that all b_{1g} and b_{2g} vibrational modes can Jahn-Teller couple, since the matrix elements of the vibrational Hamiltonian do not vanish by symmetry. Child (28) and Hougen (29) also previously addressed the question of vibronic interaction in molecules with a four-fold symmetry axis. Hougen pointed out that the dynamical Jahn-Teller effect in such molecules is qualitatively different from that in molecules with a three-fold axis. Whereas with a molecule of three-fold symmetry the dynamic Jahn-Teller vibrations belong to degenerate symmetry species, in a molecule of symmetry D_{4h}, those vibrations belong to two nondegenerate symmetry species: b_{1g} and b_{2g}. If, then, as indicated above, the symmetry species of hemoglobin is not D_{4h}, but rather C_{4v}, one may inquire whether there is evidence that degenerate states exist in hemoglobin.

The contribution of the Jahn-Teller effect is secondary to the crystal field influence on metal orbitals. This may be seen in studies of alums. Susceptibilities of vanadium, and titanium alum conform to the "spin only" formula demanding that the ratio of the fourth to the second-order part of the noncubic portion of the crystalline potential have a certain critical value (30). Van Vleck (2,3) demonstrated that this ratio results mostly from the indirect action of remote atoms in distorting or polarizing the water cluster and partly from the Jahn-Teller effect, so that there is no longer an octahedral crystal field.

Summarizing the results of the Jahn-Teller instability in hemoglobin: the porphyrin triplet state is of ^3E_u symmetry and has two-fold orbital degeneracy in addition to the normal triplet state, giving a six state manifold (31). A first result of Jahn-Teller instability in the case of the triplet states of porphyrins is that angular momentum and spin-orbit coupling are reduced (32). This is because the Jahn-Teller effect associates the two states spin-orbit coupled with vibronic states, and in order for the spin-orbit coupling to be effective, the nuclei must be shifted. A second result is that the Jahn-Teller instability and the crystal field potential effect, if in the same direction, are independent. This means that their effect can be additive and controlled by changes in the crystal field potential by means of changes in solvent, etc.

A third result, which brings us to the next section, is that the Jahn-Teller effect can contribute to zero-field splitting of the ^3E_u states. This was demonstrated by Gouterman, Yamanashi, and Kwiram (31) for zinc etioporphyrin, using the technique of optically detected magnetic resonance (ODMR), theoretically by Langhoff et al. (33), by Chan et al. (34,35) for zinc porphin, using fluorescence and Zeeman effect techniques, and by Kielman-Van Luijt et al. (36) for magnesium, zinc, copper, palladium, and platinum porphin, using magnetic circular dichroism (MCD) techniques. Canters et al. (37) also reported for zinc porphin, using optical and magnetic resonance techniques. (The porphin structure is identical to that of porphyrin except that the peripheral side chains are all hydrogen in the former, and are methyls, vinyls, etc., in the latter).

With regard to the Jahn-Teller influence on the Q band region, the study by Shelnutt et al. (38) using resonance Raman methods may be mentioned. These investigators demonstrated that excitation profiles of depolarized modes (b_{1g}, b_{2g}) in nickel etioporphyrin exhibit marked 0-0 resonance Raman intensity upon Q-band excitation. This 0-0 enhancement of depolarized modes is attributed to a weak Jahn-Teller distortion.

CRYSTAL FIELD POTENTIAL

The influence of the crystal field may be defined as either "strong" or "weak" (39). If the Hamiltonian for the electrons of the metal ion consists of two terms

$$H = H_F + V, \tag{1}$$

where H_F is the Hamiltonian for the free ion and V is the potential provided by its ligands, then three cases can be realized (1):

1. $V < \xi(r)\underline{\ell}\cdot\underline{s}$,   complexes of the rare earths,   (2)

2. $\xi(r)\underline{\ell}\cdot\underline{s} < V < e^2/r_{ij}$,   complexes of the first transition group,

3. $V > e^2/r_{ij}$,   "covalent" complexes,

where $\Sigma(e^2/r_{ij})$ is the electronic repulsion term, and $\Sigma\xi_i(r)\underline{\ell}\cdot\underline{s}$ is the spin-orbit term of the Hamiltonian H_F. The second case is usually called "the weak crystalline field case", and the third case "the strong crystalline field case". Essentially, the strong field is able to break the coupling between the total orbital and spin angular momenta, and the weak field is not. Hemoglobin exhibits both a strong and a weak field case, and the effect of the strong field is an electric Paschen-Back effect.

With d^4, d^5, d^6, and d^7 metal electrons, the transition from the weak to the strong crystalline field case corresponds to a transfer of electrons from the e_g orbital shell to the t_{2g} orbital shell. Furthermore, the spin quantum number will be lower in the case of the strong crystal field case, e.g., S = 0 for oxyhemoglobin, and higher in the case of the weak crystal field case, e.g., S = 2 for deoxyhemoglobin. In the weak field limit and octahedral configuration, the ground state is $(t_{2g})^4(e_g)^2$ for Fe^{2+}; in the strong field limit, the ground state is $(t_{2g})^6$.

The full spin Hamiltonian for the 3d ion is (40):

$$H = \beta(g_x H_x S_x + g_x H_y S_y + g_z H_z S_z)$$
$$+ D[S_{z^2} - \frac{1}{3}S(S+I)]$$
$$+ E(S_{x^2} - S_{y^2})$$
$$+ A_x S_x I_x + A_y S_y I_y + A_z S_z I_z$$
$$+ P(I_{z^2} - \frac{1}{3} I(I + 1)) + P'(I_{x^2} - I_{y^2})$$
$$- g_n \beta_n \underline{H} \cdot \underline{I},$$

$$(3)$$

where A is the axial hyperfine structure constant in units of $10^{-4} cm^{-1}$;
   D, E are the axial and rhombic fine structure constants in units of $10^{-4} cm^{-1}$;
   P, P' are axial and rhombic quadrupole constants in units of $10^{-4} cm^{-1}$;
   g   is the spectroscopic splitting factor;
   β   is the Bohr magnetic number; and
   I   is nuclear spin.

In order to describe the spin-spin interaction, the Dzyaloshinsky-Moriya interaction Hamiltonian is used:

$$H = \vec{D}_{ij} \cdot [\vec{S}_i \times \vec{S}_j],$$

$$(4)$$

where $\vec{D}_{ij}$, is a constant vector and describes antisymmetric exchange.

This exchange Hamiltonian (41,42) is used in the description of canting of sublattices (see below).

ZERO-FIELD SPLITTING

Metalloproteins often have two absorption bands in the visible region and an intense absorption band (Soret band) in the violet region (43). In order of increasing energy, these bands are referred to as the α or Q_{00}, the β or Q_{01}, and the Soret band. Higher order moments, such as the magnetic and quadrupole, influence the Q_{00} band transition. This is a "forbidden" transition, in that the components of Q_{ij} should all vanish when both ψ_i and ψ_j are even, or when both are odd (Laporte rule).

There is, however, enough vibrational motion, usually, so that the center of symmetry of a molecule is not preserved, and so these "forbidden" transitions are still seen, but at a strength one-fifth as strong as the "allowed" transitions of the Q_{01} or β band (44). The Q_{00} and Q_{01} bands are doubly degenerate, with two components polarized in mutually perpendicular directions due to degeneracy in the g-orbitals.

The prediction that excitation of an f-orbital electron of angular momentum 4 to a g-orbital of angular momentum 5 provides 9 units of angular momentum with a degenerate singlet state, $1Q^0$, and a degenerate triplet state, $3Q^0$, for the first excited configuration (44-46) was confirmed for porphyrins by integral MCD experiments (47-51). Sutherland, Axelrod, and Klein (49) later explained the different values of M_z obtained from integral and differential MCD by postulating that two components of the Q_{00} band are split slightly in zero-field, and have slightly different oscillator strengths. Sutherland and Klein (50) determined the absorption spectrum observed with left and right circularly polarized light for a randomly oriented solution of molecules in the presence and absence of a magnetic field. In zero-field, the absorption spectrum is given by (51):

$$\varepsilon(\bar{v}) = \varepsilon_o\{f(\bar{v},\bar{v}_o) + \tfrac{1}{2}\Delta\bar{v}_{ZF}^2 f^{(2)}(\bar{v},\bar{v}_o)\} + \Delta\varepsilon\Delta\bar{v}_{ZF}f^{(1)}(\bar{v},\bar{v}_o),\qquad\qquad (5)$$

where $\bar{v}$ is wavenumber, $\bar{v}_o$ is the mean position of the two unperturbed components, ε_o is their mean amplitude, $\Delta\varepsilon$ is the intensity imbalance, $\Delta\bar{v}_{ZF}$ is the zero-field splitting, $f(\bar{v},\bar{v}_i)$ is an absorption envelope which has a peak amplitude of unity located at $\bar{v}_i$, and $f^{(n)}(\bar{v},\bar{v}_i)$ is the nth derivative of the shape of $f(\bar{v},\bar{v}_i)$ taken with respect to $\bar{v}$.

The difference between the integral and the differential techniques demonstrated by Sutherland, Axelrod, and Klein (49) and Sutherland and Klein (50) indicated in the absorption spectrum equation (5), above, has been attributed to the Jahn-Teller removal of degeneracy of the porphyrin's D_{4h} symmetry to D_{2h} in conjunction with the crystal field potential in agreement with the analysis of the previous section (49), or by axial ligands with planar symmetry (52).

The zero-field Hamiltonian consists of three terms (53):

$$H_o = H_{xl} + H_{so} + H_{ss},\qquad\qquad (6)$$

where H_{xl} describes the effect of the crystal field (2,54,55), H_{so} denotes the spin-orbit coupling, and H_{ss} the spin-spin dipolar coupling. As the H_{xl} term is greater than the intramolecular spin-dependent interactions for porphyrins (cf. discussion in previous section; (34,35), and this crystal field is large, the orbital momentum of the metal electrons is "quenched" due to the presence of asymmetrical intramolecular fields (2, p. 287). However, tetragonal symmetry will not remove all the degeneracy of the Fe^{2+} electrons (54,56), but there is also no longer an axis of symmetry about which the angular momentum is conserved. Bethe (56) demonstrated that when an average magnetic moment persists despite the absence of an axis of symmetry, then there can be a first order Zeeman effect; but the selection rules are no longer the usual, and unusually large changes are permitted in the spatial quantum number which do not have the usual significance of being proportional to a component of the angular momentum (2, p. 292). The results of this is that the zero-field potential energy is reduced.

The following considerations bear upon this result. Metalloproteins have a four-fold axis of symmetry (C_4 or S_4), with the lower excited states, triplets as well as singlets, doubly degenerate and belonging to the E_u representation if the point group is D_{4h}. Furthermore, as noted in the previous section, the triplets have a three-fold spin degeneracy, and the lowest triplet state T_o of the free molecule is a manifold of six levels. As the highest degeneracy to be expected for the point groups is two-fold, the six levels of the triplets and the two levels of the singlets should be split by various interactions. van der Waals, van Dorp, and Schaafsma (57) consider two kinds:

1)   Intramolecular spin-dependent interactions: a) spin-spin dipolar coupling; and b) spin-orbit coupling; and

2)   Spin-independent perturbations of tetragonal symmetry such as: a) crystal field or solvent effects; b) polyatomic ligands on the central metal; and c) peripheral substitution of the porphyrin nucleus.

As interactions of type 1 are weak, only type 2 need be considered in the present case. Type 2 interactions, although electrostatic in nature, operate in conjunction with the Jahn-Teller coupling, which cannot by itself remove the degeneracy of the vibronic levels of the tetrapyrrole system (55, p. 791, 58-62).

A recent report of a magnetic circular emission (MCE) in zinc octaethyl porphyrin (63) gives evidence of splitting. These authors noted that if this molecule is pumped with circularly polarized radiation which has a well defined M_J value, then non-Boltzmann populations of the Zeeman sublevels of the emitting states may be attained.

Degeneracy removal comes about in the following way. The five-fold degeneracy of the d-obitals in the free ion is partially removed when the ion is placed in a crystal field having a cubic symmetry. The orbitals will group themselves into a three-fold degenerate set belonging to the t_2 representation and a two-fold degenerate set belonging to the e representation.

When the symmetry is reduced from cubic to tetragonal, degeneracies are further removed. The e orbitals are split into a_1 and b_1 in D_4, and the t_2 orbitals are split into b_2 and e. There are further effects due to spin-orbit coupling and external magnetic fields. Finally, an external magnetic field will produce a set of Zeeman levels of the spin-orbit coupled $^5T_2$ state.

As it is presently considered (64) that in forming a bond with oxygen the iron transfers an electron to the oxygen, forming superoxide ion, the iron is left formally ferric (65). (However, for a rebuttal of this point of view, see Pauling (66)). Both the oxygen molecule and the CO molecule are electron acceptors; but whereas donation from the iron d orbitals raises the energy of

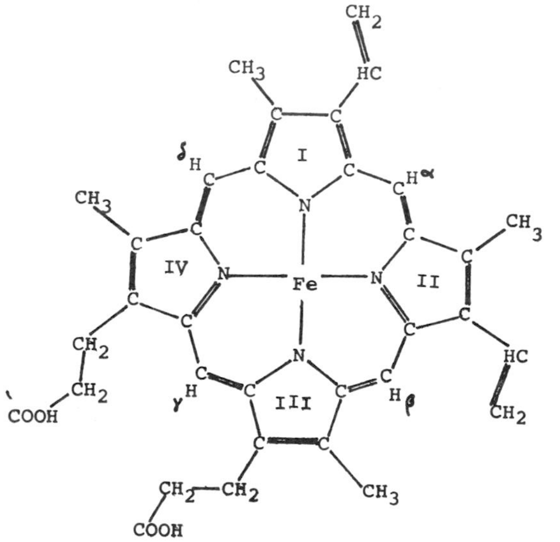

Figure 1. Fe-protoporphyrin IX or heme. In a direction perpendicular to the heme plane there is an attachment by means of a covalent bond and a nitrogen atom on the imidazonle of a histidine of a protein chain form the hemoglobin chain. The globin chains are of two types, a and b. the hemoglobin molecule consists of four subunits, two of which have a chains and two b chains. Oxygen attaches to the sixth position on the Fe which is opposite the protein attachment position.

one of the oxygen π^* orbitals, so that two electrons pair, in CO, on the other hand, the π_x^* and π_y^* orbitals are both empty and both are electron acceptors. In any of these events, from this point of view if oxyhemoglobin and carbonmono-xyhemoglobin possess a formally ferric iron, a Kramer's degeneracy will exist. Figure 2 illustrates the degeneracies discussed here apart from this final, presently speculative, one.

EVIDENCE OF MAGNETIC RESONANCE FROM RESONANCE RAMAN SPECTROSCOPY

A complete polarization study of the backscattered light from a molecule in the resonance Raman light scattering situation involves the measurement of all four polarization components of the scattered light with respect to the two polarization conditions of linear and circular polarization of the incident light. These are: 1) parallel; 2) perpendicular; 3) corotating; and 4) contrarotating (67,68).

A complete polarization study of oxyhemoglobin (69) and carbonmonoxyhemo-globin was made with incident excitation in the long wavelength absorption region, $\lambda = 4579$ Å and 4880 Å. This method has been used to characterize the three invariants of the nonsymmetric Raman tensor for randomly oriented molecules, based on a model in which the scattered light is dependent only on an induced electric dipole. With no higher order moments involved in the inelastic light scattering process, the amplitude, (i), i = 1, 2, 3 and 4, of any band measured under the four conditions should satisfy the relation: (1) + (2) = (3) + (4). As an apparatus test, this relation was seen to hold for the bands of carbon tetrachloride and benzene.

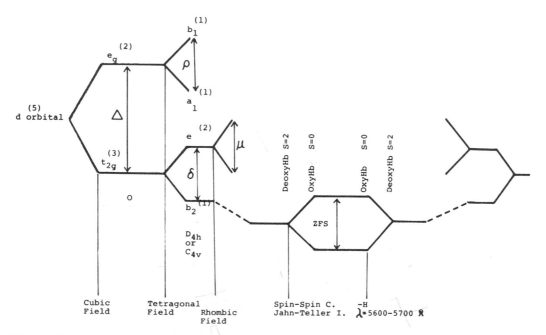

Figure 2. Energy level diagram for hemoglobin showing how the energy levels are s;lit by field and coupling influences, and how a level can be rejoined by an external magnetic field influence. These schemes are to scale.

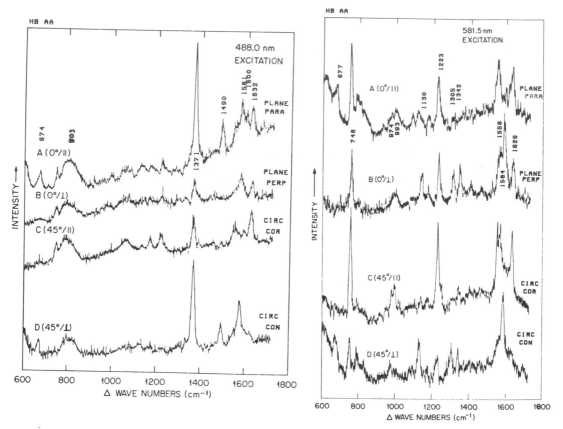

Figure 3A.   Resonance Raman spectra of carbonmonoxyhemoglobin with 4880 Å excitation at 100 mW for the four polarization conditions, incident: scattered light, tip to bottom of: 1) plane parallel; 2) plane perpendicular; 3) circular corotating; and 4) circular contrarotating.

Figure 3B.   Resonance Raman spectra of carbonmonoxyhemoglobin with 5815 Å excitation at 100 mW for the four polarization conditions, as in Figure 3A.

However, in the case of oxyhemoglobin and carbonmonoxyhemoglobin, although this relation is satisfied for short wavelength (4579 Å and 4880 Å) excitation, it is not satisfied for long wavelength (5682 Å and 5815 Å) excitation. For the latter excitations, (1) + (2) < (3) + (4) is the case (Figure 3 and Table 1).

The inequality may be interpreted as an inverse Faraday effect (11), resulting in magnetic resonance activity (70). The predisposing condition for this effect, outlined in previous sections, is a zero-field splitting (49) of a Jahn-Teller unstable state (13), resulting in a transition between the zero-field split levels of the spin-orbit and spin-spin coupled state of Fe^{2+}, $(3d)^6$ (Figure 2). A porphyrin ring-metal electron magnetic dipole moment can then be induced with circularly polarized light of the appropriate wavelength, due to the availability of a transition involving charge transfer interaction coupling metal orbitals and the porphyrin $\pi*$ orbitals (71).

TABLE I

Polarized Raman intensity data for carbonmonoxyhemoglobin AA

solution (arbitrary units) with 5815 Å excitation.

Band frequency (Δcm^{-1})	$I_{\parallel}$	$I_{\perp}$	I_{ℓ}^{*}	I_{co}	I_{contra}	I_{c}^{*}	$I_{\ell} - I_{c}$	Percentage $I_{c} > I_{\ell}$
677	22	10	32	40	26	66	-34	106%
748	66	87	153	175	45	220	-67	43%
974	30	36	66	51	24	75	-9	14%
993	24	31	55	45	21	66	-11	20%
1130	23	46	69	18	73	91	-22	32%
1223	55	70	125	135	50	185	-60	48%
1305	5	44	49	25	50	75	-26	53%
1342	11	59	70	28	45	73	-3	4%
1556	84	62	146	140	40	180	-34	23%
1584	138	25	163	55	132	187	-24	15%
1626	80	55	135	120	58	178	-43	32%

$*I_{\ell} = I_{\parallel} + I_{\perp}$, $I_{c} = I_{co} + I_{contra}$

This electric dipole-magnetic dipole transition is permitted for circular-ly polarized light at the Larmor precession frequency, but not permitted for linearly polarized light, as the d-d metal transition involved is electric dipole-disallowed. This transition involves an inverse zero-field effect (Figures 2 & 4).

Thus, the surprising result is obtained that external circularly polar-ized light, i.e., a magnetic field, of the appropriate frequency (the Larmor precession frequency) may excite a coupling (forbidden to linearly polarized light), resulting in large magnetic moment enhancement, the d-d metal transi-tion involved being magnetic dipole- and quadrupole-allowed, but electric dipole forbidden. The outcome is a switch from the hemoglobin diamagnetic state to the paramagnetic state reminiscent of a metamagnetic phase change.

METAMAGNETISM AND CRITICAL BEHAVIOR

The existence of a zero-field splitting of energy levels in a system indicates the sensitivity of that system, as an ordered system, to a magnetic field both internal and external. Application of even a weak field to a fer-

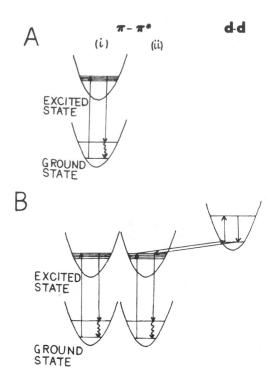

Figure 4A. Transitions excited by linearly polarized light in the long and short wavelength absorption region of oxy and carbonmonoxyhemoglobin, and by circularly polarized light in the short wavelength region. The transition moment available is

$$<\psi_i^{\pi-\pi^*} \mid \mu \mid \psi_v^{\pi-\pi^*}><\psi_v^{\pi-\pi^*} \mid \mu \mid \psi_f^{\pi-\pi^*}>$$

(where μ is the induced electric dipole moment and ψ_i, ψ_v and ψ_f are the initial, intermediate and final states).

Figure 4B. Transitions excited by circularly polarized light in the long wavelength absorption region of oxy- and carbonmonoxyhemoglobin. The transition moment available is both

$$<\psi_i^{\pi-\pi^*} \mid \mu \mid \psi_v^{\pi-\pi^*}><\psi_v^{\pi-\pi^*} \mid \mu \mid \psi_f^{\pi-\pi^*}> \text{ and}$$

$$<\psi_i^{\pi-\pi^*} \mid \mu \mid \psi_v^{\pi-\pi^*}><\psi_i^{d-d} \mid m \mid \psi_v^{d-d}><\psi_v^{d-d} \mid m \mid \psi_f^{d-d}><\psi_v^{\pi-\pi^*} \mid \mu \mid \psi_f^{\pi-\pi^*}>$$

where m is the induced magnetic dipole.

romagnet or antiferromagnet causes the magnetization to follow the direction of the field and destroys the phase. We shall consider two such phenomena which can arise from this sensitivity: the spin flop and metamagnetism. Both phenomena are describable by the Ising model of phase transitions (72, 73).

The spin flop is observed in antiferromagnets (which are ordered substances with spins antiparallel). Upon application of a field parallel to the preferred axis of magnetization, a competition is set up between the strength of the external field and that of the exchange reactions, expressed as an internal exchange field (74). When the external field, H, reaches a critical field H_{SF}, the antiparallel magnetizations of the two sublattices turn (flop) from the direction of the easy axis to that perpendicular to it (75).

The spin-flop will occur for a critical field H_{SF} given by (74):

$$H_{SF} = (2K/(\chi_{\perp} - \chi_{\|}))^{1/2},\tag{7}$$

where K is the anisotropy energy expressed in terms of a field H_A which causes the establishment of the preferred or easy axis. In the present instance, this would be the crystal field associated with the diamagnetic state of oxyhemoglobin considered as an antiferromagnet.

An increase in the external field will result in a rotation of the sublattice moments until at a critical field, H_c, the antiferromagnetic interaction is balanced by the applied field and the anisotropy field (76,77). The antiferromagnetic (AF) and spin-flop (SF) and the SF and the paramagnetic (P) phase boundaries meet at a triple point called the bicritical point.

A metamagnetic system is one in which the spin-flop region of the phase diagram has shrunk to zero area. When the crystal field or anisotropy field, H_A, is equal to the antiferromagnetic exchange field, H_E, the anisotropy is so large that the moments go over indirectly from an AF alignment to a saturated paramagnetic alignment. In this situation exhibited by the oxy-to-deoxy state transition of hemoglobin, the phase diagram is that of an Ising system (72).

A tricritical point is formed in metamagnets and may be seen in the H-T plane. Below the tricritical point and at low temperature, the H-T relation consists of first-order points. At the tricritical point the relation is described by second-order points. This phenomenon is described by the introduction of a third dimension to the H-T phase diagram, represented by $\bar{H}$, a staggered field which is an experimentally unattainable field that alternates in direction with each sublattice of an antiferromagnet (78) (Figure 5).

Due to the aforementioned residual paramagnetism of oxyhemoglobin (15,16), it is likely that this system, although primarily antiferromagnetic, is still weakly ferromagnetic due to a canting of the spins involved: those of the iron, and those of the oxygen ligand. This canting is describable by the Dzyaloshinsky-Moriya exchange Hamiltonian (Equ. (4) above).

Now, as an effective magnetic field is an average taken over the entire system of the correlations between a given reference spin and its neighbors at a varying distance r, the static pair correlation functions of the Ising model are immediately relevant:

$$\Gamma_r(T) = \langle S_o^Z S_r^Z \rangle / \frac{1}{3} S(S+1),\tag{8}$$
$$(\underline{r}=0,1,2,\ldots\infty),$$

where the brackets denote the expectation value and $\frac{1}{3}S(S+1)$ is a normalization factor. For the 2-d Ising lattice, singularities occur of the form (79):

$$\Gamma_r(T) = A + B \mid T-T_c \mid \ln \mid T-T_c \mid,\tag{9}$$

where A and B are constants. The ordering parameter, $\Gamma_r(T)$, is related to the susceptibility by

$$\chi = 1 + \sum_{r \neq 0} \Gamma_r(T)\tag{10}$$

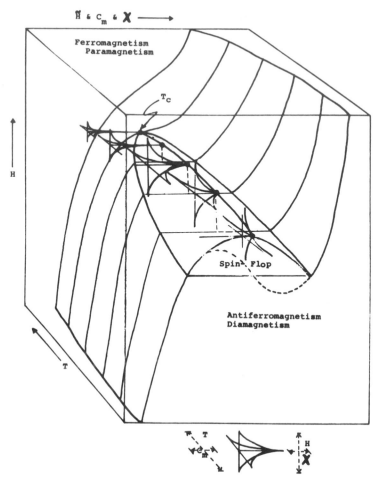

Figure 5. Three-dimensional phase-state diagram for hemoglobin. The axes are
(1) temperature, T, (2) the constant (non-ordering) field, H, and (3) either
(i) the staggered (ordering) field, H̄, equivalent to the discussed crystal
field potential, (ii) the specific heat, c_m, or (iii) the susceptibility, χ.
The empirically determined c_m-T and χ-H relations as a function of temperature
T are shown schematically along the line of critical points terminating at the
critical temperature T_c. In this scheme a change from the antiferromagnetic,
diamagnetic state of oxyhemoglobin to the ferromagnetic, paramagnetic state of
deoxyhemoglobin may be effected either (i) by increasing temperature (T) or
(ii) by increasing the external constant (nonordering) field, H. The line of
critical points corresponds to a line of bicritical points as described by
Fisher and Nelson (88). A change from the hemoglobin oxy- to deoxy-state
corresponds to a vertical movement of a representative point from the antiferromagnetism to the ferromagnetism area.

for a ferromagnetic system; and by

$$\chi = 1 - f(T) \ \Gamma_1(T) \tag{11}$$

for an antiferromagnetic system (80) where the function $f(T)$ accounts for
alternating terms of the series in the sum of Equ. (10). The theoretical
specific heat C_m, of a magnetic system may also be related to the Ising S=1/2

model (81). However, it is of relevance to the treatment of magnetic resonance that the Larmor precession theorem (82) holds exactly for the Heisenberg model rather than the Ising (83); and the Ising model is, of course, one of d x n models (where d is the spatial dimensionality of a physical system and n is the degree of isotropy) for which d=2 and n=1 in the case solved by Onsager (84,86). For d=3, n$\geq$3 a crossover from isotropic (Heisenberg) to characteristic cubic behavior occurs and terms of cubic symmetry may enter the Hamiltonian through exchange interactions (87).

REFERENCES

1. C.J. Ballhausen, Introduction to Ligand Field Theory, New York, McGraw-Hill (1962).
2. J. H. Van Vleck, Electric and Magnetic Susceptibilities, Oxford Univ. Press (1932).
3. J. H. Van Vleck, Phys. Rev. 41, 208 (1932).
4. M. Kotani, Adv. Quant. Chem. 4, 227 (1968).
5. B. R. Bleaney, K. W. H. Stevens, Reports on Progress in Physics 16, 108 (1953).
6. K. D. Bowers and J. Owen, Reports on Progress in Physics 18, 304 (1955).
7. M. Kotani, Prog. Theoret. Phys. (Kyoto) Suppl. 17, 4; Adv. Chem. Phys. 7, 159 (1961).
8. R. Schlapp and W. G. Penney, Phys. Rev. 42, 666 (1932).
9. O. Jordahl, Phys. Rev. 45, 87 (1934).
10. C. G. Darwin, Proc. Roy. Soc. A112, 314 (1926).
11. P. W. Atkins and M. H. Miller, Mol. Phys. 15, 503 (1968).
12. C. G. Darwin and W. H. Watson, Proc. Roy. Soc. A114, 474 (1927).
13. M. Bacci, Biophys. Chem. 11, 39 (1980).
14. R. S. Drago and B. B Corden, Acc. Chem. Res. 13, 353 (1980).
15. M. Cerdonio, A. Congiu-Castellano, L. Calabrese, S. Morante, B. Pispisa, and S. Vitale, Proc. Nat. Acad. Sci. 75, 4916 (1978).
16. M. Cerdonio, A. Congiu-Castellano, F. Mongo, B. Pispisa, G. L. Romani, and S. Vitale, Proc. Nat. Acad. Sci. 74, 398 (1977).
17. H. Kamimura and S. Mizuhashi, J. Appl. Phys. 39, 684 (1968).
18. S. Mizuhashi, J. Phys. Soc. Jap. 26, 468 (1969).
19. M. Weissbluth, J. Theoret. Biol. 35, 597 (1972).
20. L. Cianchi, F. Gulisano, M. Mancini, and G. Spina, Phys. Letters 59A, 247 (1976).
21. M. Bacci, Chem. Phys. Letters 68, 4907 (1978).
22. M. Bacci, Chem. Phys. 40, 237 (1979).
23. M. F. Perutz, Nature 226, 726 (1970).
24. H. Eicher, O. Bade, and F. Parak, J. Chem. Phys. 64, 1446 (1976).
25. H. Eicher and A. Trautwein, J. Chem. Phys. 50, 2540 (1969).
26. H. Eicher and A. Trautwein, J. Chem. Phys. 52, 932 (1970).
27. B. H. Hoffman and M. A. Ratner, Mol. Phys. 35, 901 (1978).
28. M. S. Child, Mol. Phys. 3, 601-607 (1960).
29. J. T. Hougen, J. Mol. Spectr. 13, 149 (1964).
30. A. Siegert, Physica 3, 85 (1936).
31. H. Gouterman, R. S. Yamanashi, and A. L Kwiram, J. Chem. Phys. 58, 4073 (1972).

32. H. Gouterman, Ann. N.Y. Acad. Sci. 206, 70–83 (1973).
33. S. R. Langhoff, E. R. Davidson, M. Gouterman, W. R. Leenstra, and A. L. Kwiram, J. Chem. Phys. 62, 169 (1975).
34. I. Y. Chan, H. G. van Dorp, T. J. Schaafsma and J. H. van der Waals. Mol. Phys. 22, 741 (1971).
35. I. Y. Chan, H. G. van Dorp, T. J. Schaafsma, and J. H. van der Waals, Mol. Phys. 22, 753 (1971)
36. E. C. M., H. P. Kielman-Van Luijt, J. M. Dekkers, and G. W. Canters, Mol. Phys. 32, 899 (1976).
37. G. W. Canters, J. van Egmond, T. J. Schaafsam, W. G. van Dorp, and J. H. van der Waals, Ann. N.Y. Acad. Sci. 206, 711 (1973)
38. J. A. Shelnutt, L. O. Cheung, R. C. C. Chang, N-T Yu, and R. H. Felton, J. Chem. Phys. 66, 3387 (1977).
39. J. H Van Vleck, J. Chem. Phys. 3, 807 (1935).
40. J. W. Orton, Reports on Progress in Physics 22, 204 (1959).
41. I. Dzyaloshinsky, J. Phys. Chem. Solids 4, 241 (1958).
42. T. Moriya, M. G. T. Rado, and H. Suhl (eds) Magnetism, Vol. 1, Chap. 3. Academic, NY (1963).
43. F. Adar, pp. 167–207 in The Porphyrins, Vol. 3, D. Dolphin, ed., Physical Chemistry, Part A, Academic Press, New York (1978).
44. J. R. Platt, pp 71–123 in Radiation Biology, Vol. III, A. Hollaender, ed., McGraw-Hill, New York (1956).
45. H. T. Simpson, J. Chem. Phys. 17, 1218 (1949).
46. P. J. Stephens, W. Suëtaak, and P. N. Schatz, J. Chem. Phys. 44, 4592 (1966).
47. M. Malley, G. Feher, and O. Mauzerall, J. Mol. Spectr. 26, 320 (1968).
48. E. A. Dratz, Ph.D. dissertation, University of California, Berkeley (1966).
49. J. C. Sutherland, O. Axelrod, and M. P. Klein, J. Chem. Phys. 54, 2888 (1971).
50. J. C. Sutherland and M. P. Klein, J. Chem. Phys. 57, 76 (1972).
51. J. C. Sutherland, pp. 225–270 in The Porphyrins, Vol. 3, Physical Chemistry, Part A, D. Dolphin, ed., Academic, New York (1978).
52. G. Barth, R. E. Linder, E. Bunnenberg, C. Djerassi, L. Seamans, and A. Moscowitz, J. Chem. Soc. Perkin II, 696 (1974).
53. G. W. Canters and J. H. van der Waals. pp. 531–582 in The Porphyrins, Vol. 3, Physical Chemistry, Part A, D. Dolphin, ed., Academic, New York.
54. H. Bethe, Ann. Phys. 3, 133 (1929).
55. A. Abragam and B. Bleaney, Electron Paramagnetic Resonance of Transition Ions, Clarendon Press, Oxford (1970).
56. H. Bethe, Zeits. f. Physik 60, 218 (1930).
57. J. H. van der Waals, H. G van Dorp, and T. J. Schaafsma, pp. 257–312 in The Porphyrins, Vol. 4, Physical Chemistry, Part B., D. Dolphin, ed., Academic, New York (1979).
58. J. H. Van Vleck, J. Chem. Phys. 7, 61 (1939).
59. J. H. Van Vleck, J. Chem. Phys. 7, 72 (1939).
60. F. S. Ham, Phys. Rev. A138, 1727 (1965).
61. F. S. Ham, Phys. Rev. 166, 307 (1968).
62. F. S. Ham, Jahn-Teller effects in electron paramagnetic resonance spectra, Electron Paramagnetic Resonance, Plenum, New York (1969).
63. R. A. Shatwell and A. J. McCaffery. J. Chem. Soc. Chem. Comm. 546 (1973).
64. M. F. Perutz, pp. 38–42 in Chemical Recognition in Biology, F. Chapeville and A-L Haenni, eds., Springer Verlag, New York (1980).
65. J. J. Weiss, Nature 202, 83 (1964).
66. L. Pauling, Nature 203, 182 (1964).
67. W. M. McClain, J. Chem. Phys. 78, 2789 (1971).
68. W. M. McClain, J. Chem. Phys. 57, 2264 (1972).
69. T. W. Barrett, Chem. Phys. Letters, in press (1981).
70. L. D. Barron, Acc. Chem. Res. 13, 90 (1980).

71. J. A. Shelnutt, D. L. Rousseau, J. M. Friedman, and S. R. Simon, Proc.
     Nat. Acad. Sci. USA 76, 4409 (1979).
72. B. M. McCoy and T. T. Wu, The Two-dimensional Ising Model, Harvard Univ.
     Press, Cambridge, Mass (1973).
73. P. A. Fleury, Science 211, 125 (1981).
74. R. L. Carlin and A. J. van Duyneveldt, Magnetic Properties of Transition
     Metal Compounds, Springer Verlag (1977).
75. G. I. van der Handel, H. M. Gijsma, and N. T. Poulis, Physica 18, 862
     (1952).
76. F. Keffer, Handbook der Physik, Springer-Verlag, NY. Vol XVIII: part 2,
     p. 1 (1966).
77. L. J. de Jongh and A. R. Miedema, Adv. in Physics 23, 1 (1974).
78. R. B. Griffiths, Phys. Rev. Letters 24, 715 (1970).
79. B. Kaufman and L. Onsager, Phys. Rev. 76, 1244 (1949).
80. M. E. Fisher, Phil. Mag. 7, 1731 (1962).
81. M. F. Sykes and M. E. Fisher, Physica. 28, 919 and 939 (1962).
82. J. Larmor. Aether and Matter, Cambridge U. Press (1900).
83. P. C. Hohenberg and B. I. Halperin, Rev. Mod. Phys. 49, 435 (1977).
84. M. E. Fisher, Rev. Mod. Phys. 46, 597 (1974).
85. P. Pfeuty and G. Toulouse, Introduction to the Renormalization Group and
     to Critical Phenomena, Wiley, New York (1977).
86. J. H. Van Vleck, Rev. Mod. Physics 17, 27 (1945).
87. A. Aharony, Phys. Rev. B8, 4270 (1973).
88. M. E. Fisher and D. R. Nelson, Phys. Rev. Letters 32, 1350 (1974).

DISCUSSION

     Dr. Tsai: Std. Oil - A few years ago we made a Mössbauer
spectroscopic experiment at Columbia University on oxyhemoglobin (OxyHb). We
have very strong evidence that the ground state of iron in OxyHb is a quantum
mixture of ferrous and ferric ion, and so I just wonder how does that affect
your analysis?

     Prof. Barrett: These experiments, not at all; but if one were to
estimate exactly what the zero field potential is, one would have to decide
whether there is a Jahn-Teller instability (in the case of a ferrous ion) or
a Kramer's degeneracy (in the case of a ferric ion). So if one wanted an
exact estimate for the zero field potential, it would make a difference, but
we are not at that stage yet.

     Prof. Hander: Univ. of NC - I was wondering whether abnormal hemo-
globins, seen in sickle cell anemia, that have different binding constants
for oxygen, might show differences detectable by magnetic resonance Raman
spectroscopy. Have you looked at this?

     Prof. Barrett: Yes. I have looked at sickle cell hemoglobin. I
think that there are two problems with sickle cell hemoglobin. The first
is, as is well known, valine is substituted for glutamic acid in the sixth
position of the beta chain. In dilute solutions, strangely enough, it acts
very normally (e.g., there is normal oxygen affinity, heme-heme interaction,
Bohr effect and reactivity with 2,3-diphosphoglycerate), and its function, normal
or abnormal, could be represented in the manner shown earlier (Figure 5). But
as you get to the concentration in the cell, then things start to go wrong. As
you concentrate the sickle cell hemoglobin solution to above about 20%, it
starts to polymerize (at room tempeature), and that's the second problem. So
sickle cells have a difference in oxygen binding (sickle cell blood has

decreased oxygen affinity). You have also substituted a nonpolar and hydrophobic amino acid (valine) for another, glutamic acid, which is negatively polarized. Not only have you changed the crystal field potential in the case of sickle cell hemoglobin, you have also offered the opportunity for polymerization. Now the existence of the first problem would have very little effect upon producing different data. The second problem, the formation of tactoids and polymerization, would probably have large effect, but we have only performed experiments in relatively dilute solution.

Prof. Hanker: What I meant to ask was whether these effects could be utilized for switches or for other switching properties?

Prof. Barrett: Yes. Well, for example, the free ferroheme in a high dielectric environment binds irreversibly to oxygen, so the "tuning" of the switch (which binds reversibly) may occur by salt effects (changes in dielectric constant) or by anesthetics (changes in hydrophobicity) affecting the crystal field potential and the dielectric constant of the surround (usually the proteins) of the porphyrin. Yes.

Dr. Carter: NRL - Given the planar nature of heme, you would expect the induced magnetic dipole moment to be rather small. If you were to have a conjugated system, say three conjugated ligands arranged in a twisted prism, you could anticipate a very large induced magnetic dipole moment, and I wonder if you know of such a system for which McClain's test or rules have been tried?

Prof. Barrett: Firstly, in the resonance Raman experiments I discussed, the hemoglobin in solution is spun in a cell very fast in order to prevent heating by the incident laser light, so if you had an oriented polymer, you would get a much better effect, and not an averaged effect over orientations. The interaction with the metal ions is, however, via the porphyrin ring vibrations, the interaction occurring by charge transfer. The fact that a magnetic resonance occurs with light of wavelength at about 5600 $\overset{\circ}{A}$ (i.e., frequency 17,857 cm^{-1}) is due precisely to the above mentioned "tuning," i.e., to the crystal field potential, which results in a critical cubic splitting parameter of 18,500 cm^{-1} (estimate by Y. Tanabe & S. Sugano, (1954) J. Phys. Soc. Japan 9: 766). The incident circularly polarized light is thus of such an energy as to populate magnetic substrates or to mix the $^1A_1$ and $^5T_2$ states. Without the crystal field quenching of the iron ion angular momentum, magnetic resonance would be at another frequency. In answer to your question about McClain's theory: complete polarization studies have only been attempted at exciting wavelengths at which the model has held (i.e., there is equality between the sum of the linear polarization measures and the sum of the circularly polarized measures) and where one would expect equality. The experiments discussed here are the only ones that I know of which are a complete polarization test at long wavelength (alpha band absorption region). As far as I know, there is no other experiment that has demonstrated that equality does not hold, so there is only an induced electric dipole influence as far as other experimental reports are concerned.

CHAPTER XXVI

MICROTUBULES: BIOLOGICAL MICROPROCESSORS?

S. R. Hameroff and R. C. Watt
Departments of Anesthesiology and Electrical Engineering
University of Arizona
Tucson, AZ 85724

INTRODUCTION

Advanced technologies including geodesic domes, photo-optics and holog-raphy have apparently mimicked biological functions. Molecular switching and computer-like signal processing could similarly be regulating cellular biol-ogy in a class of protein polymers known as microtubules (MT). Quantal trans-fer modes suitable for switching and previously linked to protein mediated bi-ological regulation include electronic semiconduction, charge transfer, super-conductivity, tunneling, excitons, phonons, conformons, polarons, photons, protons, solitons, and/or calcium or other ions. The cylindrical grid-like MT structure, connecting proteins, and intracellular trabecular networks (Porter 1) could provide programmable matrices for information transfer resulting in temporal and spatial control of protein mechanical functions and cellular ac-tivity. Media of information transfer among the four nanometer (nm), 55,000 dalton subunits could include conformational states coupled to any of the pre-viously mentioned modes. In this paper we will refer primarily to a general-ized model of electron transfer coupled to protein conformational state.

Microtubules (MT) are cylindrical polymers found in all living cells. Their functions include cellular orientation, structure, and guidance of cyto-plasmic movement. MT are contained in cilia, flagella, mitotic spindles, centrioles, kinetochores, desmosomes and other organelles and are intimately involved with mitosis, cellular growth, and differentiation (Roberts & Hyams 2, Dustin 3, Stephens & Edds 4). Associated proteins which bind at specific sites on MT walls include contractile filaments which move cilia and flagella, transport substances, contact other MT in a trabecular network and regulate membrane proteins (Amos & Klug 5, McIntosh 6, Matsumoto & Sakai 7, Vallee & Borisy 8). Within neurons MT course the lengths of axons and dendrites and are responsible for axoplasmic flow and trophic maintenance of the neuronal membrane as well as glial and postsynaptic cells (Singer 9, Ochs & Ranish 10, Paulson & McClure 11). Nerve membrane depolarization has been correlated with increased density and polymerization rates of intraneuronal MT (Alvarez 12, Alvarez & Ramirez 13). Circumstantial evidence has linked MT to memory and intellect (Seite, et al 14, Cronley-Dillon & Perry 15, Cronley-Dillon, et al 16, Jorgensen & Meier 17).

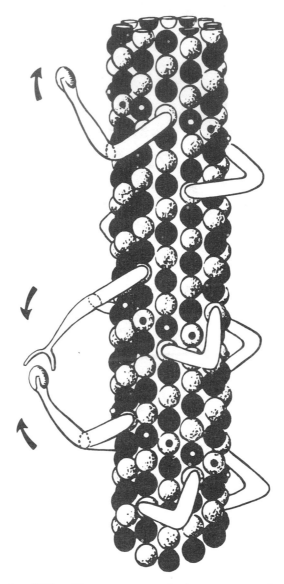

Figure 1. Microtubule (MT), 25 nanometers (nm) in actual diameter, shown
with attached functional sidearm proteins. Spherical subunits (α or β tubulin) represent 55,000 dalton, 4 nm diameter proteins. Programmable "on-off"
conformational coupling to charge or energy transfer may regulate biological
functions through MT and sidearm protein activities.

This paper reviews some theories of biological regulation by charge/
energy transfer in proteins, describes the structure and functions of microtubules and presents a model of information processing, logic, and transduction based on known MT structural geometry and programmed switching among
neuronal MT subunit arrays pulsed by the traveling nerve action potential.
Likely conformational switches within MT subunits are excited electron resonance states within hydrophobic pockets of aromatic amino acid residues (tryp-
tophan, tyrosine, etc.) (Gutfreund 18). By weak Van der Waal's hydrophobic
interactions, anesthetic gases reversibly inhibit protein excited state luminescence and MT mechanical activities (Ueda & Kamaya 19, Middleton & Smith
20, Allison & Nunn 21, Nunn, et al 22). Key intra-protein hydrophobic environments could integrate and transduce several input modes to determine conformational and mechanical activities. Aspects of the model are analogous to
information and computer technologies including programmable Boolean switching
matrices, transistor circuits, bubble memory, charge transfer devices, surface acoustic wave resonators, and/or holography. Attempts to understand biological and neurological signal processing could yield technological insight
and medical benefits. Coupling among MT and fabricated devices could theoretically provide therapeutic responses in widely diverse MT-involved pathology as well as possible interfacing of biological and machine intelligence.

MODELS OF FUNCTIONAL CHARGE/ENERGY TRANSFER IN PROTEINS

Models of charge and/or energy transfer, resonance, and long-range coherent interactions within proteins have been proposed (Szent-Gyorgyi 23, Frohlich
24). Oxidation/reduction electron movement within proteins spatially fixed
in an organelle or membrane has been compared to solid state electronics
(Rosenberg & Postow 25, Cope 26). Specific protein conductivities among spatially arrayed aromatic amino acid resonance orbitals (Szent-Gyorgyi 23) are
thought to regulate semiconductive protein functions in membranes, mitochondria, and intercellular gap junctions (Pappas, et al 27, Politoff 28, Gutman
& Lyons 29). Intraprotein electron dipole oscillations may be coupled to
mechanical conformational changes and necessary for enzyme function (Frohlich
30). Functional long-range coherent transitions among spatially arrayed
charge sites in a membrane or other matrix may respond to sudden slight fluctuations of a surrounding electric field (Adey 31). Electron superconductivity (Cope 32) and intermolecular quantum mechanical tunneling over several
nanometers (nm) (Miller 33) is suggested to occur widely in biological systems.

Quantumized functional biological energy transfer has been described as
packets of protein lattice conformational energy ("phonons", "excitons",
"conformons") (Avery & Pavlidou 34, Shohet & Reible 35). Other models couple
conformational energy to charge transfer ("polarons") (Cope 26) and propose
resonance among spatially arrayed excited states in macromolecules and organelles (McClare 36). Spatially locked conformational wave patterns in protein
systems have been linked to nervous system function (Drost-Nausen 37). Oxidative phosphorylation, photosynthesis and muscle function may all have conformationally coupled free energy transduction systems. Transfer of excited
electron resonance energy has been demonstrated between MT and membrane proteins by fluorescent labelling (Becker & Oliver 38). Communicative photon
perception by MT and other protein structures has also been described (Carlson
& Stephens 39).

MICROTUBULES

Since the 1960's electron microscopy, x-ray diffraction, immunofluorescence and other techniques have identified MT as ubiquitous structures shaping

and directing cellular movement, growth, morphology, and function (Wilson 40, Porter 41, Baker & Amos 42). Most microtubules are assemblies of thirteen longitudinal protofilaments which are each a series of polar, tubulin dimers (Figure 1). A dimer consists of two slightly different 55,000 molecular weight monomers (α and β tubulin) which are each 4 nm in diameter (Dentler, et al 43, Borisy & Taylor 44, Lee & Timasheff 45). Leftward helices of α and β tubulin interfaces in 3, 5, and 8 start patterns have been observed (Amos & Klug 5, Bryan 46, Burns 47). MT outer diameters are 25-30 nm and inner diameters of the MT cavities are 14-15 nm (Tilney 48). Functional MT lengths may apparently range from hundreds of nm to several meters within some mammalian neurons (Allison & Nunn 21, Atema 49). Tubulin dimer subunits are synthesized by DNA/RNA regulated ribosomes and subsequently self-polymerize or are assembled into MT on patterned organizing structures (Tucker 50).

Programmed variability in the array of MT subunits' primary structures due to ribosomal genetic influences has been observed (Behnke & Forer 51, Bryan & Wilson 52). Potential nongenetic modifications of assembled MT structure include GTP (Bryan 46), cation binding (Bhattacharyya & Wolff 53, Borisy, et al 54, Borisy & Olmsted 55), phosphorylation (Bhattacharyya & Wolff 56, Bryan 46), glycosylation (Behnke 57), and enzymatic addition of tyrosine to the C-terminal end of α tubulin (Argarana, et al 58). GTP binds at two different sites per tubulin dimer: a tightly bound site and a freely exchangeable Mg^{++} dependent site ($K_d = 1.3 \times 10^{-7}$ M) coupled to tubulin conformational changes (Bryan 46). Low concentrations of calcium (Ca^{++}) stimulate and fortify MT assembly but millimolar (mM) Ca^{++} prevents polymerization. Tubulin has one high affinity Ca^{++} site ($K_d = 3 \times 10^{-6}$ M) in the protein interior and 16 low affinity Ca^{++} sites ($K_d = 2 \times 10^{-4}$ M) which are probably involved in inhibition of assembly ($K_i = 2 \times 10^{-4}$ M) (Solomon 59, Ochs & Ranish 10). Magnesium (Mg^{++}) is necessary for MT assembly and GTP binding. Excessive zinc (Zn^{++}) disrupts MT and induces aberrant polymerization resulting in sheets of protofilaments (Seite, et al 14). Lithium (Li^+) below 1 mM stimulates MT assembly and protects assembled MT from drug induced depolymerization (Cronley-Dillon, et al 16). Other environmental cations may have long term toxic effects. Excessive brain levels of aluminum (Al^{+++}) and other cations binding to MT may cause dementia in which neuronal MT become abnormally tangled (Hirano 60, Iqbal, et al 61).

Drugs clinically used for their MT inhibition and consequent anti-inflammatory and anti-mitotic effects include colchicine, vinblastine and podophyllotoxin (Borisy & Taylor 44, Drost-Nausen 37, Bryan 46). Major tranquilizers, anticonvulsants, and general and local anesthetics bind to intraneuronal MT and at high doses may inhibit axoplasmic flow, depolymerize MT or disconnect filamentous attachments between MT and membrane proteins (MacKinney, et al 62, Edstrom 63, Haschke, et al 64, Cann & Kinman 65, Allison & Nunn 21). Multiple complexes of MT and interconnecting proteins such as cilia, mitotic spindles and centrioles perform specific functions in which they guide, signal, or direct cellular constituents through time and space. These include ciliary, flagellar and ameboid movement, secretion, phagocytosis, axoplasmic transport, mitosis, growth and differentiation (Dustin 3). Within neurons MT extend from axons to dendrites through the cell body (Palay 66). Neurotransmitter secretion and membrane excitability function are linked to MT structural integrity (Matsumoto & Sakai 7). In both myelinated and unmyelinated cat neurons, action potential frequency has been correlated with intraneuronal MT polymerization and density (Alvarez 12, Alvarez and Ramirez 13). Morphological maintenance by proximal and retrograde axoplasmic transport (1-400 mm/day) of specific substances including synaptic receptors (Young, et al 67) trophically regulates neuronal membrane composition as well as glial and postsynaptic cells (Paulson & McClure 68). Movements of filamentous contractile ATPase proteins attached to MT surfaces account for axoplasmic transport and many other facets of MT function (Ochs 69).

Several types of MT associated proteins (MAPs) bind to MT surfaces, often at regularly spaced intervals in a spiral whose pitch differs from the inherent MT 3, 5, and 8 start helices (Tilney 48, Burns 47). Among these proteins are filamentous bridges which extend laterally and often contact other MT (McIntosh 6), contractile ATPases such as dynein which perform orchestrated mechanical work, and a variety of 100,000 to 400,000 molecular weight proteins (Vallee & Borisy 70, Sandoval & Cuatrecasas 71). Porter (1) has demonstrated protein trabeculations interconnecting intracellular MT and other filamentous polymers. Filamentous bridges among MT are seen in complex geometric arrays of multiple MT throughout biology (Vallee & Borisy 8, Connolly 72). One type of array, layers of MT sheets with alternating 90 degree orientations polymerize within nuclei of cat sympathetic neurons within minutes following stimulation of those neurons (Seite, et al 14). Evidence for gross MT involvement in memory, recognition, and consciousness include correlation of brain tubulin content with chronic sensory input in rats, (Jorgenson & Meier 17) and colchicine induced loss of experimental memory function in goldfish (Cronley-Dillon & Perry 15). Correlation of intraneuronal MT polymerization density with nerve stimulation and action potential frequency implies possible conditioning and information storage. Documented MT functions include cellular skeletal support, motility, transport, and memory (Porter 1).

CHARGE/ENERGY TRANSFER MODEL IN NEURONAL MICROTUBULES

General anesthetic gases reversibly inhibit certain MT functions (Nunn 73, Nunn, et al 22) and inhibit intraprotein excited states in all bioluminescence models tested (Ueda & Kamaya 19, Middleton & Smith 20). Conformationally coupled information transfer among sensory cilia tubulin subunits has been proposed (Atema 74). We describe a model of excited state transfer, switching and mechanical coupling among neuronal MT subunits and associated proteins. The purpose of this model is to demonstrate possible MT capabilities for biological information processing as an approach to understanding structural/functional correlates of conscious awareness.

The repetitive geometric array of MT subunits may serve as a matrix of directional transfer and transduction of biochemical, mechanical, or electromagnetic energy quanta or charge. A simple model of unidirectional oxidative/reductive electron transfer will be assumed to occur between α and β subunit interfaces of a tubulin dimer or between adjacent dimers. Behaving as "mixed function oxidase" MT could accept electrons from biochemical reducing agents or other sources and ultimately donate them to molecular oxygen (O_2^- metabolized by superoxide dismutase) (Heikkila & Cabbat 75). Intraneuronal electron transfer between α and β tubulin subunits concomitant with, and parallel to the traveling nerve action potential will be considered. Neuronal conduction velocities (10 to 100 meters/sec) would result in nanosecond time intervals for 4 nm tubulin subunit transfers, and thus be consistent with observed nanosecond range protein conformational oscillations (Lakowicz & Weber 76).

MT structure can be viewed as a cylindrical, leftward spiral chessboard grid (Figure 2). With the following assumptions the continuous grid could function as a programmable switching matrix capable of information processing, storage, and integrated transduction of electromagnetic, mechanical, and biochemical energies. Many other assumption sets might also be considered.

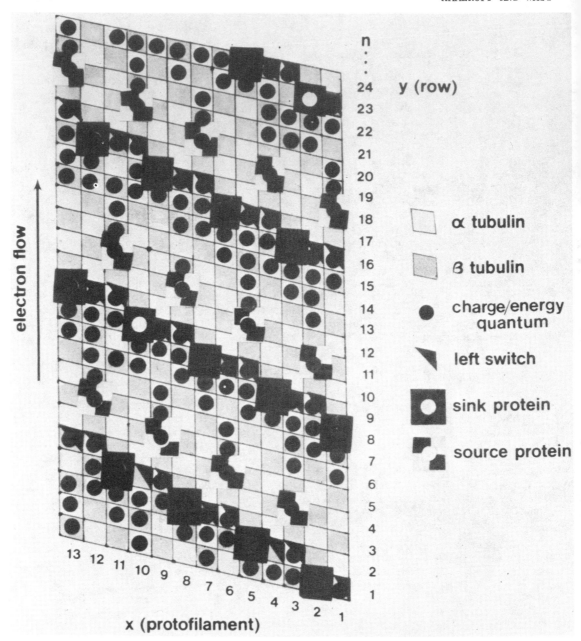

Figure 2. Unwrapped microtubule (MT) grid as programmable switching matrix. "Sink" and "source" sidearm protein attachment patterns ("leftward 3, up 1") represent electron microscopic evidence of MT associated protein attachment (Burns 47). Left switch loci may be determined by various programming modes. Charge/energy quanta may be pulsed by traveling nerve action potential.

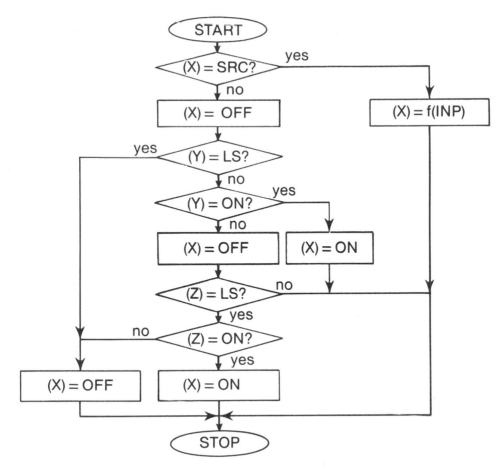

(X)—condition of a given tubulin subunit
(Y)—condition of subunit directly below X
(Z)—condition of subunit to adjacent right of X

SRC—source protein   LS—left switch protein
INP—factors affecting source charge

Figure 3.   Flow chart describing a decision process for MT quantal pulsed
transfer and switching. Nerve action potential can drive MT transfers.

1. At time (t) either one or no electron occupies any given α or β
    subunit, and electron occupancy correlates with a particular
    protein conformational state.
2. With each nerve action potential, electrons advance one subunit
    if an adjacent subunit in the direction of the action potential
    will have an electron vacancy.
3. In the direction of the action potential, each electron has two
    possible "moves" to fill electron vacancies; straight ahead along
    one of the protofilaments, or leftward along the three start
    helical row.
4. Switching mechanisms exist at each subunit which direct electron
    movement either straight or leftward. Possible substrates for
    such a switching mechanism might include genetically programmed
    alterations in primary protein structure, polymerization effects,
    or changes due to environmental interactions. Tubulin binding to
    Ca^{++} or other cation, GTP, tyrosylation, glycosylation, or other
    factors could induce conformational and energy states such that
    electron transfer from the monomer occurs leftward only. Thus,
    heterogeneity of electron flow, occupancy and conformational
    states, and possible standing wave patterns, consequent field
    vectors and resonance effects would be specific MT integrated
    functions of genetic, experiential, and present time input.
5. Charged MAPs bind at sites of electron abundance ("sink proteins":
    pulsed electron streams accepted) or electron paucity ("source
    proteins": pulsed electron streams supplied). These MAPs may
    extend laterally as contractile filamentous bridges which contact
    other MT in the geodesic cellular skeleton, transport cytoplasm
    and organelles, or regulate membrane function. Sequential,
    coordinated MAP activities may be controlled by pulsed MT transfers
    (Figure 4).

Unwrapped MT structure viewed as a switching matrix is shown in Figure 2.
Electron occupancy and conformational switching decisions based on left switch
programming and neural pulsed transfer are represented in a flow chart in
Figure 3. MT programming could channel electrons such that specifically arrayed subunits, M(2,1), M(5,2), etc., would have high electron occupancy rates,
be continuously reduced, and maintain particular conformational (and receptor)
states. Proteins binding at such sites could act as electron sinks and transfer modulated trains of electrons and/or excited conformational states to
other MT, organelles, or membrane. Proteins attracted to tubulin sites programmed to be devoid of electrons could behave as electron sources returning
electrons from coupled sink proteins, other MT, or organelles. Left switch
sites sufficient to explain one particular "leftward 3, up 1" observed pattern
of MAP attachments (Burns 47) is expressed in Table 1 as a Fortran subprogram.

Functional mechanical motions of MAPs including ATPase sidearm proteins
such as dynein could be regulated by transfer patterns over time. A specific
model of axoplasmic transport based on MT programmed sidearm protein activities is shown in Figure 4. Unidirectional, specific transport of a synaptic
bound enzyme or precursor is shown in Figure 4 as a function of "on-off"
states of the sidearms' anchoring MT subunits. Each sidearm is shown anchored
to two subunits, two rows apart. If either row subunit is occupied ("on") and
the other row subunit is not occupied ("off") the sidearm protein conformationally points toward the "on" row. Thus, unidirectional "bucket-brigade"
type axoplasmic transport may be regulated. Since four possible sidearm signals may be specified, "pinwheel" or multidirectional actions are also programmable. Mechanical or biochemical "sensory" perturbations (Atema 74) of
laterally projecting MAPs could also modulate MT function. Sink-source protein pairs and leftward switches could then be viewed as variable transistor

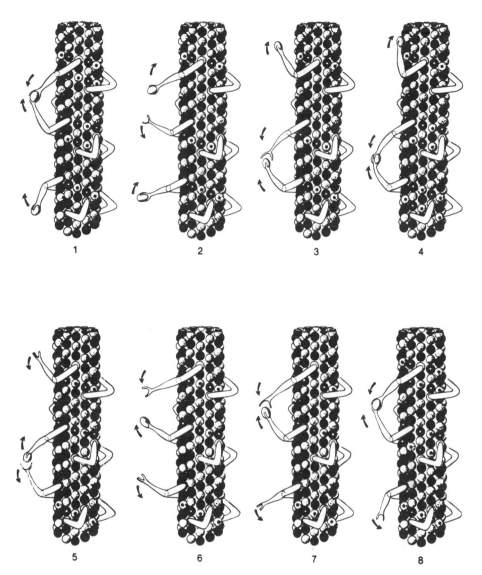

Figure 4. Axoplasmic transport. A single column of MAP "sidearm" proteins in a "bucket brigade" model of axoplasmic transport of specific enzyme or precursor. Each sidearm is anchored to 2 subunits, 2 rows apart. In this particular model, sidearms point towards an unopposed "on" subunit. Rotational and multidirectional MAP movements and transfer are also programmable. Ciliary and flagellar bending may be similarly viewed.

Table 1
Fortran subprogram plotting left switch sites which would channel electrons
through a specific set of MT loci known to bind funtional proteins (Burns 47).

In a 2 dimensional array M(X,Y) is 0 or 1 (left or straight).

FOR Y=1,24   FOR N=0,23   100 M(X,Y)=0

FOR X=1,13   FOR M=1,3   NEXT M

M(X,Y)=1   X=X+M   NEXT N

NEXT X   Y=Y+N

NEXT Y   IF X = 14 GO TO 100

X=2   X=1

Y=2   Y=Y+3

or logic circuits programmable by electronic, biochemical, or mechanical interactions. Other possibly analogous technological functions occur in charge
coupled devices, acoustic surface wave resonators, magnetic bubble memories,
and Boolean switching matrices.

MT signalling could occur by modulated, pulsed traffic through associated
proteins or by low intensity radiant field effects of nanosecond fluctuations
in electromagnetic vectors. Such signalling could be perceived by other MT
or various structures which may respond via phase transitions, conformational
changes, or other reactions. Dynamic electrical fields have been detected
oriented to mitotic spindles, coupled to embryonic neural growth axes, and
theoretically linked to organization patterns of cellular growth and functions
(Burr & Nelson 77). MT spatial regularity of 4 nm intervals could possibly
promote coherence and resonance among MT subunit excited states. In the
brain, nerve action potentials traveling through parallel MT arrays could
induce cascades of excited states and resultant wave fields. Interference
patterns within the "coherent-like" wave fields (possible vectors: electric,
magnetic, ultra-violet, biochemical, mechanical, gravitational, etc.) could
reconstruct image type information as in holography (Hameroff 78). Quantum
optical mode locking of coherent laser light, superconductivity, and super-
magnetism manifest second order phase transition as maximal resonance is ap-
proached (Sargent 79). Excited state resonance among spatially arrayed tubulin subunits could be similar. Phase transitions in consciousness might depend on MT density, MAP loci, charge/energy conformational state and occurrence of pattern changing action potentials. Thought, awareness, and recall
could thus represent continuous tuning and detuning of various subsets of MT
loci.

CONCLUSION

Intracellular biological communication and information processing is
postulated to occur via "computer-like" functions in microtubule (MT) subunits
and associated proteins. Such speculation is prompted by the lack of other
structural or functional correlates of cellular information processing and
the possible tendency for technology to emulate biology. If so, beneficial

interfacing between MT and devices or field might include MT mediated therapy in many disease processes or more direct (sub)consciousness interactions. In our laboratories, we are currently studying MT roles in nervous system injury response.

REFERENCES

1. K.R. Porter & J.B. Tucker, "The ground substance of the living cell," Sci. Am. 244, 56 (1981).

2. K. Roberts & J.S. Hyams, "Microtubules," Academic Press, London, New York (1979).

3. P. Dustin, "Microtubules," Springer Verlag, Berlin (1978).

4. R.E. Stephens & K.T. Edds, "Microtubules - structure, chemistry, and function," Physiol. Rev. 56, 709 (1976).

5. L.A. Amos & A. Klug, "Arrangement of subunits in flagellar microtubules," J. Cell. Sci. 14, 523 (1974).

6. J.R. McIntosh, "Bridges between microtubules," J. Cell. Biol. 61, 166 (1974).

7. G. Matsumoto & H. Sakai, "Microtubules inside the plasma membrane of squid giant axons and their possible physiological function," J. Membrane Biol. 50, 1 (1979).

8. R.B. Vallee & G.G. Borisy, "Removal of the projections from cytoplasmic microtubules in vitro by dissection with trypsin," J. Biol. Chem. 252, 377 (1977).

9. M. Singer, "Neurotrophic control of limb regeneration in newt," Ann. N.Y. Acad. Sci. 228, 308 (1974).

10. S. Ochs & N. Ranish, "Characteristics of the fast transport system in mammalian nerve fibers," Neurobiol. 1, 247 (1969).

11. J.C. Paulson & W.O. McClure, "Microtubules and axoplasmic transport," Brain Res. 73, 333 (1974).

12. J. Alvarez, "Microtubules in non-medullated fibres: effect of the action potential," Neurosci. Lett. 15, 15 (1979).

13. J. Alvarez & B.U. Ramirez, "Axonal microtubules: their regulation by the electrical activity of the nerve," Neurosci. Lett. 15, 19 (1979).

14. R. Seite, N. Mei & Vuillet-Luciani, "Effect of electrical stimulation on nuclear microfilaments and microtubules of sympathetic neurons," Brain Res. 50, 419 (1973).

15. J.R. Cronley-Dillon & G.W. Perry, "Tubulin synthesis in developing rat visualcortex," Nature, Lond. 261, 581 (1976).

16. J. Cronley-Dillon, D. Carden & C. Birks, "Possible involvement of brain microtubules in memory fixation," J. Exp. Biol. 61, 443 (1974).

17. O.S. Jorgenson & E. Meier, "Microtubular proteins in the occipital cortex of rats housed in enriched and in impoverished environments," J. Neurochem 1, 381 (1979).

18. H. Gutfreund, in "Enzymes: Physical Principles," Wiley, London, N.Y. (1972).

19. I. Ueda & H. Kamaya, "Kinetic and thermodynamic aspects of the mechanism of general anesthesia in a model system of firefly luminescence in vitro," Anesthesiology 38, 425 (1973).

20. A.J. Middleton & E.B. Smith, "General anesthetics and bacterial luminescence," Proc. R. Soc. Lond B 193, 159 (1976).

21. A.C. Allison & J.F. Nunn, "Effects of general anaesthetics on microtubules," The Lancet 2, 1326 (1968).

22. J.F. Nunn, J.A. Sharp & K.L. Kimball, "Reversible effect of an inhalational anaesthetic on lymphocyte motility," Nature 226, 85 (1970).

23. A. Szent-Gyorgyi, in "Introduction to a Sub-molecular Biology," Academic Press, N.Y. (1960).

24. H. Frohlich, "Long range coherence and energy storage in biological systems," Int. J. Quant. Chem. II, 641 (1968).

25. B. Rosenberg & E. Postow, "Experimental Methods in Biophysical Chemistry," C. Nicolaw, ed., Wiley, New York (1973).

26. F.W. Cope, "Evidence for semiconduction in Aplysia nerve membrane," Proc. Natn. Acad. Sci. 61, 905 (1968).

27. G.D. Pappas, Y. Asada & M.V.L. Bennett, "Morphological correlates of increased coupling resistance at an electrotonic synapse," J. Cell Biol. 49, 173 (1971).

28. A.L. Politoff, in "Intercellular Communications," Plenum Press, 127, N.Y. (1977).

29. F. Gutman & L.E. Lyons, in "Organic Semiconductors," Wiley, New York, (1967).

30. H. Frohlich, "The extraordinary dielectric properties of biological materials and the action of enzymes," Proc. Nat'l. Acad. Sci. 72, 4211 (1975).

31. W.R. Adey, "Models of membranes of cerebral cells as substrates for information storage," Biosystems 8, 163 (1977).

32. F.W. Cope, "Solid state physical mechanisms of biological energy transduction," Ann. N.Y. Acad. Sci. 227, 636 (1974).

33. J.R. Miller, "Intermolecular electron-transfer by quantum-mechanical tunneling," Sci. 189, 221 (1975).

34. J. Avery & C.M. Pavlidou, "General perspective of quantum-mechanical foundations of energy transduction," Ann. N.Y. Acad. Sci. 227, 651 (1974).

35. J.L. Shohet & S.A. Reible, "Models for energy transduction and transfer in biological-systems," Ann. N.Y. Acad. Sci. 227, 641 (1974).

36. C.W.F. McClare, "Chemical machines, Maxwell's demon, and living organisms," J. Theor. Biol. 30, 1 (1971).

37. W. Drost-Nausen, "Phase transitions in biological systems: manifestations of cooperative processes in vicinal water," Ann. N.Y. Acad. Sci. 204, 100 (1973).

38. V.S. Becker & V.M. Oliver, "Fluorescence techniques for following interactions of microtubule subunits and membranes," Nature 254, 152 (1975).

39. J.G. Carlson & R.E. Stephens, "Mitotic acceleration induced in grasshopper neuroblasts by small doses of monochromatic ultraviolet-radiation," Photochem. Photobiol. 20, 1 (1974).

40. L. Wilson, "Properties of colchicine binding protein from chick embryo brain," Biochem., N.Y. 9, 4999 (1970).

41. K.R. Porter in "Ciba Foundation Symposium on Principles of Biomolecular Organization," Churchill, London (1966).

42. T.S. Baker & L.A. Amos, "Structure of the tubulin dimer in zinc-induced sheets," J. Molec. Biol. 123, 89 (1978).

43. W.L. Dentler, S. Granett, G.B. Witman & J.L. Rosenbaum, "Directionality of brain microtubule assembly in vitro," Proc. Nat'l. Acad. Sci. 71, 1710 (1974).

44. G.G. Borisy & E.W. Taylor, "The mechanisms of action of colchicine," J. Cell Biol. 34, 525 (1967).

45. J.C. Lee & S.N. Timasheff, "In vitro reconstitution of calf brain microtubules - effects of solution variables," Biochem. 16, 1754 (1977).

46. J. Bryan, "Definition of three classes of binding sites in isolated microtubule crystals," Biochem. 11, 2611 (1972).

47. R.G. Burns, "Spatial organization of the microtubule associated proteins of reassembled brain microtubules," J. Ultrastruc. Res. 65, 73 (1978).

48. L.G. Tilney, "How microtubule patterns are generated," J. Cell. Biol. 51, 837 (1971).

49. J. Atema, in "Microtubule and Microtubule Inhibitors," M. Borgers and M. DeBrabander, eds., Amsterdam-Oxford, North-Holland (1975).

50. J.B. Tucker, "Shape and pattern specification during microtubule bundle assembly," Nature, Lond. 266, 22 (1977).

51. O. Behnke & A. Forer, "Evidence for four classes of microtubules in individual cells," J. Cell. Sci. 2, 169 (1967).

52. J. Bryan & L. Wilson, "Are cytoplasmic microtubules heteropolymers?," Proc. Nat. Acad. Sci. 68, 1762 (1971).

53. B. Bhattacharyya & J. Wolff, "Thyroid tubulin: preparation and properties," Biochem. 13, 2364 (1974).

54. G.G. Borisy, J.M. Marcum, J.B. Olmsted, D.B. Murphy & K.A. Johnson, "Purification of tubulin and associated high molecular-weight proteins from porcine brain and characterization of microtubule assembly in vitro," Ann. N.Y. Acad. Sci. 253, 107 (1975).

55. G.G. Borisy & J.P. Olmsted, "Nucleated assembly of microtubules in porcine brain extracts," Science 177, 1196 (1972).

56. B. Bhattacharyya & J. Wolff, "Stabilization of microtubules by lithium ion," Biochem. Biophys. Res. Commun. 73, 383 (1976).

57. O. Behnke, "Studies on isolated microtubules - evidence for a clear space component," Cytobiologie 11, 366 (1975).

58. C.E. Argarana, C.A. Arce, H.S. Barra & R. Caputto, "In vivo incorporation of (14C) tyrosine into the c-terminal position of the alpha subunit of tubulin," Arch. Biochem. Biophys. 180, 264 (1977).

59. F. Solomon, "Binding sites for calcium on tubulin," Biochemistry 16, 358 (1977).

60. A. Hirano, in "Alzheimer's Disease and Related Conditions," G.E.W. Walstenholme & M. O'Connor, eds., Churchill, London (1970).

61. K. Iqbal, H.M. Wisniewski, I. Grundke, J.K. Korthals & R.D. Terry, "Chemical pathology of neurofibrils - neurofibrillary tangles of Alzheimers presenile dementia," J. Histochem. Cytochem. 23, 563 (1975).

62. A.A. MacKinney, R.S. Vyas & D. Walker, "Hydantoin drugs inhibit polymerization of pure microtubular protein," J. Pharmacol. Exp. Ther. 204, 189 (1978).

63. A. Edstrom, H.A. Hansson, H. Larsson & H. Wallin, "Effects of barbiturates on ultrastructue and polymerization of microtubules in vitro," Cell Tiss. Res. 162, 35 (1975).

64. R.H. Haschke, M.R. Byers & B.R. Fink, "Effects of lidocaine on rabbit brain microtubular protein," J. Neurochem. 22, 837 (1974).

65. J.R. Cann & N.D. Hinman, "Interaction of chlorpromazine with brain microtubule subunit protein," Molec. Pharmacol. 11, 256 (1975).

66. S.L. Palay, "Synapses in the central nervous system," J. Biophys. Biochem. Cytol. 2, 193 (1956).

67. W.S. Young, J.K. Wamsley, M.A. Zarbin & M.J. Kuhar, "Opioid receptors undergo axonal flow," Sci. 210, 76 (1980).

68. J.C. Paulson & W.O. Mclure, "Inhibition of axoplasmic-transport by colchicine, podophyllotoxin, and vinblastine - effect on microtubules," Ann. N.Y. Acad. Sci. 253, 517 (1975).

69. S. Ochs, "Energy metabolism and supply of $\sim$ P to fast axoplasmic transport mechanism in nerve," Fed. Proc. 33, 1049 (1974).

70. R.B. Vallee & G.G. Borisy, "The non-tubulin component of microtubule protein oligomers. Effect on self-association and hydrodynamic properties," J. Biol. Chem. 253, 2834 (1978).

71. I.V. Sandoval & P. Cuatrecasas, "Proteins associated with tubulin," Biochem. Biophys. Res. Commun. 68, 169 (1976).

72. J.A. Connolly, V.I. Kalnins, D.W. Cleveland & M.W. Kirschner, "Immunofluorescence staining of cytoplasmic and spindle microtubules in mouse fibroblasts with antibody to tau protein," Proc. Natn. Acad. Sci. 74, 2437 (1977).

73. J.F. Nunn & A.C. Allison, Effects of anesthetics on microtubular systems, in "Cellular Biology and Toxicology of Anaesthesia, B.R. Fink, ed., Williams and Wilkins, Baltimore, MD (1972).

74. J. Atema, "Microtubule theory of sensory transduction," J. Theor. Biol. 38, 181 (1973).

75. R.E. Heikkila & F.S. Cabbat, "Chemiluminescence from 6-hydroxydopamine: involvement of hydrogen peroxide, the superoxide radical and the hydroxyl radical, a potential role for singlet oxygen," Res. Comm. Chem. Path. & Pharm. 17, 649 (1977).

76. J.R. Lakowicz & G. Weber, "Quenching of protein fluorescence by oxygen - detection of structural fluctuations in proteins on the nanosecond time scale," Biochemistry 12, 4171 (1973).

77. H.S. Burr & O. Nelson, "Electrodynamic correlates of cell biology," Proc. Nat. Acad. Sci. 32, 73 (1946).

78. S.R. Hameroff, "Chi - neural hologram - microtubules; bioholography, and acupuncture," Am. J. Chi. Med. 2, 163 (1974).

79. M. Sargent, "Mode locking in quantum optics," Appl. Phys. 1, 139 (1973).

DISCUSSION

Dr. Nagel: NRL - Are these self-assembling?

Dr. Hameroff: Yes, they polymerize upon a basic substrate known as a microtubular orienting center or MTOC. They are unidirectional and will start from an MTOC and polymerize outward. There are several classes. Some microtubules are more stable and seem to be around all the time, but others are labile and depolymerize and repolymerize repeatedly. As I said, stimulating neurons causes polymerization of these microtubules within minutes, very soon, so it may represent a conditioned or learned response mechanism. The polymerization factor is something that we are studying for possible clinical application, for example following nerve injury. Considering genetic engineering Dr. Ulmer said yesterday he could synthesize tubulin. Perhaps one could inject microtubule precursors into an area that has been injured to promote neurite sprouting and synaptogenesis. Dr. Raphael Gruener, a neurophysiologist at the University of Arizona works with embryonic neurons and muscle cells which are put together and form neuromuscular synapses. We are using his model to look for factors which might enhance synapse formation via microtubule actions. Factors which might favorably affect polymerization include cation concentration as well as perhaps field-induced effects. For example, low intensity ultra-violet light has been shown to stimulate mitotic acceleration. Mitosis is effected by mitotic spindles which are comprised of microtubles, and low intensity UV stimulates mitosis. We have been hoping that a field effect might promote neurite sprouting in the right direction and enhance synaptogenesis and nervous system recovery.

Dr. Greene: NRL - I have one short question. Did you say that you were able to make an artificial synapse? Does that mean it is possible to make an interface between one of our ordinary today electronic devices and something specific?

Dr. Hameroff: The question is whether it may be possible to interface some kind of device and an axon. That was mentioned yesterday with osmium tetroxide, although that may be toxic to the neuron. I would think it might be possible. Our group at the University of Arizona has talked about this in terms of running prosthetic limbs. Eventually it may be realized. Other types of field interactions might be possible: if holographic mechanisms occur subcellularly, information may be retrieved or perhaps instructed by field interference. I am very much interested in how anesthetic gases work. What they seem to do with the firefly luciferase molecule is bind in the hydrophobic pocket and apparently quench or inhibit solid state processes which would otherwise lead to the conformational change necessary for the appropriate function of that protein. Most people think in terms of lipid solubility as an explanation of anesthetic effect, but I think you can make a better argument that they work via proteins. There are pockets within proteins that have the same solubility as in lipid phase and match olive oil solubility data.

Prof. Hanker: Univ. of NC - Dr. Hameroff was kind enough to refer to our suggestion yesterday of the possibility of making interfaces between diagnostic or prosthetic devices and axons. He mentioned the problem of the toxicity of osmium tetroxide. I did not mean to infer that osmium tetroxide should be applied to living nerves. The activation of devices depending upon a tissue/device interface does not require contact of living tissue with any toxic component including osmium tetroxide. On the other hand, either a physiologic or biochemical signal is all that is required. From the neuron, for example, release of the enzyme acetycholinesterase at the neuron/device interface would be utilized to deposit a conductive metallic compound within the confines of the device; the conductive metallic compound could, of course, complete or activate a circuit. The result is an electron device whose fabrication was completed by a biochemical or physiologic signal.

Dr. Hameroff: Yes. Of course, the cholinesterase molecule is transported along the axon by the microtubules.

SECTION SIX
After Dinner Speech

CHAPTER XXVII

TALK FOR "MOLECULAR" ELECTRONIC DEVICES WORKSHOP

Alan Berman
Director of Research
Naval Research Laboratory
Washington, DC 20375

The Director of Research at a place like NRL or at any large National or industrial laboratory has a curious job. In some sense, the position is much like the Vice President for investment in a very large bank. As scientists and engineers, we tend to have very little sympathy with the problems of investment bankers. Nevertheless, their problems are real and rather interesting. A Vice President for investment must divide up the bank portfolio into home mortgages, industrial investments, stock holdings, bonds, money market certificates, short term paper, long term paper, and various forms of interbank credit. In doing this, he has to understand things such as the discount rate, projected rates of inflation, and the probability of appreciation of various properties. In some sense, a Research Director is supposed to perform an analogous function. The only difference is that the Research Director makes investments in various areas of technology.

In simplest terms, part of my job is to be sure that insofar as they can be cured by current technology, the short term problems of the Navy are cured. However, I also have responsibility to make a series of investments in basic research which will yield technologies, so that in the period 15, 20 or 30 years from now, systems will be in being which will insure technological competence of the U.S. Navy and or Department of Defense.

Fortunately, the U.S. Navy and Department of Defense don't rely on the judgment of any one person who has the limited competence that I have. Investments are made by many people. In some sense, each profits by the mistakes of others. When it comes to making investments in technology related to computers and computer architecture, I have made my share of mistakes. I am not embarrassed to admit to my mistakes, since many people in positions such as mine have made similar mistakes in judgment, when they bet on the wrong technology at the wrong time. In the early 1960's, I took responsibility for a very large program known as Project ARTEMIS. The exact details of the program do not matter much. It was an active sensor program of some sort. The real point was that for the program to be successful we had to be able to perform 10^9 computations per second. As reasonable scientists and engineers, we sat down and extrapolated existing computer technology. In the early 60's the state-of-the-art of computers permitted something like 10^5 computations per second. Foreseeing no reasonable way in which the current 1960 generation of computers would move up to the rate of 10^9 computations per second, we decided that we would leapfrog technology and place our bets on optical correlators and optical computers. I thus made a very large investment in optical computers. The program struggled on for about six to eight years before it was put to a merciful death by some budget cutter. The program was completely unsuccessful in that we were never able to demonstrate a reliable real-time computer that could manage 10^9 operations per second.

What was wrong? Basically, the problem was not in the theory of the optical computer. Our problem was that we could not deliver or pump the data into the processing system in real time. Approximately six to eight years after that program was terminated, the so called Surface Acoustic Wave Bragg Cell was developed. As you know, this allows an injection of a wave train at RF frequencies which causes densification and rarefactions on the surface of a lithium niobate chip. A coherent signal from a laser is focused on the surface of the chip, and the cell then acts as a defraction grating. It scatters the light in directions proportional to the wavelength of the signal. Another technology, namely the Charge Coupled Device Technology, also needed to be invented to make optical computation feasible. In 1960, when I laid out my first optical computer, I needed to devise a real-time system which created a mask on a film negative which then would be continuously moved in front of a lens to form a reference function. This required a rather impressive chemical factory in which a light beam was played on film and the film was developed in near real time and then transported across the front of the lens in time to be cross correlated with incoming signals. At the detector the signals would be displayed on a scope. These would be swept by an electron beam, and then processed. Effectively, in 1960, we lacked an ability to develop a real-time replica signal and an ability to provide a real-time display of the output signal.

Today's technology has made optical computers quite feasible. Right now as one scans what is available in computers, most modern high speed computers based on semiconductor technology of the current generation, can do about 10^6 and 10^7 operations per second. At the laboratory level optical computers using Bragg cells and CCD detectors can manage computations at the rate of 10^9 per second. In other words, we can solve the problem that I tried to work on and failed some 20 years ago.

Both optical and semiconductor technology will be improved. If one makes a somewhat conservative extrapolation of current optical technology, it is safe to estimate that optical computers probably can be improved by one to two orders of magnitude. Thus, I would think that by the mid-eighties optical computers will be capable of doing computations at the rate of 10^{10} or 10^{11} computations per second. The more optimistic salesmen in the world of optical computers suggest that 10^{12} computations per second will be possible. Certainly, if one parallels optical processes, such rates of computation should be possible. In the world of semiconductor technology, the great hope for the future for making computers faster is the so called VHSIC program. This foresees that semiconductor technology will go to submicron lithography. Eventually, computers with the capability of 10^8 to 10^{10} computations per second will be achieved. As an interesting outside contender, there is the Josephson Junction Technology, which also looks as though in the late 80's it will get into the range of 10^{10}, 10^{11} computations per second.

All three of these technologies contain problems and limitations. The number of computations which can be made with an optical computer is limited by some rather basic principles of Physics, such as the defraction limit of lens, and by the speed that we are able to pump data into the computing elements. I would guess that it is unlikely that optical computers will within the next ten years perform much above the rate that I previously quoted. 10^{10} or 10^{11} computations per second is the limit unless there is a break-through in the field of x-ray lasers, which I have some reservations about at the moment. Josephson Junction Devices are, of course, limited by the cryogenic problems associated with them and also, essentially by dimensional considerations. In the world of semiconductor devices, as one goes to submicron lithography, very real limitations are encountered other than those imposed by lithographic dimensional limitations. There is, of course, the classic problem of making nonresistive connections to very small elements. The second is the sheer mechanics of generating ultra submicron structures. In other words, if some-one wanted to develop components at the hundredth or thousandth micron level, rather severe problems would be encountered. Finally, as one gets down to submicron level descrete components, random cosmic rays tend to cause soft upsets. To offset this, one must use redundant channels. Pretty soon one does not gain very rapidly by going to smaller and smaller components because the need for redundant circuits uses up the capability almost as fast or possibly faster than it is generated by going to finer scales of lithography.

Other approaches still exist. One would think that three-dimensional rather than two-dimensional devices will help. However, I don't think that they will get us beyond the barrier of 10^{10} or 10^{11} computations per second. As a kind of Vice President for investment, I must ask myself a question, what would be wrong with computers capable of performing operations at the rate of 10^{11} per second. The answer is nothing. Lots of people would be delighted to have them, if in fact, they were available and performed reliably. Are there requirements which could usefully employ computers that perform at rates 10^{12}, 10^{13} or 10^{14} per second. The answer comes out, yes indeed. Although I have not thought through civilian, medical, or social applications in any serious details, I certainly am familiar with military, scientific and space exploration type requirements. I think that in these fields there are, in fact, many systems that would profit from data handled at these rates.

If I have the vision of such a need some 10, 20 or 30 in the future, what are the technologies that I ought to be investing in? At the moment, I see three possible directions to go. Two of these are outgrowths of the areas that I have discussed here tonight. The third relates to the topic of your Workshop. Optical computing using variants of the Bragg cell and CCD detectors obviously could be improved if we had x-ray lasers. Therefore, I suppose that I should underwrite investments in the development of x-ray lasers with some level of enthusiasm. Although, I am skeptical of our ability to produce a reliable, usable x-ray laser, nobody has ever given me a existence proof that it cannot be done. Three-dimensional semiconductor devices are certainly possible. In fact, at rather rudimentary levels, we are building these devices at NRL. Certainly I know of other industrial academic institutions that are toying with such a technology.

In the area of Molecular Devices, which I think may eventually be the winner in the competition for the race to 10^{12} operations per second sweep-stakes, much remains to be done. One needs in the next 10 years a tremendous investment in this field. Part of the investment is purely an intellectual investment. I think we are, to some degree, limited in our ideas. The question of how you would configure a molecular based computer, how you would couple data into it, how you would pump the data, how changes of state are detected, how data would be buffered, stored, displayed, routed to separate address, must be dealt with, together with all of the problems of normal computer architecture. This will be a tremendous challenge to our knowledge of basic Physics, Chemistry, and Computer Architecture.

One of the impressive aspects of the U.S. computer industry has been its ability to mass produce electronic circuitry of diminishing size with ever-increasing complexity, reliability, and operating speeds. Before considering the benefits that may be associated with a computer based on molecular sized electronic components, it is desirable to consider three problems associated with the current large computer.

While tens of thousands of active elements can now be placed on a single silicon chip, it now costs more to assemble these chips onto printed circuit boards and then to assemble these boards into a working computer than it costs to produce the chip. I don't know what current industry costs are, but I would guess that the cost of the chip is not more than one or two percent of the total cost of an assembled and tested electronic system. This is primarily because of the two dimensionality of both the silicon chips and their assembly. This leads to another related problem, namely the operating speed of the computer. Since the speed of the electrical impulse is no greater than $0.3nm/10^{-9}$ second, the length of the wires hooking together the chips tends to provide a clear limitation on the ultimate speed of the computer. One obvious way to circumvent this problem is in the future to build, as I have suggested, three-dimensional microcircuitry. If, for example, all of the microcircuitry could be included in a three-dimensional block, one centimeter on side, the transport of information from one element to another would not take much more than 30 picosecond compared to the three and a half nanoseconds with current devices. This would be an improvement of a hundred fold. Further, most silicon devices are limited by the drift velocity of holes. The third problem that plagues modern large computers is the heat generated by the resistive elements in the microcircuitry. Unless a new approach is developed to computer architecture, heat dissipation problems will provide the ultimate limit to the capability of semiconductor-based computer designs.

The enormous number of elements that might be combined in one cubic centimeter, if one were to use molecular scale devices, certainly staggers the minds of current designers. It is apparent that if a switching element plus its insulator could be contained in a cubic molecular volume of ten to a hundred Angstroms on side, a cubic centimeter of molecular circuitry could exceed the sum of all memory elements manufactured to date. Obviously the potential is enormous. A highly speculative description of how such a computer might be made has been given by a number of authors. In the wonderful world of uninvented devices, life would be much simpler than it is for our current generation of computer architects. The number of electrical leads would be relatively few. Most of the input timing impulses and numerical input data would be transmitted by optical or RF pulses. The output is envisioned as being via multichannel optical techniques in which each channel source would be highly directional. At the microscopic or molecular level, such highly directional output might be achieved by developing a linear array of oriented chromophores which, when excited, will radiate in a preferred direction. If several of the chromophores could be excited nearly simultaneously, the spontaneous radiation might stimulate the remainder to radiate, producing, in essence, a small highly directional micro laser. Another possible technology for the central processing unit of a molecular or chemical computer might take advantage of the sensitivity of a two-dimensional charge coupled device built into the side of a chemical computer. As currently imagined, electron impulses might be injected into the receiver cells over a small potential barrier using a molecular tunneling device which could be readily switched on or off by a very small signal. Such a use of a CCD as an output device would provide a high density of output channels for a low controlling charge input.

I think the possible advantages of a computer based on molecular level of electronics are fairly obvious. When one evaluates whether one should invest one's time, assets, or career in this field, one must consider the following points:

- In going from a modern day two dimensional computer to a three dimensional molecular configuration, wiring costs must be significantly decreased and fabrication more fully automated, or the device will not be economically feasible.

- By reducing the switching elements to molecular size the memory density could be increased by several orders of magnitude and the power input decreased very significantly.

- Three dimensional construction plus switching elements of molecular size could enhance computer speed by several orders of magnitude. To use this speed, faster data pumps will need to be developed.

These possible advantages are all very significant. However, the technical barriers which now appear to limit the utility of such devices must be overcome. The decade of the 80's should be the time where chemists, physicists, and engineers will begin to become sensitive to the possibility of useful switching devices at the molecular level.

The bottom line for any investment or research manager is "would you invest in this program". In this case, my answer is a qualified yes. While I am willing to make modest investments in research supporting molecular computation, many questions need to be answered before anyone would make large scale investments in the field. Much thought has to be given and persuasive arguments have to be presented in each case to justify the reality of the conjectures that I have alluded to. Your arguments must be plausible. Solid research must be performed to show the feasibility of these concepts. I am confident that eventually the community of people represented here tonight will, in time, be joined by others, and that ultimately you will succeed in solving the problems and realizing molecular based computers.

Ladies and Gentlemen, I believe you have an exciting intellectual and professional challenge ahead of you if you pursue work in this field. It is a challenge where the stakes are high and the results of success will be extremely important to the quality of life throughout the world. Thank you.

GLOSSARY

GLOSSARY FOR

BIOLOGICAL AND MOLECULAR ELECTRONIC SWITCHING

Acceptor - A molecule or group (or moiety) that accepts one or more electrons (like TCNQ or $-NO_2$).

Allosteric Interactions - A process which is regulated by a species (enzyme) at another site.

Amino Acids - The building blocks of proteins. There are 20 common amino acids, the same basic structure, different side groups (R):

$$R\!-\!\underset{\underset{3}{NH_3^+}}{\overset{}{CHCOO^-}} \;=\; R\!-\!\underset{\underset{2}{NH_2}}{\overset{}{CHCOOH}}$$

Amino Acid Sequence - The linear order of the amino acids in a protein.

Amplification (biotechnical) - Replication of a gene library in bulk.

Antiferromagnet - There is more than one sublattice of atomic moments. In the ordered state the magnetic moments of one lattice align oppositely to another and cancel exactly.

Axons - The core of a nerve fiber which conducts impulses away from the nerve cell.

Bacteria - Unicellular microorganisms containing a single very large DNA molecule per cell (the chromosome).

Bacteriophage - A virus that grows in bacteria.

Bistable Switching - A regime in which there exist two separately identifiable states (e.g. 1 and 0, ON and OFF, or two molecular tautomers.)

Canting - Certain substances that are primarily antiferromagnetic exhibit a weak ferromagnetism due to the canting or impercise alignment of antiparallelism in the spins.

CCD - Charge Coupled Device - An electronic device which is capable of precisely transferring and manipulating small amounts ("buckets") of electronic charge. Used for computer memory, optical and IR imaging, etc.

365

Centrioles – A tiny cylindrical organelle located at the center of a centrosome.

Charge Transfer Interaction – The interaction by charge transfer of electronic levels in disparate electronic species.

Charge-Transfer or Ion-Radical Salt – When the ionization potential of a donor is low and the electron affinity of an acceptor is high, electron transfer may occur to give a phase markedly different from the weak pi-complex. In a 1:1 stoichiometry, the crystal structures may consist of segregated linear chains of each molecular species.

Chlorophyll – The intensely colored pigment used for light harvesting and primary charge separation in photosynthetic organisms.

Cilia – Microscopic hair-like appendages which extend from the cell surface.

Clone – A group of genetically identical cells or organisms reproduced asexually from the same cell.

Codon – A sequence of three adjacent nucleotides in messenger RNA that code for an amino acid (or chain termination).

Colony – A group of contiguous cells, usually derived from a single ancestor, growing on a solid surface.

Complementary Base Sequences – Polynucleotide sequences that are related by the base-pairing rules.

Contractile ATPase – An enzyme which exerts catalytic influence on ATP (adenosine triphosphate) in contractile muscle.

Contrast Curve – In lithography, it is a plot of resist dissolution rate versus the incident radiation dose.

Critical Behavior – A phase change characterized by critical points, an order parameter, coexistence curve, etc.

Crystal Field Theory – The theory which treats a metal complex as if the only interaction between the central metal atom and its set of nearest neighbor molecules or ions is a purely electrostatic one.

Curie Temperature – T_c, is the ordering temperature for ferromagnetic ordering.

Curie-Weiss Law – The presence of interactions between the atomic magnets modifies Curie's law such that $\chi = C/(T-\Theta)$, where Θ is called the Weiss constant. Susceptibility data is often displayed as "Curie-Weiss" plots of $1/\chi$ vs. T to exhibit the intercept on the T axis, Θ. If this is at $T > 0$, then $\Theta > 0$ and ferromagnetic interaction is dominant. If the intercept is at $T < 0$, then $\Theta < 0$ and antiferromagnetic interaction is dominant. (If $\Theta = 0$ there is no interaction, the material is a paramagnet and Curie's law is recovered).

Cytochemistry – The chemistry of plant and animal cells.

Cytoplasmic Movement – Movement of the protoplasm outside of the cell nucleus.

Dendrites - The branched parts of nerve cells which transmit impulses toward the cell body.

DNA Deoxyribonucleic acid - The genetic material of all cells and many viruses. Most DNA molecules consist of two interwound strands of four basic units called nucleotides or bases, A, C, G, T. Their structure is such that A in one strand is always found opposite T in the other strand, and vice versa. Similarly, C and G always pair with each other. DNA molecules can be either linear or circular (for micro-organisms, i.e. bacteria and viruses).

DNA polymerase - An enzyme that can fill in single-stranded gaps in double-stranded DNA by inserting the proper complementary bases opposite the bases in the intact strand.

DNA replication - The process by which the two complementary strands of a DNA molecule separate and a new complementary strand is synthesized by DNA polymerase on each of the separated strands. This process gives rise to two daughter DNA molecules identical to the parental molecule.

Donor - A molecule or group that gives up one or more electrons (like TTF or $-NH_3$).

Donor Acceptor Complex - (See Weak PI Complex).

Dynamic Memories - Digital electronic devices which store binary information in the form of electric charge on a capacitor. Due to leakage of this capacitor, it is necessary to "refresh" the memory by recharging it at frequent intervals typically $10 \rightarrow 100$ times per second.

Dynein - A large protein which catalyzes ATP hydrolysis in the presence of Mg^{2+}.

Dzyaloshinsky-Moriya Interaction - An interaction Hamiltonian used to describe spin-spin interaction.

E-Beam - Electron beam.

E. Coli, Escherichia coli - The most extensively studied species of bacteria, isolated from the gastrointestinal tract of most mammals including man. The present degree of understanding of E. coli is probably an order of magnitude greater than that of any other bacterium, as is the capability for manipulating it in precise ways by genetic techniques.

Electron Microprobe - Method for quantitative chemical analysis. An electron beam impinging on the sample excites characteristic X-rays which are analyzed.

Electron Spin Resonance (ESR) - A magnetic sample is placed in a uniform magnetic field. An electric field of (usually microwave) frequency ν is then applied. Energy is absorbed by the sample when $h\nu$ = energy level splitting induced by magnetic field plus internal field.

Enzyme - A protein molecule that catalyzes (increases the rate of) a chemical reaction.

Episome - A circular gene fragment.

Extrinsic Phase - Ion-radical solid whose formation is accounted for by invoking chemical species other than those implied by the name of the solid.

Femtosecond - 10^{-15} sec.

Ferromagnetism - An example of cooperative behavior characterized by a spontaneous macroscopic magnetization in the absence of an applied magnetic field and resulting from an exchange interaction between electrons such that spins are parallel.

Flagella - A long filamentous appendage of certain cells which frequently assists in locomotion.

Four Point Probe - A device for measuring electrical resistivity of materials by passing a known constant current between two precisely spaced outer electrodes and measuring the voltage produced between two precisely spaced inner electrodes.

Gene - A sequence of DNA base pairs that codes for a single species of protein, which is itself a sequence of amino acid units in a chain. Proteins (enzymes) are thus gene products.

Genetic code - Dictionary of codons or code words consisting of three adjacent nucleotides which specify the twenty amino acids and stop signals in protein synthesis.

Gene Expression - A gene is expressed in a cell when it is transcribed into RNA and the RNA is translated into a functional protein.

Hard Errors - Data processing errors encountered in digital electronic hardware which result from the failure of an electronic device and not just the loss of information.

Heisenberg Exchange Interaction - The most commonly assumed form of strong interaction between atomic magnets. It is written $JS_i \cdot S_j$ where S_i and S_j are spins on sites i and j. It is _symmetrical_ in that the three components of the vector S are equivalent.

Heisenberg Model - A model, in which for a description of magnetic and other systems, the magnetic moments are related to a quantum mechanical three-component spin operator, and the assumption is made that the energy is proportional to the scaler product of these operators. There is no exact solution for a three-dimensional lattice.

Heme - A complex between a protoporphyrin and iron (II). Protoporphyrin is a derivative of a tetrapyrrole compound.

Hemoglobin - A complex four chain molecule, one chain of which has Fe^{2+} surrounded by a porphyrin ring with either an alpha or beta protein attached, and, if in the oxy form, an oxygen molecule in the sixth position of the metal ion. The heme of hemoglobin is Fe-photoporphyrin IX.

Host-Vector - A system designed for preparation of recombinant DNAs, consisting of a vector or molecular vehicle to carry the recombinants and host cells for growth of the vector.

Hydrogen bonds – An important but relatively weak chemical bond as in $-OH\cdots NH_2-$, $-OH\cdots Cl-$, or water. It is responsible for the α-helix structure of proteins and holds complementary base pairs (A and T, C and G) together in DNA, etc.

Inducible Enzymes – Enzymes whose rate of production can be increased by the presence of inducers in the cell.

Intrinsic Phase – Ion-radical solid where initiation may be discussed by involving only the donor and acceptor, their redox states, and their mutual interactions.

Inverse Faraday Effect – The resonance enhancement of internal magnetic moments.

Ion Radical Salt – (See Charge Transfer Salt) Often involves a donor or acceptor molecule (like TCNQ) that becomes charged and contains an unpaired electron in the valence orbitals (like $TCNQ^{\bar{\delta}}$).

Ising Model – A model in which the magnetic moments are assumed to be classical, one-dimensional "sticks" capable of two orientations. Solutions for the model exist for the one and two dimensional cases.

Jahn-Teller Instability – This instability theorem states that a complex which has an even number of electrons and a degenerate ground state will distort so that degeneracy is removed and produces a configuration which is lower in energy.

Langmuir-Blodgett Technique – A process for generating adsorbed films by repetitively dipping a substrate into a liquid which is covered with a monolayer of the desired film material. If the material is an aliphatic organic compound with a polar end, then each dip will result in the deposition of the film whose thickness is twice the length of the compound.

Larmor Precession Theorem – In a magnetic field an electron in orbital motion may be regarded as a vector precessing about the direction of the magnetic field.

Ligand Field Theory – Crystal field theory modified in such a way as to take account of the existence of moderate amounts of delocalization between the metal and ligand orbitals.

Linker – A small fragment of synthetic DNA that has a restriction site useful for gene splicing.

Lithography – The process of transferring two dimensional images by irradiation of radiation sensitive resist material with either photons or charged particles, in the desired pattern followed by development and etching.

Macromolecule – A large molecule, usually composed of a sequence of a limited number of different kinds of basic subunits. DNA, RNA, proteins, and polysaccharides are all examples of macromolecules.

Magneto-Crystalline Anisotropy – A property of a magnetic material whose magnet moments show a preferred direction with respect to crystal axes.

Manganese Stearate – A soap in which two stearate chains combine with one divalent manganese to form $Mn(C_{18}H_{35}O_2)_2$.

MER - A repeat unit as in polymer but differing from the monomer due to condensation reaction plus any bonding rearrangement.

Metamagnetic Transition - The conversion of a antiferromagnet to a ferromagnet by the application of a strong external magnetic field. The ferromagnetic state exists only in the presence of the field.

Microtubles - Cylindrical protein polymers composed of multiple strands of α and β tubulin assembled in a helical fashion.

Mitotic Spindles - Microfilaments that pull chromosomes apart during cell division.

mRNA, messenger RNA - The kind of RNA that is synthesized from genes and that acts as the intermediate in the conversion of information stored as a base-pair sequence in DNA into an amino acid sequence in a protein.

Multistage Redox System - A molecule system capable of reversible transfer of n electrons in n steps.

Mutation - A change in the genetic material of an organism. Mutations can be base-pair changes, deletions, additions, or inversions of a series of base pairs.

NAND (Not and) - A logical operation in which a false result is obtained only if all input conditions are true and a true result is obtained if any input condition is false.

Néel Temperature - T_n, is the ordering temperature of antiferromagnets.

NMP - N-Methyl Phenazinium

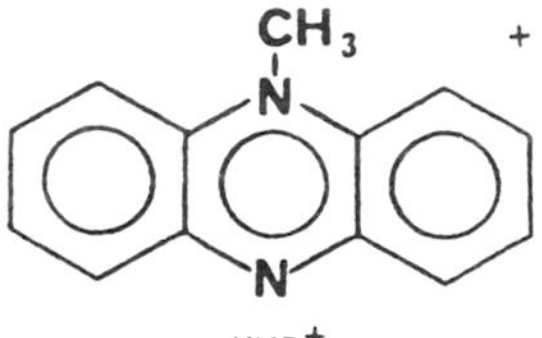

NMP^+

NOR - (Not or) - A logical operation in which a true result is obtained only if all input conditions are false and a false result is obtained if any input condition is true.

Nuclear Backscattering - Method for quantitative chemical analysis. Incident nuclei are scattered from the nuclei in a sample. Depending on the rebounding energy, the masses of the elements in the sample can be determined.

Operator - In molecular biology, a region of DNA that interacts with a repressor protein to control the expression of an adjacent gene or group of genes.

Operon - A gene unit consisting of one or more genes that specify a polypeptide and an "operator" that regulates the transcription of the structural gene. The regulator and the coding genes are adjacent on the DNA molecule.

Organelles - The highest level of organization in the heirarchy of cell
   structure in which various supra molecular complexes are assembled into
   such things as nuclei, mitochondria and chloroplasts.

Palindrome - A self-complementary nucleic acid sequence, that is, a sequence
   identical to its complementary strand; perfect palindromes (for example,
   GAATTC) frequently occur as sites of recognition for restriction enzymes.

Paramagnet - A material whose atomic magnets weakly interact and normally
   do not form an ordered magnetic arrangement but will order in an
   external magnetic field. The tendency toward alignment is opposed by
   thermal agitation.

Phonons - A quantum of acoustic or vibrational energy.

Phosphodiester bond - The type of covalent bonds that link nucleotides together
   to form the polynucleotide strands of a DNA or RNA molecule. Phosphodiester
   bonds can be cut by endonucleases and exonucleases, formed by DNA
   polymerase, and repaired (reformed) by DNA ligase.

Photosynthesis - The conversion of light energy (photons) into chemical
   energy by natural or artificial means.

Photosynthetic Membrane - Natural membranes in photosynthetic organisms in which
   all the light reactions of photosynthesis take place.

Phthalocyanine -

Pi-Amphoteric Molecule - A molecule which behaves as an electron donor or
   acceptor, depending on specific experimental conditions.

Picosecond - 10^{-12} sec.

Plasmid - Extrachromosomal, autonomously replicating, circular DNA segment.

Plastoquinone - An electron carrier in photo systems.

PMMA (Polymethylmethacrylate) – A popular resist polymeric material in E-Beam and X-ray lithography.

Polarons – An excited state of an electron that is coupled to a semilocalized hole state (+ charge). The location of the hole is partially trapped by relaxation of the atoms near the hole.

Polymerase – Enzyme that catalyzes the assembly of nucleotides into RNA and of deoxynucleotides into DNA.

Porphyrin – A macrocylic tetrapyrrole compound.

Porphine   Porphyrin System

Primary Events of Photosynthesis – The earliest photochemistry in photosynthesis.

Prokaryotes – Simple, unicellular organisms such as bacteria and blue-green algae. Prokaryotes have a single chromosome and lack a defined nucleus and nuclear membrane.

Promoter – A DNA sequence at which RNA polymerase binds, and then initiates transcription.

Protein – The major structural and catalytic macromolecules in cells. Proteins consist of linear chains of 20 different kinds of building blocks called amino acids. Each triplet of base pairs in a DNA molecule codes for a different amino acid, so that the sequence of base pairs is converted into a sequence of amino acids during protein synthesis.

Proximity Effect – Loss of resolution in charged particle beam lithography caused by scattering of the incident particles in the resist layer and substrate.

Push-Pull Olefin – A molecule containing donor and acceptor group separated by one or more double bonds like $H_3N-HC=CH-NO_2$.

Radical Anion – A charged ion or group whose charge includes unpaired electron near or in the valence orbitals.

Raman Spectroscopy - Inelastic light scattering by molecules due to the induction of a dipole moment by the incident, usually laser, light.

Reaction Center - A natural complex between protein, chlorophylls, and other electron transfer components. The primary events occur within the reaction center.

Reading Frame - There are three reading frames in any nucleotide sequence, since there are three nucleotides per codon. Generally only one reading frame of a gene will translate into a functional protein.

Reading - One-way linear process by which nucleotide sequences are decoded, for example, by protein-synthesizing systems.

Recombinant DNA, chimeric DNA, hybrid DNA - DNA molecules of different origin that have been joined together by biochemical techniques to make a single molecule, usually circular and usually capable of some specific biological function, especially self-replication in an appropriate cell.

Registration - In lithography, it is the process of aligning new patterns to be defined with existing patterns on the same substrate.

Regulatory sequence - A DNA sequence involved in regulating the expression of the gene (for example, promoters, operators).

Relaxation Time - The time required for an excited molecule (or moiety) to decay to a less excited or ground state.

Repressor - The protein that binds to a regulatory sequence (operator) adjacent to a gene and which, when bound, blocks transcription of the gene.

Replicon - An autonomous genetic element that replicates as a single unit, having an origin at which replication commences.

Resonance Raman Spectroscopy - As for Raman spectroscopy, except that the irradiating light source resonates with what is usually the electronic absorption band corresponding to an induced electric dipole. Magnetic effects are possible.

Ribosomal RNA, rRNA - The nucleic acid component of ribosomes, making up two-thirds of the mass of the ribosome in E. coli, and about one-half the mass of mammalian ribosomes.

Ribosomes - Small macromolecular cellular particles (200 Å in diameter) made up of rRNA and protein and held together by weak noncovalent forces (e.g. van der Waals, hydrogen bonding, etc.). Ribosomes are the site of protein synthesis.

RNA - Ribonucleic acid - All cells contain both DNA and RNA, and some viruses have RNA as their genetic material. RNA differs from DNA in that is has the sugar ribose instead of deoxyribose, it is usually single-stranded instead of double-stranded, and it has the base U (uracil) in place of the base T (thymine). RNA is used as the molecule that transmits information encoded in the DNA base sequence to the protein-synthesizing apparatus of the cell (see mRNA) and as major structural components of ribosomes.

Short Intermolecular Contacts – Crystallographically observed interatomic
    distances between molecules which are shorter than the sum of accepted
    van der Waals radii.

Single Event Upset – A soft error caused by an X-ray or cosmic ray.

Soft Error – In digital electronic systems, the loss of information caused by
    a transient failure of an electronic device (sometimes radiation
    induced).

Soliton – A solitary wave moving in a non-dissipating or nondispersive mode
    in a dissipating medium.

Stacked Porphyrin – Metal porphyrin group bridged via the metal atom so that
    the porphyrin centers are directly over one another like a stack of poker
    chips.

Stearic Acid – A fatty acid, a long-chain molecule with a carboxylic acid
    (COOH) group at one end: $H_3C-(CH_2)_{16}-COOH$.

STEM – Scanning Transmission Electron Microscope.

Synthetic DNA – DNA of a desired nucleotide sequence that has been synthesized
    chemically rather than enzymatically.

Synthetic Endonuclease Site – A synthetic DNA that contains the specific base
    pair sequences recognized by a site specific endonuclease. See Linker.

Tautomerism – Chemical isomerism characterized by relatively easy inter-
    conversion of isomeric forms in equilibrium, like

$$-\overset{\displaystyle OH}{\underset{\displaystyle |}{C}} =CR \rightarrow -\overset{\displaystyle O}{\underset{\displaystyle ||}{C}}-CHR-$$

Termination codon – A codon that specifies the termination of translation.

Termination sequence – A DNA sequence at the end of a transcriptional unit
    that signals the end of transcription.

Tetraazaanulene –

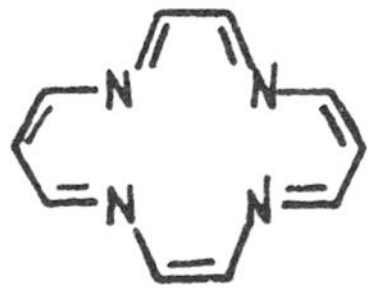

TCNE – Tetracyanoethylene

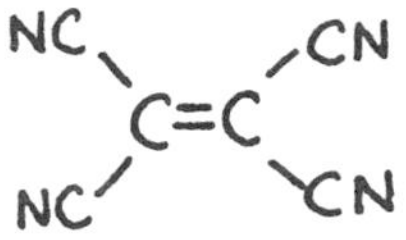

TCNQ - Tetracyanoquinodimethide

TNAP⁻ - Tetracyanonapthoquinodimethene

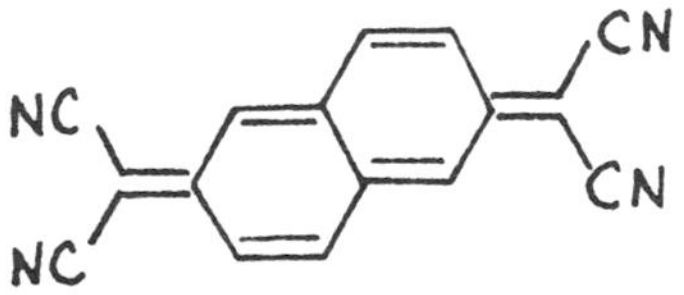

Transcription - The process of synthesizing an RNA chain using a DNA molecule
    as a template.

Translation - The process in which the genetic code contained in the nucleotide
    sequences of mRNA directs the order of amino acids in the formation of
    peptide.

Tricritical Point - A point representing an equilibrium state in which three
    phases coexist.

p-Tricyanovinylphenyldicyanamide

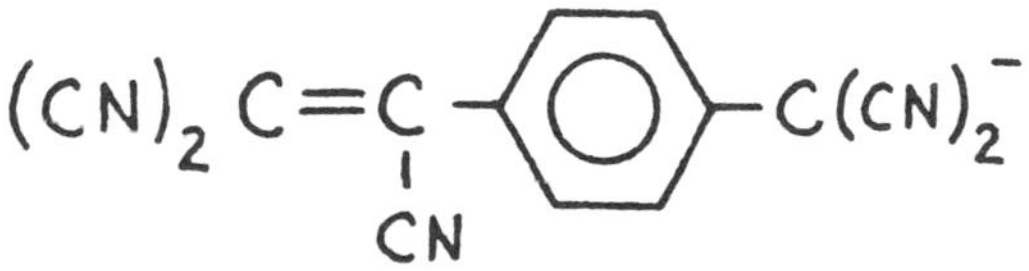

Trinitrofluorenone - (TNF)

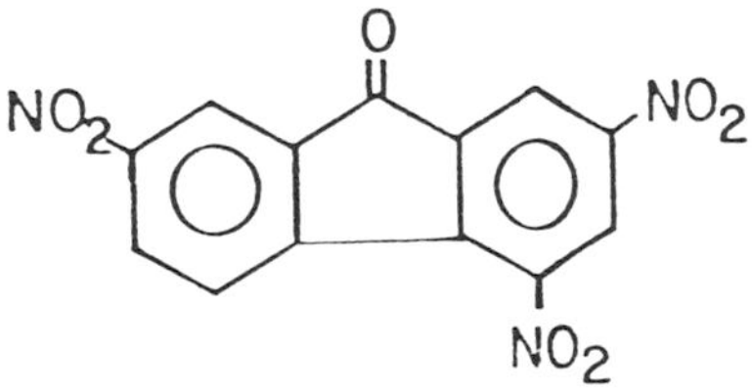

tRNA - Transfer RNA.

TTF - Tetrathiafulvaline

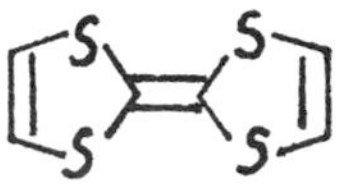

Ubiquinone - An electron carrier which is ubiquitous in cells consisting of a benzoquinone derivative with a long isoprenoid side chain (Coenzyme Q).

Vector - An agent consisting of a DNA molecule known to autonomously replicate in a cell to which another DNA segment may be attached experimentally so as to bring about the replication of the attached segment.

Virus - A DNA or RNA molecule surrounded by a protective protein coat. The viral DNA or RNA is capable of replicating itself inside an appropriate type of cell. Some viral DNA's can be covalently inserted into the chromosomal DNA of the cells they infect, in which case the viral DNA is replicated as part of the cellular DNA and does not kill the cell.

Wild type - The genetic state of an organism isolated from nature.

Weak-ferromagnet - This is an antiferromagnet, whose sublattices are not exactly opposed (i.e., they are canted), so that there is a small net magnetic moment.

Weak Pi-Complex or Donor-Acceptor Complex - A crystallographic phase formed from two or more molecular components and manifesting no charge-transfer in the ground state. The geometries of the components are unperturbed compared to the isolated components. However, charge transfer between the components can readily take place and may lead to enhanced electrical conductivity.

Zero-field Splitting - The splitting of degenerate energy levels in the absence of an external magnetic field.

INDEX